Frances Osborn Wallace.
October 1951.

OP
ABC

THE HUNTERS AND THE HUNTED

THE HUNTERS
AND THE HUNTED

BY

SACHEVERELL SITWELL

NEW YORK
THE MACMILLAN COMPANY
1948

FOREWORD

THERE are flames of fire at the feet of all the pagan statues. The old wine has turned sour in the goatskin. The new wine is fermenting. The snapdragon nods upon the sculptured cornice, and in a flowering meadow within the walls the statue of Venus has fallen among the violets.

So fell the antique world which now lies in ruins. So will fall our world in its own sweet time. But it will not die so beautifully. Rather, we are trapped in the ruins. Here and now we do not pronounce the names of Moloch, nor those of the rival charioteers. The streets of our city are to be strewn, not with phosphorus and anti-personnel bombs, but with rose petals, rosemary, and sprigs of myrtle.

We are supposing, and it may come true, that the reign of plenty has returned again. We are beginning, even now, to create beauty from the tank's slime and the tractor's mud. For the world was young and gay, once. It belongs to the young. It will be young again when flowers grow on the dumps and scrap-heaps. Our Muse is to be that one of whom Dr. Lemprière tells us in his dictionary that she holds a mask in her right hand, and is distinguished from her sisters by her shepherd's crook. And he adds that her dress appears shorter, and not so ornamented as those of the other Muses. Not, then, the tolling of the tocsin, but the ringing of an *entr'acte* bell. And, for our goddess, Thalia, the Muse of Comedy, which has as many meanings as there are kinds of laughter. But read on, we ask you, and you will hear them, one and all.

TO
BRYHER

CONTENTS

LIST OF ILLUSTRATIONS

PROLOGUE

EARLIER, there had been torn and ragged moonlight, after a stormy sunset. To all quarters of the winds, in the imagination, near and far, from the gilded cock upon the steeple, that crows and claps his wings, down to thunderous Acroceraunia. For such was the moonlight. Like a vision of a mysterious land, but suddenly it begins to pour with rain. The timber houses and their gables are entirely hidden. Not a light shows in a window. You cannot look up, or look to right or left, because of the pelting rain. It drips down off your face and hands. It runs from your clothes. It pelts and jangles on the muddied cobbles.

In the deserted street we meet a man coming towards us leading his horse. We cannot see his face or distinguish anything else about him except that his horse is tired and droops its head, and that a big black dog runs beside it in the gutter.

But we know our way. Here is the door. It is a few steps down from the level of the street. A few more steps lead down, inside, into a huge room like a vault or cellar, brilliantly lit after the dark outside, and full of men and women sitting at benches and tables, eating and drinking. It is the Ratskeller, under the town hall, below where the Baltic ships' models hang from the ceiling with their rounded hulls and the antlered lights are made from horns of deer.

They are drinking Rhenish brought from the huge barrels in the cellar, the ' Bacchus ' cask, the ' Rose ' cask, or those of the ' Twelve Apostles ' ; or foaming tankards. They are eating venison, black bread, and cheese. Young and old, for there are men and women of all ages, and seeing but unseen, we take our place among them. But the first thing we notice is that there is no tobacco smoke. Where are we ? Is this the tavern where Hoffmann drinks with the students and tells them of his loves, Olympia, Antonia, and Giulietta ; of Doktor Mirakel, Coppelius, and Spallanzani ? The beer cellar where the first *putsch* was planned ? How many will remember the evil genius, the medium or automaton, the dwarfish doctor and their companions planning disaster for the world ? For that was no less extraordinary than what we see before our eyes. Over in a corner that man is already sitting whom we passed, a moment ago, in the street outside. Some instinct tells us it is he. And, as we look, his black dog jumps up and sits beside him. Are we to surmise that he has been here all the time ? But, in fact, he is unimportant compared with all the others, an impostor or mountebank, someone who goes round from town to town and is no longer, even, young. He is in his middle age. Lost, for him, is the golden opportunity.

And, at once, the Ratskeller is transformed for ourselves, and for him, into the court of the Duke of Parma, or anywhere else that fame and fortune beckoned. It need have no name. But always with the inn or Ratskeller as background, as the reality of the dream. For music we will have the accordion or mechanical piano ; or, if we prefer, the wheezing hurdy-gurdy. It does not matter. I remember an old musical box that would do as well. It could be the Café Royal, the Dôme, the Deux Magots, the Caffè Greco ; anywhere that painters and poets spend the evening. Other persons pretend to themselves that they are of their company.

But the peasant models stand for hire on the stone stairs above the fountain. We see the scarlet bodice and snowy head-dress of the *ciociari* from the plain of Naples ; the beautiful costume of the Alban hills with glittering golden necklaces and earrings ; the wide, flopping Tuscan straw. In the distance, they dance the saltarello to the burr of tambourines, under the vines or on the golden threshing floor. Or in another town, where there were once painters, we dine early and go for evening drives in the Cascine amongst the flower-girls and nightingales.

Those are, or were, the lands of art. We speak of Rome and Florence. What are they now? But coloured postcards are being hawked around. You may buy a paper-knife with a mosaic handle, or an alabaster model of the leaning tower of Pisa. You may find a gondola which conceals an ash-tray, or a mandoline no bigger than your little finger. Better still, they are selling roses and carnations.

There is a stand of paper windmills, on the way down to the sea; and a shrimp stall, and an advertisement of jellied eels. And the automatic slot machines. There are the fishing nets spread out to dry, and low tide, and a trawler hooting in the bay. How beautiful the world can be! There are wild roses in the hedges, and the thrush flies from the pear tree on the wall. There is country quiet all through the night, and dawn like a child born to a safe income throughout life. When I think what the world has been, and what it could be, I could walk up and down, and wring my hands, and weep.

But where are Olympia, Antonia, and Giulietta? There are three loves in the life of everyone, or all three loves are the same. If I were a painter, I would paint a fresco of the banquet of the gods. That would be my opportunity. And while they feasted an orchestra would play the waltzes of the demi-monde. But the three goddesses could be in our midst. Listen to their names: Olympia, Antonia, and Giulietta, for those names will do as well as any other! Olympia is of the beauty that does not have to speak. In her silence lies her provocation. Antonia is of another order: an actress, a dancer, or a film star. In her name we hear her disguises and, in fact, the way she alters her style of hairdressing. Sometimes she wears a mask. Giulietta is the courtesan who draws us after her to Venice, which comes to every young man, if only in the imagination. It will be evident that these can be three shades or incarnations of the same person. Or it could happen the other way. But Olympia is of the sort that will burn our youth through in agony and suspense. Antonia smiles for the public, but looks at us and lifts her finger to her lips. We float with Giulietta by the decaying palaces and on the green lagoon.

Olympia ! Do you remember when we met in the mornings and afternoons, and all day and night ? Maybe this old music will remind you of it. Antonia ! I used to fetch you from the dancing school. You carried your shoes wrapped up in paper, and a little leather case. Giulietta ! I speak, not for myself alone, but for all young men. Or, shall we say, for all men who have been young. But I will come to that later. For Olympia is here, in the Ratskeller, seated in our midst. You can hear the rain still pouring down outside. She has taken shelter here, like Dido in the cave, when she was hunting with Aeneas and they were overtaken by the storm. Here for an hour or two, and then gone. Yet here all the time, and every night. It is in her attitude that she is passing by, and will not stay.

But Antonia has often had to lunch alone at snack bars. In a hurry. She eats a sandwich, or drinks a glass of milk. For the types are eternal. It is not a case of place and time. She takes the bus or Underground. She stays for the week-end in a little house in Surrey, where there are ponies to ride across the common, black and white Nuns in the dovecote, and a large family of auburn-haired and freckled children, not much older than herself, and takes the morning train to Waterloo. O listen to the barrel-organ ! It torments me with the same old tune. Antonia, you knew the organ-grinder, who was an old woman with a handkerchief upon her head ! The old woman has not altered. It is not long ago. Giulietta is the hidden side of your nature, and that which, in Olympia, is on the surface but not

4

true. Though it has come true since, and was the half-truth then. We said Venice because there is no other town like Venice. The faded city of pleasure, at once Cleopatra's galleon and a drawing-room. Or a barge tied so long at anchor that it disintegrates. But it could be any other place that you prefer, so long as there is architecture, and not mere nature in her changing moods. There must be the background of intelligence. Even though we be ignorant ourselves. There have to have been painters and architects. There need be no flowers or trees.

For this is an interior drama, and the externals are of no more importance than objects exposed in the shop-windows, which we cannot afford to buy. In the windows of the shops round three sides of the Piazza, and in the midst, the church of porphyry and serpentine with golden mosaic and Oriental domes. For those objects which we cannot afford and do not even particularly want to buy are the symbols of our state of mind, which turns in upon itself and is not interested in anything else at all but the progress of our own emotions, that alter from day to day and hour to hour. In this sense, ourselves, or our like, are permanent inhabitants of the arcades. Or, if you prefer it, the arcades of Bologna ; or, better still, the arches of the Rue de Rivoli, with shops that are more expensive still, in front and behind us, and round every corner. But it must be a town. For the country equivalent is of another kind. We will write of that later, if there be time for it. But the pavement is essential, and we would have it somewhere that it is hot and we can come out without a hat or coat. If there be an alternative we would choose the Russian winter, as it used to be, with hothouse rooms and a sleigh to be driven in across the snows.

For we have to be anonymous and leave no mark. We have to have inhabited a room in a hotel. Someone else will move in on the day we leave. Their luggage must be already waiting in the hall. Contact with the exterior world comes when we buy cigarettes at the tobacconist's, or gardenias and tuberoses from the stall. For those are the flowers of the season. Of the time and place. Brought in, by barge, from the terra firma. Or from gardens on the Mediterranean ; from the terraces of Bordighera where the Malmaisons grow beside a tideless sea.

Why not the gardenias and violets that are sold upon the London streets ? Because we should pass friends and acquaintances and persons whom we know. Because it is improbable we should be staying in an hotel. Because it is necessary for our state of mind that we should be like a country child who comes to London for the first time, and feels lost in it. Could we recapture that sensation, then it might be London. But, for that matter, Venice is well enough known to us, though now, owing to circumstances, it is as though we remember it from another life and were sworn to keep the secret of its monuments and paintings.

In a sense I have been there since I was ten years old, when I was taken to Venice for the first time. Florian's had been open, day and night, since the eighteenth century. Giulietta ! What does it matter whether it was Venice or Paris ; whether, in fact, you ever existed, for this is an adventure or a metamorphosis of someone who lived and breathed, who took up the flowers and put them in water in her room, who told me to go early and book a table for our dinner. With whom I wandered — did I not, another time ? — in the glorious orange grove. Behind the glade of cypresses. Or past the fun-fair and the shooting galleries. For you can have which you prefer. Below the statue which has its finger to its lips.

The spiders' webs that hang on the yew hedges could be the masks of the evening's entertainment. Antonia ! I bought you once a black domino, and another time a green one, from the shop in Long Acre. There are several such shops in that neighbourhood but this one, in particular, had masks in the window and a pile of black sombreros. Near there are the shops where they make the ballet shoes, a part of tradition, for the makers are Italians from Milan. Olympia ! Your foot would never fit into a ballet shoe. But you both are combined to form the ghost of Giulietta. She is both of you at once, in the same person. You are all three the same, but different. Antonia ! There was a mandoline hanging on your wall, which I never heard you play. So that it was like the music lesson from the old opera, where the hidden accompaniment was in the orchestra, where you but made the motions of music with your hands. I was your Pygmalion. I loved the statue, but did not know it was alive. Not till too late.

But with your other embodiment it was quite different. Let me give you my arm so that you can jump out upon the water-steps ! For we were rowed here to the restaurant. Not like the trip by bus or Underground. Can you imagine anything more beautiful on an August night ! Very late. Ten o'clock, or after. But it is hot, and we would wait till it is dark. The great bell struck the hour from the Campanile and we saw summer lightning over the sea towards the mountains. It was time to sit at Florian's and listen to the band. And, in fact, it should always be time to listen to music. But there could be more appropriate music. Though this is its own music.

We had seen the lutes in the hands of the cherub children of Gianbellini. But I prefer the barrel-organ or the hurdy-gurdy. What little fame I had was in London. I cannot go back on that. And my first memories of music are by a summer sea. If all towns were forbidden me but one, I would yet choose London. My three phantoms I met in London. I would have met them in another life, and we would meet again, were it possible, but we know that cannot be. They are immortal, in the sense that they are always there. The person who is mortal is my mortal self.

BOOK I

THE HUNTERS
AND THE HUNTED

THE HUNTERS
AND THE HUNTED

(i)

Chrysorrhoas

WE are walking along a river underneath some trees. They are high and lofty, having been long planted, and are most clearly distinguished in their different kinds. We can tell the walnut, the cedar, and the cypress. There are lemons and apples, too, but these, in hallucination, are in fruit against the season, which is eternal spring.

The character of the landscape is that of the gardens outside a town. The stems of the pines and cypresses are a silvery blue and somehow the suggestion of the pine cone is conveyed in the shape of the bough, the whole tree itself being the form of a pine cone when that ripens and the scales begin to open. We can smell the cedarn smell, so intense that we wonder whether Lebanon is near. The cones are as big as a goose's egg ; and we see the two sorts of cedar, that which is dark green with light-green leaves, and the silvery white, the leaves of which have a bluish bloom upon them. There are black firs, as well, and smaller trees of bush-like growth.

But not a soul is astir. There is not an animal abroad. It is a spring morning in an hallucination, for now we see buildings in between the trees. A wonderful city of the Orient appears among the branches.

We come to a bridge which is in a style of architecture we have never known before. With a tower at either end, overshadowed by an enormous cedar tree. The towers are roofed with gilded tiles. The bridge is a high arch, so lofty that a large house stands underneath it, and in shape it is an arc or the segment of a circle. It has a balustrade, six windows, and as many fluted pilasters ; a design like a conventional flower over each of the windows, and an arching roof. A bridge perhaps as long and high as the Rialto.

But the mystery is that the bridge stands in isolation. We are left to think, for ourselves, what persons may have crossed it and looked out from its windows up and down the river.

A little further, a pavilion rises between the trees. In shape it is like a tower or belfry. It is a conglomerate of roofs and porches, with pillars upon which vines are trained. Such porches, in the form of phiales or fountains, were a feature in Byzantine monasteries.[1] Of what does this tower or belfry remind us ? Of the cathedral of St Basil in the Red Square at Moscow ; but that has Tartar influence ; or, at least, it suggests Tartar buildings there have never been.

But where is the population ? There is the golden dawn behind these towers and kiosques, but not a living being. We walk a little further, down the river of paradise, to where there are plane trees with lopped stems which have sprouted into leaves, as though having grown for centuries near to human dwellings. But not a stork's nest, nor the voice of any bird. It is all sleeping in enchantment. And we come, suddenly, on the most fantastic of all the buildings.

A huge plane tree grows from the back of it, and another, hidden until we come in front of it, can just be seen. It consists of a centre and two projecting wings, of the same architecture as the bridge over the river. These buildings, at each end, stand with their foundations in the water. They are washed by the river.

---

[1] There are specimens on Mount Athos ; in the courts of Xeropotamou, Iviron, and more particularly at Vatopedi.

But there are a pair of pavilions, exactly alike, on the terrace under the plane tree, and this is the most peculiar of all the visions of the morning. They are octagonal, with conical roofs, apparently, in themselves, gleaming with gold, but of such fashion that it is impossible to tell whether they are open porticoes of pillars, or if the whole structure is enclosed by solid walls. This is the mystery. For they are immensely tall, one hundred feet high, it could be, to the top of their conical roofs. We have to think that they are given the proportion of their own poetical or magical importance. They must be famed twin pavilions of the Dark Ages, known to all travellers, and recognised.

Our longing is for whoever inhabits this pair of pavilions to come forth and be seen. Whoever it be that is their inhabitant, would descend no lower than the terrace. He would never come down the steps. He stays above in magical isolation, upon the far bank of the river. For, indeed, the river of paradise flows between.

What we see before us are twin pavilions in an Oriental idiom, midway between the pagan temple and the nomad tent. Twin pavilions, pitched side by side, under the giant plane tree. Descended from what race? Ah! who can tell? Goth, or Ostrogoth? They could be tents of the Gothic conquerors. For all the barbarians had their distinctive styles. They could be Arabian, but made to glitter with the Byzantine gold. They are, according to one interpretation, hung with stuffs. Between the pillars there are embroidered hangings; while the whole shape of the tent is that of an Arabian helmet, as that continued down even into the Mamelukes. The domes of the tomb of Sultan Barqûq, in the desert outside Cairo, are two such casques or war helms.

We can see in them, as well, the kiosques and pavilions of the Ptolemies, made of wood and painted canvas and boughs and fronds of trees for their entertainments at court, as described by Callisthenes. The rudiments of such buildings appear in the wall paintings of Pompeii and Boscoreale. The tradition of their splendour, and even some survival in popular form in the ancient cities of Asia Minor, are to be expected. Alexandria, Ephesus, and Antioch had a late classical architecture of which Bernini's Rome is the phantom by circumstance, or if you prefer it, by historical recurrence.

But, also, the twin pavilions are a pair of tholoi. They are circular temples of the Greeks come down, after many changes, to their present and last form. For the shape of the pavilions is that of a tholos or rotunda. Such is the temple of the Sibyl, near the falls of Tivoli, with its eighteen Corinthian columns in an open colonnade. But this is but a Roman copy of a Greek original, for the circular temple was one of the most beautiful inventions of Hellenic architecture.

There were two tholoi, in particular. One was at Delphi, in the valley nearly below the Castalian fountain, and famous in antiquity as among the chief beauties of the sacred site. The other, much admired by Pausanias, was at Epidaurus. A building with exterior and interior colonnades, but of uncertain purpose ; some holding that it was built over the sacred spring of the Asclepeion, and others that it served as a prytaneum for the celebration of sacred feasts and magic rites in the labyrinth that lay below. Its uses are conjectural, but this is certain, that the interior was of black and white marble with a colonnade of fourteen Corinthian columns, while on the outside the peristyle was composed of twenty-six Doric pillars.[1]

What we are describing, in fact, are the great panels of mosaic

[1] The architect was the younger Polycletes, who was a sculptor as well, and who designed the theatre of Epidaurus, which is the most perfect of Greek theatres. The most celebrated work of Polycletes was a sculpture representing the bodyguard of the King of Persia. The interior of the tholos had frescoes by Pausias of Sicyon, of Love and Drunkenness. It was Pausias who made a painting of his mistress Glycere, sitting naked on the ground and making garlands of flowers.

in the mosque of the Omaiyades, at Damascus. These were only uncovered from their whitewash in 1931. They adorn the long walls of the court of the mosque, for this was a basilica, having been built in the fourth century by Theodosius I to enclose a casket with the head of John the Baptist. But the mosaics date from 715, when the Caliph El Welíd converted the basilica into a mosque, and had it decorated by craftsmen from Byzantium. According to the Arab geographer Muquaddasi, who wrote at the end of the tenth century, the mosaics were the gift of the Byzantine Emperor, and he adds that not a tree or city of the known world but was figured on the walls. They were counted as one of the wonders of Islam, but in deference to the Moslems they were uninhabited. Not a living being is portrayed.

The main panel of mosaic is that park through which the river runs. Cedar trees and cypresses grow on the banks, and between their stems are seen fantastic buildings, now gleaming in the foreground, or brought forward, as it were, to the proscenium, which is the river-bank. But are they, really, cities and famous buildings of the eighth century ? Perhaps it is only a scenic interpretation of those porticoes and colonnades.

In the mosaic, persons and statues are conspicuous by absence; and, so far as human beings are concerned, it may be because the scene is uninhabited that it has this fairy-tale improbability, which is as though we saw it one early summer morning while the world was sleeping. Or else the buildings, still gleaming with the Eastern gold, have been deserted. Are they, then, authentic cities in the mosaic ? The oldest description of Damascus, by the geographer Istakhri, is so detailed that one town in particular may be identified. The river which flows through the great panel of mosaic (it is more than a hundred feet long) could be the Barada, meaning ' cold ', called by the Greeks the Chrysorrhoas or golden stream, which is the Abana of the Old

Testament. It waters the villages of the Ghûta and their um-
brageous gardens in the plain of Damascus. House piled on
house, as in the valleys of the Lebanon. Our first building may
be the bridge of Damascus, over the Abana, and we may have
seen the minarets of Damascus. But this is only in the third
generation after the Prophet. It is to be noted that the minarets
are more like the towers of basilicas, for their distinctive form
is not yet established, it is so early.

If it be Damascus, then it is probable that we may find a
reminiscence, if no more, of other wonders of the Dark Ages.
We would look for something of Aleppo, or of Antioch, which
was rebuilt by Justinian after the catastrophe of the earthquake
in which half a million persons perished. But, as well, there
may be representations of more distant places. Other towns
and buildings might be recognised, all standing on the banks of
the stream which flows, like the river of paradise, through the
scene. They have been reduced to the most simple expression of
their forms, so that a town consists of no more than its most
conspicuous building with a few small houses put in to give it
scale. Cordoba, under the same Omaiyade dynasty as Damascus,
may be depicted, actually or in imagination. Muquaddasi says
definitely that all the towns of the known world were on the walls,
and we have to believe him, or take it that none were there at all.

There could be suggestions in the mosaic of the palace of
the Byzantine Emperors at Constantinople, occupying the
present site of the Old Seraglio, upon the Golden Horn, and
forming the highest achievement of the arts of decoration in the
West, and probably in all human history. The pair of tholoi
may have been a feature of the Imperial palace. But, for a
glimpse of that, we need not be tied down to the eighth century ;
we can see it in its apogee at any time we like, after the great
buildings of Theophilus and Basil the Macedonian had been
added to it in the ninth century.

(ii)

Palatine Way

The Processional Way, as described in the *Book of Ceremonies*, led from the doors of St Sophia. Near to that, upon its pillar, stood the equestrian statue of Justinian, four times the size of life. This was seen by the Spaniard Clavijo, as late as 1400, upon his embassy to Tamerlane. There was " a great plume on his head the shape of the tail of a peacock ", and in his huge fist he held a golden orb.

The Palatine Way led from St Sophia to the gates of the Chalce, guarded day and night by Doryphores and Hoplites, two of the seven detachments of the Imperial Guard, with drawn swords. We are to imagine that we pass, unchallenged, through the Chalce, looking up at the walls and ceiling where we see Justinian and Theodora, the conquered towns of Italy, Libya, and Spain, and Belisarius bringing the loot and the prisoners to the feet of the Basileus. There are a banquet and festival in celebration of triumphs over the Goths and Vandals, all in mosaic.

Next we advance into an immense series of porches called the Scholae, leading to the Great or Summer Consistory, where stands the Imperial throne behind curtains which are drawn away on days of ceremony to reveal the Emperor seated in majesty. A little further, to one side, stands the church of the Saviour, built by Constantine the Great, with a special body of clergy attached to it, and a Skevophylax or guardian of the sacred treasures. Near to this, Constantine caused a statue of himself, a bronze Apollo cast with a new head which was his own portrait in a halo of golden rays, to be set upon a column of eight drums of porphyry, and in the plinth he enclosed the twelve baskets from the miracle of the loaves and fishes, the alabaster box of spikenard ointment, the adze with which old Noah shaped the ark, and the crosses of the two thieves.

Within the great gate of Daphne stands the Octagon, where the Imperial robes and crown are kept. Also the church of St Stephen, and a pair of oratories at which the Emperor pauses to worship during the Palatine processions. At this point we notice the Excubitors and Candidates, so called from the white uniforms they wear, two more detachments of the Imperial Guard. Other guards carry golden bucklers, a gilded battle-axe, and golden helmets with red plumes. And there are the ' axe-bearing barbarians ', the Varangian Guard, Norsemen of huge stature, of whose tawny fairness Anna Comnena leaves an admiring description in her *Alexiad*. It was recruited, partly, of Saxon English who fled here after the battle of Hastings, and partly of Danes from Thyland, or Thule, in the dunes of Jutland.

We come now to the first of the great buildings of the palace. It is the Triclinos of the Nineteen Couches, a banqueting hall called from the beds or couches, *accubita*, at which the guests feasted in the ancient pagan manner. The Emperor had at his table twelve guests in symbol of the Twelve Apostles, and the other persons feasting at eighteen tables, twelve to each, numbered two hundred and sixteen. The feast was served on golden plate ; and the three golden vases of dessert, owing to their weight, had to make a circus entrance in three chariots, harnessed and upholstered in scarlet. They were then raised to the table by ropes which descended from a ceiling of golden foliage, and wound up on a machine.

The hall next to this is the Magnavra, a detached hall in the form of a basilica with three naves, and containing the throne of Solomon. Also the trees of mechanical birds which sang, and the golden lions at foot of the throne which lashed the ground with their tails and roared aloud. The ambassador Luitprand, Bishop of Cremona in the ninth century, here prostrated himself before the Emperor upon a disk of porphyry, and when he raised his head saw him seated on his throne, high up near the ceiling of the hall, lifted there by some hidden mechanism, and having changed his robes, in that interval, for others that were more gorgeous still. But even more curious, the Magnavra had a golden organ and the silver organs of the Blue and Green factions which played during the Palatine processions, while the pavement was strewn with roses.

Near to this are the great kitchens where the banquets are prepared. We see the scullions in their high caps, and a certain number of persons who are in charge of the making and repair of the robes of ceremony. There are also the Noumera, another detachment of Guards, and the rowers of the dromons or state barges upon which the Imperial family take the soft airs of the Bosphorus, or cross over into Asia. At a reception given to the Saracen ambassadors by Constantine VII, in the middle of the tenth century, these state watermen were stationed near to the throne. And we pass a stable where the riding mules are kept, and a barrack for the eunuchs.

But we continue to the Triconchos, by way of the Sigma, an entrance hall which is shaped like an apse or hemicycle. In front of this, a fountain or phiale is heaped with almonds and pistachios on days of ceremony, and runs with spiced and aromatic wines. The Triconchos is a huge and diverse mass of buildings, consisting, among others, of the Heros or arsenal with mosaics of weapons and armour upon the walls ; a hall called Margaritos or the 'Pearl' with eight pillars of rosy marble ; and the Camilas, which has a roof flecked with gold, and in the interior, mosaics with scenes of harvesting and reaping.

Through the Triconchos we reach the Lausiacos and Justinianos, two long vaulted halls at a right angle to each other, gleaming with golden mosaic, and forming a high porch or vestibule, dividing the Triconchos from another building.

This is the Chrysotriclinos, built by Tiberius II in the sixth century, and the most glorious structure of the whole Imperial Palace, where the Immortals are on guard.[1] It is an octagon, after the pattern of St Vitale at Ravenna and the Kutchuk Aya Sophia (Little St Sophia or church of SS. Sergius and Bacchus) at Constantinople, but apparently more than twice the size, with eight arches leading to eight apses. Mosaics of flowers and trees, with gold and silver, form the ornament, and the floor is strewn with rose petals, rosemary, and sprigs of myrtle.

Upon days of ceremony, curtains woven with birds and animals upon a gold ground hung before the silver doors, and from silver poles or masts upon the floor. Constantine Porphyrogenitus had a dining-table of silver made specially for this hall ; and in an adjoining chamber the Empresses displayed their new-born sons when they were eight days old, for which occasion the hall was draped with golden tissues. But the feature of the Chrysotriclinos was the Pentapyrgion, a gigantic display cupboard with five towers, made by Theophilus, in which the treasures of the crown were exhibited : golden thrones and beds, golden tables and golden vessels of all sorts, crowns and diadems, golden robes and vestments, and a plane tree, all of gold, and glistening with pearls.

(iii)

The Porphyra

We come now to the great additions of Basil the Macedonian, dating from the second half of the ninth century, and beginning

---

[1] The Immortals were a special corps of ten thousand cavalry formed by Michael VII Ducas in 1078. Their name was taken from the horsemen who were the household cavalry of the old Persian Kings.

with the Kenourgion, two splendid halls which he attached to the Chrysotriclinos ; the first, in the form of a basilica with sixteen columns, eight of green Thessalian marble and eight of onyx. Upon the walls were mosaics of Basil I and his generals presenting him with captured towns, while his warlike exploits were in mosaic upon the ceiling. The hall next to this, which may have been his bedroom, had a peacock in mosaic upon the pavement ; figures of eagles, in the corners, about to take wing ; and wavering lines, like rivers, formed of the green Thessalian marble. Basil and his Empress Eudoxia and their children were in mosaic on the walls and ceiling. There was also a summer garden, open to the Bosphorus, with its walls adorned with hunting scenes in mosaic.

The founders of the Macedonian dynasty built, as well, a new cathedral, not less magnificent in its decorations and the treasures it contained than the coronation church of the Virgin of the Pharos (Lighthouse), which had been completed twenty years before by the previous dynasty. That was a building of five cupolas roofed with copper and had doves of white gold, studded with emeralds, and carrying cruciform sprigs of pearls in their beaks, that hung from the ceiling. This new church, for one better, had six domes of bronze. The riches of the interior were beyond description. An iconostasis of gold and silver worked with precious stones and pearls, and an altar formed of a composition " more precious than gold itself ". In front was an atrium with two phiales, one of red Egyptian porphyry, and the other of veined Anatolian marble. The jets sprang from a pine cone, and from the rim of the fountain bronze figures of cocks and rams and bulls spouted water into the basin.

More churches and oratories were built under Basil I. The church of St Elias, which was octagonal with seven altars ; and the oratory of the Saviour where the floor was entirely covered with a thick silver leaf, enriched with inlay and niello. The treasures of the Indies were lavished upon its sacred fittings. Another oratory, that of St Paul, was not less marvellous with its floor formed of circular plaques of precious marbles with surrounds of silver. Next to this he built the Pentacubiculum, of five halls or *cubicula* used for banquets.

Leo VI, the son of Basil, not so great a builder as his father, rivalled with him in the church of St Demetrius, next to those of St Elias and the Virgin of the Pharos, built, in fact, like the cathedrals of the Kremlin, touching on one another. This was the custom among the Byzantines. SS. Sergius and Bacchus (Little St Sophia) had, for instance, next door to it, the church of SS. Peter and Paul, now destroyed, with which it shared in common the atrium, the porches, and the marble columns of the entrance.

And we must mention the Mouchroutas, deriving from the Arabic word which means a ' cone ', dating from the end of the eleventh century. It was also called *persicos domos*, the ' Persian house ', and had a staircase leading to it, of blue, white, and green, with purple from the mussel shell, and cupolas wrought into honeycomb vaults and stalactites. The craftsmen were Greeks who had worked at Koniah in Asia Minor for the Seljuk Sultans then in the zenith of their powers. Seljuk art was under direct Persian influence, and the Mouchroutas may have been not the least fantastic of all the palace buildings of Byzantium.

But we have left till last the most remarkable of all the structures in point of architectural conception, beginning with a building of an earlier dynasty, the Porphyra, upon a square base ending in a pyramid, and made of red porphyry flecked with white. This was the tower of the Porphyrogeniti, princes and princesses ' born in the purple '.[1] It was to this tower in the shape

[1] Anna Comnena describes the Porphyra, as follows, in the seventh book of her *Alexiad* : " This purple room was a certain building in the palace shaped as a complete square from its base to the spring of the roof, which ended in a pyramid ; it looked out upon the sea and the harbour where the stone oxen and lions stand. The floor of this

of a pyramid that the Empresses came when they were about to give birth to their children. Also, according to ancient custom, it was from this tower that the Empresses made gifts of purple to the court ladies, though by purple is intended what we call scarlet.

The structures in pyramidal form must have been the most novel and interesting of all the later Byzantine buildings. Basil I was not the builder of the Porphyra, but he erected other palaces in this shape, and it has been suggested that as an iconoclast Emperor he was anxious to be an innovator, and to introduce architectural forms hitherto unknown. Of such may have been the apartments constructed by him, which from their great elevation were called the 'Eagle'.

(iv)

The Purple Buskin

Of all these wonders we would wish, more specially, to see certain mosaics and the palaces built in form of a pyramid. For we must remark that it is unfamiliar to find Byzantine mosaics that do not depict saints and holy figures. Our desire would be to behold the scenes of reaping and harvesting upon the walls of the Triconchos : and those others, due to Theophilus the Iconoclast, who having forbidden all portrayal of religious subjects ordered mosaics of trees and flowers and animals,

room was paved with marble and the walls were panelled with it but not with ordinary sorts nor even with the more expensive sorts which are fairly easy to procure, but with the marble which the earlier Emperors had carried away from Rome. And this marble is, roughly speaking, purple all over except for spots like white sand sprinkled over it. It is from this marble, I imagine, that our ancestors called the room 'purple'." Cf. *The Alexiad*, p. 170, translated by Elizabeth A. S. Dawes : London, Kegan Paul, 1928. The Princess Anna Comnena, daughter of Alexius I Comnenus, was herself born in the Porphyra in 1083. She died in 1148 weapons and warlike arms, the hunting of lions, and scenes of fruit-gathering.

Also we would wish to visit the studios of the mosaic workers and the establishments where the silk stuffs of Byzantium were dyed and woven. The slow growth of centuries must have permeated the workshops of the palace, for the art of mosaic was to flourish for a thousand years from the age of Constantine to the mosaics of the Kariye Djami at Constantinople, which were completed by 1321. The secular mosaics, especially, would be our object, and we may imagine, if we will, the cartoons of reaping and harvesting, remembering that these are cornlands of Cappadocia and of the Asian provinces. The silk stuffs were an Imperial monopoly reserved for the use of the Emperors and their court or given as presents, and a view of the workshops, say, early in the eleventh century during the reign of Alexius Comnenus, would be among the highest aesthetic experiences ever possible to human beings.

Under Coptic and Sassanian influence, and in the certainty that the older patterns were produced again and again, we would recall such subjects as that of the Byzantine horsemen spearing lions ; the combats of lions and dromedaries ; the parrots ; or that of the Basileus, full face, in habit of ceremony, riding in a quadriga or four-horse chariot. Of such are the fragments found in the early tombs of kings and bishops, in Western Europe, representing, it is to be presumed, actual gifts of the Byzantine Emperors, and having their origin under the shadow of the churches and palaces that we have described. Often the designs are disposed in circles, so that the figures face each other heraldically in all the strength and simplification that are the secret of their effect. The more precious of these stuffs were sometimes signed and dated, and we should distinguish between those which were woven stiff with gold and silver thread or wire and those which were patterned silks.

The colour of these miraculous fabrics can be nearly in-describable. Tones of rose or lemon, peach or apricot, as though dyed from the fruits and flowers ; half-shades and demi-tints of white and saffron ; ivory and all the shades of green ; with warmer sepia and brown, and hot depths of browns and blues and blacks and yellows. For background the Imperial purple was preferred, in its three shades of scarlet, violet, or red. And just as the tradition of these fabrics continued even after the Turkish conquest in the silk stuffs of Brusa, which were woven by Greek workmen, so the formalities of Byzantine ceremonial costume were retained under the Sultans. The turban and silken fur-trimmed robe of the Phanariot denotes his office, from Grand Logothete to Hospodar, in the Moldavian and Wallachian principalities, down to 1849. Such was the tradition of Byzantium and its silken stuffs. We may conceive of the slow and leisurely process of their manufacture, reposing in its ancient secrets and conscious, it could almost be, that theirs was an age in which the hand of man could do no wrong. For, indeed, the mosaics and the silks ; the carved capitals ; the marble panels, often with designs of peacocks with spread tails drinking from a fountain, familiar from examples in Italian and Sicilian churches ; such relics show that the arts of the Dark Ages, so called, are of that primal order in which the individuals of any human race resemble each other so closely that they could be mistaken for the children of one father. But we intend by this a spiritual and not a physical resemblance, in the sense that the aesthetic values are identical. Their breeding is true as that of the animals and birds ; and that through the centuries until, as much for this as for any other reason, growing impoverishment and the mere lack of precious materials, gold and silver, porphyry and fine marbles, brought down their diminution and decay.

For an example, the red Egyptian porphyry from the quarries in the desert had been kept specially for busts and portraits of the Emperors and their families and for use in the palaces and in churches that were of Imperial foundation. This supply was lost when Egypt fell to the Moslems, though for some little time yet Rome could be looted of its stock of porphyries. As for the purple codices of Byzantium, written in uncial letters of gold or silver upon vellum dyed blue or violet and polished with an agate, these are found rarely, if at all, after the fall of Constantinople to the Crusaders, and date, chiefly, from the age of Justinian and the sixth and seventh centuries. There exist one or two manuscripts in the Imperial autograph of one or other Emperor of the Comnenus family. In a particular instance, the text on each page is written in the form of a cross, the writing being in purple ink powdered with gold. This Imperial ink is said to have been a mixture of vermilion and cinnabar, or purple. In these purple codices the use of such precious materials is proof of Imperial provenance. These, too, were painted under the shadow of the Chrysotriclinos and the Porphyra.

It may be that the mere nature of the materials employed ; the hard substances like porphyry and serpentine ; the manipulation of solid uncial letters of gold or silver upon vellum ; the convention of an art in which the technique was imposed by the use of a multitude of cubes of glass ; it may be that this is responsible, primarily, for the Byzantine stiffness. So much of what has come down to us is carved in ivory, for caskets, thrones, or doors. Their cups and chalices and sacred vessels made use of such precious substances as sapphire, amethyst and heliotrope, chalcedony and cornaline, jasper, haematite, agate, onyx and alabaster, ophite, lapis lazuli. In these, in their sculpture and mosaic, in their golden coins, we find an analogy, which is not real, between works of untrained incompetence and those of purposeful deformation.

In this connection it is a mistake to be influenced by our

judgement of Russian mediaeval art. We should not compare the buildings of the Imperial Palace at Constantinople with the churches and palaces of the Kremlin. The bulbous domes of the 'third Rome' are a barbarian conglomerate of Slav and Tartar. Not the product of the Dark Ages, but of a Middle Ages, prolonged almost into modern times. Haphazard, fortuitous, not the results of design and plan. The Russian Middle Ages are the worst advocate for the authentic, true Byzantine arts. Their art of the three golden periods is pre-determined ; it is not the accident of ignorance or chance.

In this spirit we would imagine for ourselves the cartoons of the mosaic workers, the studios of the goldsmiths and lapi-daries, and the looms of the silk weavers. It begins to live for us in the thought of the curious and fantastic figures to be seen in their distinctive robes and headdresses : the lilac of the Emperor's brothers and the Patriarch ; the blue of the other Princes ; the ladies-in-waiting who carried in their hands an apple of red enamel set with pearls, of which custom we seem to hear a distant echo from the other end of the world when the Spaniard Clavijo, on his embassy to Tamerlane, found the Khan in a garden be-longing to one of his palaces at Samarcand, sitting near a fountain in which some red apples were playing in the waters. But persons of all ranks are to be recognised within the palace precincts by their distinctive costumes. Anna Comnena is at her most typical in those passages of the *Alexiad* in which titles are described. She mentions how her father, the Emperor Alexius I, invented a new name by compounding the names of Sebastos and Autocrator, and bestowed upon his brother the title Sebastocrator, exalting him a step above the Caesar who was now counted third in the acclamations. But the coronets of the Sebastocrators and Caesars were more sparingly decorated with pearls and jewels than that of the Emperor, and had no globe. At the same time Taronites, who had married the Emperor's sister, was created Protosebastos and Protovestiairos, and gazetted, later, as Panhypersebastos. Anna Comnena continues : " Now my father was inventor of all these new honorary titles. Some he made by compounding names, of which I gave an instance above, and the others by applying them to new use. . . . And if anyone were to reckon the art of ruling as a science and a kind of high philosophy, as if it were the art of all arts and the science of all sciences, then he would certainly admire my father as a skilful scientist and artist for having invented those new titles and functions in the Empire. . . . Now when his father Michael Ducas was ousted from the throne, Queen Maria's son, Constantine Porphyrogenitus, doffed the red buskins of his own accord and assumed ordinary black ones, but Nicephorus Botoniates, who succeeded his father as Emperor, bade him take off the black buskins and wear silk shoes of varied colours, as he felt some reverence for the young man, and liked him for his beauty and his high descent, for he grudged him indeed the splendour of entirely red buskins, but allowed him to have a few spots of red showing in his woven shoes. Then after Alexius Comnenus had been proclaimed Emperor, the Queen Maria, Constantine's mother, in obedience to the Caesar's suggestion, demanded from the Emperor a written pledge, which would be inviolable by being written in red and sealed with a gold seal, to the effect that not only she and her son should suffer no harm, but further that her son should be the Emperor's partner, allowed to wear red buskins and a crown, and be acclaimed as Emperor together with Alexius himself. Nor did she fail in her request, for she received a Golden Bull granting all she asked. Next they took from Constantine the woven silk shoes he used to wear, and gave him red ones, and in the future he put his signature in red after that of Alexius to all deeds of gift and to Golden Bulls, and in processions he followed him, wearing the imperial diadem." Anna Comnena, indeed, uses this phrase to describe an accession to the throne : " Fortune gives to a man the imperial crown and makes his boots purple ".[1]

An office closely connected with the throne in its important function of signing documents and Golden Bulls was the Cartulary of the Inkstand. There was a special inkstand with its pen, and the ink was of cinnabar, producing red letters. The material used as sealing-wax was gold—hence the Golden Bulls. But, in addition, there were many other curious characters in their appropriate costumes, the holders of high-sounding offices. The Great Primicerios, for instance, was chief of the household and held high appointment in the army. There were the Great Domestics of the East and West, exercising authority in their different spheres, the former post being an office to which the gigantic, yellow-haired Bohemund, ' hero-villain ' of the *Alexiad*, aspired. And the mixture of admiration and repugnance with which Anna Comnena regards Bohemund reaches to its climax in the passage where she describes his escape from the Greeks by feigning his own death and being carried in a coffin aboard a bireme in the port of Antioch. During the voyage he caused his attendants to mourn for him and pluck out their hair, whenever the vessel put in at a harbour, and even, in order to make his corpse appear stale and odoriferous, strangled or killed a cock and kept it upon his chest within the coffin. " And when a cock has been dead for four or five days its smell is most disagreeable for those who have a sense of smell. But that villain Bohemund enjoyed this fictitious evil all the more ; though I for myself am astonished that he being alive could bear such a siege of his nostrils." [2] In the meantime, he lay inside breathing through holes in the lid of the coffin and being fed at night, or

---

[1] It will be remembered that, at the taking of Constantinople in 1453, the body of the last Byzantine Emperor, Constantine XIII Palaeologus, was identified by his purple buskins.

[2] The passages quoted are taken from *The Alexiad of the Princess Anna Comnena*, the first complete translation into English, by Elizabeth A. S. Dawes. Another indis-

when the ship was out to sea. But when the vessel reached Corfu Bohemund emerged from his hiding-place, showed himself insolently in the streets in his foreign and barbaric garb, demanded an interview with the Byzantine governor of the island, and sent back defiant messages to the Emperor Alexius threatening to raise all Italy against him.

Other titles carrying appointment in the army or the navy were that of Phalangarch or Protostrator, Thalassocrator, or more simply Dux of the fleet. Any persons who have seen the patterned silken robe and huge striped turban of Theodore Metochites, Grand Duke or Admiral of the Fleet, in the mosaics of the Kariye Djami at Constantinople, work of the fourteenth century under the Palaeologi, will be able to conceive of a Thalassocrator of the eleventh or twelfth centuries when the Byzantine genius and luxury in costume was at its height. We read, also, of the Grand Hetaeriarch of the Foreign Palace Guards, and of a particular official, the Exousiocrator of Alans, a race of barbarians who have disappeared from history and left no trace behind. And we conclude this list of actual but improbable personages with the Decurion, the Toparch or Topoteretes, and the Tagmatarch. With last of all, but not least, the Great Drungary of the fleet, who was in charge of the triremes, biremes, dromons, whether worked with sails or rowed by banks of oars.

It is to be remembered, where Byzantine costume is concerned, that the Russian boyar of the time of Ivan the Terrible, become familiar through the stage pictures in Mussorgsky's opera of *Boris Godunov*, derived his high fur hat and brocaded fur-lined gown from Byzantium ; and that the extravagances of Byzantine costume can be studied in paintings by Carpaccio and Gentile Bellini ; in the frescoes of the Battles of the Christian Emperors Constantine and Heraclius by Piero della Francesca

pensable work, in some sense supplementary to the above, is *Anna Comnena : a Study*, by Georgina Buckler ; Oxford University Press, 1929. Our list of Byzantine titles, and much other matter, is derived from this latter authority.

in the church of San Francesco at Arezzo, where only in the light of this knowledge can the extraordinary, Russian-looking dresses be explained ; and, lastly, in the bronze doors of St Peter's at Rome, by Filarete, in which the identical hats and dresses are to be seen, while the fact that these bronze reliefs were executed between 1433 and 1445 makes them anterior to the fall of Constantinople and coincident with the living existence of these splendours. Become, though, a legend in their own time, for the restored empire of the Palaeologi was a period of impoverishment. Coming after sixty years of domination by the Frankish Emperors, it never attained to what Constantinople had been before the fall of the city to the Crusaders in 1204. Till then, Byzantium had a history of nine centuries behind it and three periods, at least, which were Golden Ages for the arts.

A blessed age, when the hand that sculptured, or the hand that drew, worked in magic and had no counterfeit. Their purpose was not to please. It was their object to exalt or frighten, to intoxicate, or to fire with wild fantasy. Their works were rare as music before the age of mechanical reproduction, and such were their formal qualities of magic or inspiration that even those who dwelt in midst of them never tired from familiarity. They inspired awe and terror. The mosaic of the Pantocrator, the Ruler of the World, was intended to terrify.

(v)

Mosaic of the Pantocrator

Of this, there is the tremendous instance at Daphni, near Athens, in a mosaic of the eleventh century in the dome of the church. But by dome, a shallow, flat curve is not intended. The church of Daphni is immensely tall in proportion to its size. It gives the impression of a giant stature and could be compared, almost, to a half-orange stuck upon a spear. This image of Christ Pantocrator, with the rainbow round it, consists of the bearded countenance and the two hands. Its raiment is suggested by wild lines and folds to be compared with furious scale passages in music. They gather the attention and direct it. That is their purpose, and to distract it from themselves they draw the eyes towards the theme, which is the frown, and parted hair and beard, and hands. It is long hair, touching on the shoulders, and the marks of the comb are shown in golden lines. It falls with redoubled thickness by the ears. But it is combed hair ; black hair of the Syrian with an auburn streak in it. Especially thick, too, above the temples, like a pelisse, or a fleece, and with a loose lock of hair upon the forehead. The beard begins by the side of the ears, but it is a scanty beard, not the full beard of the Bedouin, for it has a bare patch upon the chin and grows but sparsely below the underlip. The moustache, downward curving, descends into this, and it is this expression of the mouth which is characteristic of the countenance, if we except the frowning eyes.

Most of the forehead is hidden. What we see are the lines of the forehead and the knitting of the brows, which has caused two vertical lines above the nose, but they are not straight lines. They curve and open in harmony with the eyebrows. The eyes bear marks of agony and suffering. The eyelids are livid and leaden, as of one who has never slept, and this which in human beings is to be seen upon the lower lids, below the eyes, has spread to the upper eyelids. Out of this the eyes are staring. The nose is long and thin and aquiline with both edges outlined in drawing, ending in the curved nostrils above the thin lips. The sides of the face are long and thin, with hollow cheek-bones, and the beard grows from the shrunken hollows. What is its meaning ? It is the face of a being who has endured appalling suffering, and who, unquestionably, has risen from the dead.

Now for the hands. The left hand holds the book of the Gospels, a book of loose sheets bound, concertina fashion, with a loose back, and the sign of the cross upon the binding. This is held close to his shoulder and against his chest. But it is not the Bible. It is the hand that holds it. This emerges from a sleeve, immensely and wonderfully foreshortened in the mosaic, and taking advantage of the hollow of the dome. The thumb and index finger are upon the book. The other three fingers, side by side, are in repose, and their only function is to keep the edges of the book together. The expression or drama, therefore, is in the thumb and first finger, and for this purpose the ball of the hand has been exaggerated. Also, the canon of the three finger-joints has been distorted. The two lower joints are as though stiffened together, while the first joint is twisted and flattened so that it is equivalent to a head or caput, in which the nail is the mouth and eyes, as it were, resembling the flat head of a serpent, only the snake, like a fish or an insect, has a mask that wears a set expression. It never alters. Like the head of the praying mantis, about to strike, about to bring down its fearful limbs or saws ; like the head of the caterpillar upon the leaf.

Such is the one hand. Of the other hand we see only the fingers, and not the thumb. They are high up, on the level of the shoulder, as though the arm is extended, and here the character is implicit in all four fingers. The first and second fingers are apart and separate. The others keep close, as is their nature. The whole hand is about to enter into argument. It waits till the lips open. We see the nails of all four fingers like so many serpent countenances swaying from one body, the line of the quick and the line of the cuticle and the edge of the nail in outline, each with the same expression; the first and second fingers sprawling like a pair of legs belonging to a body that has tumbled, until we see that it is all in the wild and gaunt fury of their beckoning, upon the ground of the garment, the folds of which are like straight arrow shafts, and are flecked with gold in the mosaic.

The hands are more tremendous, even, than the terrifying countenance of the Christ Pantocrator. We shall not find their equivalent in any painting by El Greco. The hands in El Greco are white and perfumed in comparison. Those have intrigued and made gestures, but they have not suffered. Nor should we find any face in pictures by El Greco to compare with this. His is an effeminate Byzantinism. The only hands that can compare are in Picasso's *Guernica*, that ultimate prophecy of our own time, in which the hysteria and agony are clown-like and of the circus; the hands are like pseudopods; they are embryonic hands; the weeping women in the many different drawings are hideous as that Spanish circus act in which one clown is the squalling baby, and the other is its mother; the faces are moonlit apparitions foreshortened or elongated by the fateful hour; and we see the ghost or phantom of a mare, mad with fright, which has been let out of the bull-ring for a worse fate which is impending.

We could find similar hands, drawn according to that canon; but there is, of course, no parallel to the face of the Christ Pantocrator, for the hands are the instrument of the mind. They are in the world. They deal with the hideous happenings. But the countenance is immortal and outside it. In the very nature of this contrast, and in view of his tireless experiments, it is impossible to expect of the Spaniard Picasso that he should become, of a sudden, the supreme religious painter. He has seen the tragedy and transformation of death in the mean gutter, but we cannot expect of him that he should raise the dead. His phantasmagoria is at the moment of explosion. They will be lying, spattered and dismembered, in the kennel. Here, in the mosaic, we have every earthly horror in the hands. But, above, there is the face of the Pantocrator in the hour of judgement.

It is an Oriental countenance, but with nothing of Oriental serenity or calm. It is not longing for annihilation. Neither is it the Indian sadhu with knotted, tangled hair ; the fakir rubbed with ashes ; nor the wild-haired dervish. For the long hair is combed. We must turn the head round into profile, when we shall see that this thing of eternity is the face of a man of thirty-three or thirty-six ; but if, again, we look at it full face, considering it without the long hair or beard, then we are appalled by the wasting, burning agony. It is the face of a being who is dying in a high fever. The strength of the hair and beard, the moustache, are of that growth which continues after death. We look instinctively at the nails of the hand to see if they are long, for the nails grow after death. But we know the hands : the nails are not long. The face has shining, livid lights upon it, exactly as when we see a person dying in a darkened room and it is impossible that someone so weakened should live through the night. But the horror of sickness is not here. It is because we know him for a supernatural being, strongly marked, though, with his racial affinity, for he is a Jew or Syrian of Semitic countenance, of the physical type that was according to the tradition of his appearance, particularly in the manner in which his beard grows upon his lower lip and chin, which accords with the earliest known accounts of him, and with those extra-ordinary relics, the Sudario of Turin and the Volto Santo of Lucca. The nature and origin of both these are as mysterious as anything whatever that has come down to us from the past.

The first affects to be the shroud in which the body of Christ was wrapped, after he had been taken down from the cross, and it bears upon it the imprint of a human face, produced by some unknown agency, akin, perhaps, to that which produces the 'ghost' of a drawing or photograph upon the thinner sheet which protects it within the pages of a book. Whatever it be, and whether the result is art or accident, it is the most beautiful countenance imaginable, but on the excessively rare occasions upon which it has been examined it has been dated, in uncertainty of its process, as Byzantine, of the eleventh or twelfth century. The other, the Volto Santo of Lucca, is a crucifix, a robed and crowned figure upon the cross, according to tradition rescued from the sea, and beyond question a Byzantine work dating from before the destruction of all carved images by the Iconoclasts of the eighth century. This, too, conforms to the same tradition of appearance as the face upon the Sudario, and probably the pair of them, and the Pantocrator of Daphni, are the most authentic, as they are the most awe-inspiring and tremendous of all portrayals of Jesus Christ. All three are likenesses of the same person ; but the Sudario is the head of a dead man ; the Volto Santo is the head of a dying man upon the cross ; while the Pantocrator of Daphni is the same person, come through his agony, and given supernatural majesty and terror. The two first, that is to say, are powerless, because they are inanimate. They are dead, or dying, and cannot suffer any more. They have come to the extremity. But the Pantocrator, if we believe it, is the only person who has lived beyond the grave, who has been raised from the dead, and this is the only countenance that makes it credible. We can believe it ; or believe that, if it ever happened, such would be his bodily appearance after the miracle. This, and no other. In all Christian art there is not another portrayal which has this supernatural truth, which convinces of life after death, and the immortality of the soul.

He bears the marks of the agonies inflicted upon him in the living world. He is still suffering ; and we are given this witness upon an earth in which all the evidence is to the effect that human beings have been forgotten, or left to their fate. We can think of no other countenance that could be looked upon by the starving, or by those in pain. It is a work of rage and fury ; Oriental, but with none of the calm of the Orient. At the same time its facial expression reveals that it is not only considering the poor. Its concern is with every degree of mind ; and it is as terrifying now as then.

How curious it would be to climb into the dome, were there a scaffolding, and see it, bit by bit, by the light of a box of matches! To be within a few inches of the eyes, and mouth, and hands ! To strike the last match, with trembling fingers, and look into its eyes, and wasted cheeks, and frowning lips ! If there must be a god and a saviour, this is he. All others are meaningless.

(vi)

Mauresque

The pine trees of the huge mosaic are glaucous and resinous, that is to say, they glisten with a purplish or bluish tinge. They are not the colour of nature, any more than the cypress. Their shadows are violet or chocolate, and they are unguent-dropping. They exude gums and amber. But not a movement in the branches, nor the flash of any wing. The park lies sleeping in enchantment, as we left it. There is, indeed, something strange and curious about the deserted kiosques and pavilions. They are empty, but not uninhabited. Their population have gone away, or are not yet woken. They have been sleeping for ten centuries, and in the landscape it has been a perpetual dawn or early morning before they are awake.

More of the Dark Ages lies sleeping in the golden mosaic

than in sunken churches and in mildewed tombs. The secret consists in so much that we have lost and may never, now, regain. To that extent there were magicians who had the power to transform the visual world of human beings. They are the magicians of the Dark Ages and their secrets of instinct are lacking in our mechanical or scientific world. We have as much to learn from them as they from us. There have been other Golden Ages, but none that is so magically remote. The landscape of the mosaic is a sacred park or paradise more full of enchantment than any of the landscapes of the great masters. It is as old again as the Italian Primitives ; not spoiled by religion nor haunted by a story ; while, because it was created for the early Arab conquerors who were forbidden to draw the animal or human form, it is Oriental and intangible. It is even Indian in the old meaning of the word, when India lay to East or West and the only criterion was that it should be huge and remote and golden. The kiosques and pavilions in the mosaic would be Indian to Columbus and the Conquistadors, and they, like ourselves, would wait impatiently for their inhabitants to come forth. The Inca, we remember, filled a room as high as the hand would reach with gold, and may have lived in a palace built in the form of a pyramid. None of these histories is more strange than what we see before us.

What makes the mosaic the more mysterious is that it bears no inscription in Greek letters, or indeed in an alphabet of any kind. The Capella Palatina, most beautiful of all interiors with its mosaic walls and fretted Saracenic ceiling of gold and cedarwood, has inscriptions in Latin, Greek, and Arabic. The Greek workmen left inscriptions in their own alphabet at Cefalù and at Torcello, and it becomes their sign manual upon the mosaics as much as the signature in Greek letters upon El Greco's paintings. Here there is no such evidence, but the work of art is Byzantine-Greek in origin, and constructed for the

Arabs. It belongs to the aesthetic condominium of Greek and Arab, Spaniard and Moor.

While we wander through the sacred park of the mosaic, before we conjure up our vision of its inhabitants, and the hunt rides past before our eyes, there is time to think of early Kings, of Swinthila, Recesvinto, Wamba, or Don Rodrigo. Both Kings, Swinthila and Recesvinto, reigned in the seventh century. It is known that the Visigothic Kings kept a court of extraordinary magnificence, modelled upon that of Constantinople, and that they copied the Eastern Emperors even in their legal forms. But they were famed, particularly, for their wealth of jewellery and for their golden crowns. Of their barbaric splendour there remain, found by a miracle of chance, the crown of Recesvinto, discovered at Guarrazar, near Toledo, and now in the Musée de Cluny at Paris, and the crown of Swinthila, from the same treasure, in the Royal Armoury at Madrid. They are, more properly, votive crowns, for they have chains by which they were hung up in the sanctuary. The crown of King Swinthila, apart from this hanging chain, consists of a piece of rock-crystal from which depend four chains of golden leaves, *percées à jour*, and these support the upper rim of the crown proper, from the lower rim of which there are pendent letters, hanging down, spelling out the inscription : SVINTHILANUS REX OFFERET.[1] Large single pearls and sapphires hang down from these. But, from its size, it is a crown which could also be worn upon the head. In all, no fewer than eleven golden crowns were discovered at Guarrazar, though a great part of the treasure was sold by the peasants who found it, in 1858, to the goldsmiths of Toledo, by whom it was melted down for the value of the gold. These golden diadems must be among the most wonderful relics of the barbaric arts ; but one of the

[1] The golden crown in the Musée de Cluny bears the inscription : RECESVINTHVS REX OFFERET.

revelations of the great exhibition of Barcelona in 1929 lay in certain illuminated Visigothic manuscripts of later date, works of the ninth and tenth centuries ; notably a commentary on the Apocalypse from the cathedral of Burgo de Osma with a miniature of the Four Horsemen, resembling contemporary Persian drawing of the school of Rhages ; another codex of the Apocalypse from Seo de Urgel ; and a commentary and homily upon the Venerable Bede from the church of San Feliú at Gerona.

But this is not the Moorish part of Spain, and in order to satisfy our conscience, while giving at the same time an indication of the wonders of Mauresque art, we would instance the eleventh-century ivory caskets of Cordovan workmanship, of which the most beautiful extant specimens are to be found in the treasuries of the cathedral at Pampeluna in the Pyrenees, at Braga in Northern Portugal, and in the Victoria and Albert Museum, the two former of these being proved by inscriptions upon them to have been made for the same person, a minister of the Khalif Hisham II, under the direction or inspection of his chief eunuch. These caskets of ivory are completely covered with carvings in relief, with ornamentation of leaves and flowers, and with cusped medallions containing figures of men seated in Moorish fashion upon the ground, hawking, or fighting with wild beasts, and with many other single figures of lions, stags, or other animals. They are, undoubtedly, among the most precious objects that have come down to us from the Dark Ages. It would seem natural in these ivory boxes that their carved subjects should represent the chase, as though the imagination of the Moorish craftsman was fired by the distant provenance of the material upon which he was working and by its romantic origin from somewhere unknown in the dark continent of Africa.

The ivory cross of King Ferdinand I of Castile, given by that monarch to the convent of San Isidro at León, and now in the Archaeological Museum at Madrid, is in the same Mauresque

MOORISH IVORY CASKET
11th Century, Pamplona Cathedral

style with figures of animals, and men struggling with wild beasts. All such bestiaries, however, are to be compared for a supreme example with the carved monsters on the stone capitals of the two-storeyed cloister at the abbey of Santo Domingo de Silos, in its distant valley, only to be reached, till recent years, by early-morning diligence from Burgos. These carved animals, which show Persian influence in their suppleness and nervous line, were the work of Mussulman slaves attached to the monastery. This cloister is a thing unique of its kind. Not only is a scheme of decoration carried out by Mussulman craftsmen a feature without parallel in a Christian abbey, but, also, the Mussulmans seem to have considered themselves released, in part, from their obligation of abstract representation, and they worked in a freedom of fancy that is nowhere to be found in mosque or *medersa*, or even in the inner courts of Moorish palaces, so that from both points of view, Mussulman and Christian, Santo Domingo de Silos is incomparable and alone.

Even so, this Oriental idiom had its influences. It is to be followed in Languedoc, in the wonderful sculptures of the school of Moissac, works of Romanesque and Eastern origin that must be connected with the Mussulman carvings of Santo Domingo de Silos and with which the sculptured figures of Chartres, magnificent as they may be, do not compare. The arches of the cloister at Moissac, resting alternately on single and on clustered columns, have carved capitals of the greatest intricacy and Oriental richness. But it is the portal of the abbey, more particularly, with its astonishing tympanum of an enthroned Christ surrounded by symbols of the Apostles and by the twenty-four elders of the Apocalypse ; the great stone rosaces of the lintel ; the column of crossed lions, one pair above another, with the gaunt, attenuated Prophets upon alternate faces of the central pier of the great doorway opening into the church ; Isaiah and St Peter at the sides ; and the sculptured bands of birds and rats that course up and down the lateral piers ; but, above all, the inner faces of the porch with sculptured scenes, in compartments, upon two floors. below double arches, and above, another row of sculptures all framed in more carved pilasters and sculptured courses. Here is the great school of European sculpture and effects, in stone, as wildly magnificent and sumptuous as in the golden mosaics and silken stuffs of Byzantium. Here is the same god whom we will worship in the Birds of Paradise and in the Trogons.

The same sculptors or their pupils worked at Beaulieu, where, under the tympanum above the central doorway, there are bands of fabulous animals and the central pier of the door has the same elongated figures in a canon of proportion all their own ; and at Souillac, where the central pillar has the sacrifice of Abraham, and carved figures of wrestlers in this peculiar and Eastern idiom that is found nowhere else, and that never comes again. The feeling for stone is extraordinary in these carvings.[1]

But mention must be made, also, of the Moorish textiles. A Cordovan historian, writing in the beginning of the thirteenth century, says of Almeria that what made it superior to any other city in the world was its various manufactures of silks and other articles of dress such as the *dibaj* (silken stuff of many colours), a sort of silken cloth surpassing in quality and durability anything else manufactured in other countries ; and *tiraẓ* or costly stuffs on which the names of Khalifs, Amirs, and other wealthy individuals are inscribed, some of which are so rich that a suit made out of them will cost many thousands ;[2] for striped

---

[1] The sculptures of Moissac, and of Souillac and Beaulieu, were executed between 1120 and 1180.

[2] Compare these " brocades with beautiful drawings, and the names of Khalifs and Amirs woven in them " with the coronation robes of the Holy Roman Emperors in the Schatzkammer at Vienna. Those are, in reality, the robes of the Norman Kings of Sicily, woven by Arab craftsmen from Palermo, acquired by the Hohenstaufens through Constance, wife of Emperor Henry VI, and added to the treasury of the Holy Roman Emperors.

silks and brocades there were a thousand looms, and the same number were continually employed in weaving the stuffs called Iskalaton (scarlet). There were also one thousand for weaving robes called Al Jorjani (Georgian), and another thousand for weaving robes called Isbahani (from Isfahan). The manufacture of turbans of gay and dazzling colours for the women employed an equal number of hands. And he, or another Moorish author, adds that at Murcia " there are several manufacturers of silken cloth called *Al washin thalathat* " (variegated, of many colours), and mentions the cloth of gold of Zaragoza.

Later, after the fall of Cordoba, the Kingdom of Granada became famous for its silks. The geographer Edrisi tells of three thousand villages, in the territory of Jaén alone, where silkworms were reared. He remarks that Almeria was then the principal city of the Mussulmans in Spain. Stuffs were manufactured there, known by the names of *holla*, of *debady*, and of *siglaton*, *espahani*, and *djordjani* ; curtains were made patterned with flowers, stuffs ornamented with nails, and other cloths known as *attabi* and *mi djar*. Also, apparently, Samite or *Xamet*, deriving from Syria or Damascus. These manufactures continued at Granada after the conquest. In the travels of Philippe le Bel, father of Charles V, we are told of the zacatin or silk market ; and an Italian traveller, a few years later, writes that " one enters a place called Alcaiceria which is enclosed within two doors, and full of alleys where the Moors sell silks and embroideries of every kind ", and he alludes to " good taffetas, sarcenet, and silk serges ". Toledo, as well, was famous for its stuffs.

But it is necessary, also, to speak of the Toledan steel. Not the rapiers of later date known by the name of *perrillo*, because they were marked on the blade with the figure of a dog, praised by Cervantes, and made by a Moor of Granada who had been swordsman to Boabdil, and became a Christian. Their secret lay in the tempering, which was done at night, in order to tell in the darkness the colour of the heated steel when it was dipped into the water. The choicest blades of that time were so elastic that they were curled up like the mainspring of a watch and packed in boxes.

The secret of their excellence was the Tagus water, and the fine white river sand. Estoques reales or swords of state ; and montantes or double-handed falchions ; or the sword of Boabdil with its hilt of solid gold enamelled in blue, white, and red, with Cufic lettering, and axle of ivory, worn hanging round the neck between the shoulder-blades, with a little bag, the *tahali*, hung, also, from the leather girdle. The round leather shields or adargas of the Moors were not less renowned, being formed of a pair of hides cemented together with a paste composed of herbs and camel-hair.

Spain had been celebrated for swords as long ago as Roman times. The ancient Iberian city of Bilbilis, now Calatayud in Aragon, was known for its swords that were tempered in the waters of the Jalón. Bilbilis was famous for its armourers, goldsmiths, iron mines, and horse fairs. Ford reminds us, in his *Handbook*, that Bilbilis was the birthplace of the Roman poet Martial, who went to Rome to the court of Domitian, " neglected business, and took to writing epigrams and composing *seguidillas*, like his later countrymen Salas and Quevedo ".

(vii)

Tirra-lirra

The enchanted palaces of the Dark Ages came to life for a few moments, but the mirage fades again. It was only the conjuring up of a vision, or even a dream within a dream, for we have never seen with our eyes the mosaics of Damascus, and it is merely that their magical emptiness and remoteness and their mysterious buildings led us to wander there away from the wreck of falling cities. Here at least there is no starving and taking of hostages, no shivering from the cold ; no internment, nor the noise of steel wings, night and day. The sacred places of the arts are deserted and uninhabited as those buildings in the mosaic, and our only hope must be that a few of the population are sleeping, and not dead. All, all, however, is interior creation. How could it be otherwise ? Such things are but fictions ; or the shadows of what has been, or what could be.

As for ourselves, once again we are unimportant compared with all the others, an impostor or mountebank, someone who goes round from town to town and is no longer even young, having written books and poems for twenty years or more. Lost is the golden opportunity. And, at once, the scene is transformed for us all into the court of the Duke of Parma, or anywhere else that fame and fortune beckoned. It need have no name. But always with the park or paradise of the mosaic for background, for the reality of the vision.

And, suddenly, the miracle happens. A gigantic fanfare of hunting horns breaks, with no warning, from the far corner of the wood. A phrase of four notes or syllables, the first note three times repeated, then the fourth or higher note, long held. After that, the whole phrase once more, and the dying of its sentence in four more notes, fading away into the distance. But the body of the horns is gaily flourishing, and it is taken up again and again from further away. This is no ordinary hunt. Horns are blowing in every direction. Next the flourishes themselves form the prelude for the fanfare, and it proclaims itself and dies mournfully away. And once again ; while the flourishes challenge and give answer, near and far.

We listen, and do not know which way to turn or move. But no living thing, human or animal, can be seen. It is so curious that there comes no sound, no trampling of the dead twigs, with so large a body of men and horses moving in the wood. But nothing stirs. There is no breath of wind. The dead silence itself becomes a bass or drone, an empty humming ; and upon that ground, suddenly, and more tremendous as though nearer, the fanfare breaks solemn and portentous. What can be its meaning ? And we listen, not daring to move, and not wanting to, for fear of losing the enchantment.[1]

It is even not a little frightening, like a message out of another world. Not the tirra-lirra, tarah-ti-rarah of the hunting horn. They are massed hunting horns. The ghostly hunt is bound by some compact. Or is it nothing more than that the wood is dark and lonely ? And when we hear them again, they have fled into the distance, down the haunted glades. But not for long. There comes the thunder of galloping hooves. A furious and wild urgency and expectation, with the flourishes searching the wood, as it were, a dozen times at once, letting no corner of it escape them, and in midst of it, the fanfare and answering tirra-lirra of the fairy horns. And at last, voices, if you listen intently — but now for certain — and a crashing of the twigs and briars. We are about to behold the huntsmen and the hunted.

They come riding out of the trees into a clearing, with the massed horns behind them, and solitary calls sounding in every direction. But not galloping. They are moving at a set pace like an army on the march, and the fanfares and alarums are in perpetual accompaniment. They are on a journey : moving down to the coast or frontier, hoping to reach it in safety by forced marches, but now lost, or overtaken by the darkness. Or, at another moment, they are only riding back from hunting.

---

[1] A reminiscence of the introduction and opening scene of Act II of *Tristan and Isolde.*

The hunt is still on, even, and it is that they are separated from the hounds and huntsmen. Hence the fanfares and the scattered hunting calls. What a magical moment ! It is impossible to move or stir, for we know them. They are the knights and ladies of *The Triumph of Death* in Orcagna's fresco. But we will not have it that this is entirely a mediaeval hunting party. They are knights and ladies out of an earlier time : or they are timeless. Looking at them, we need not be tied down to any particular place or time. It is the hunting party out of *The Triumph of Death* in the Campo Santo at Pisa, a penultimate work of the Dark Ages before they merged entirely into the Gothic, before they lost their urgency and terror, while it is something far older and more inexplicable because it is a state of the world with which we have no connection and have lost all contact.

Death is in front of them, and behind them, in the painting. They have ridden past the bodies of the three Kings lying in open coffins in various stages of decay. In the fresco we saw them before this moment, when they had just reined in their horses, when they had come face to face with death. But this time they have not been spared. The roof of the cloister was set alight by an incendiary shell, and molten lead poured down upon the walls. We are told by an ' official spokesman ' that the results are most interesting, though regrettable, and that it is now possible, owing to the destruction of the surface, to see the frescoes of the Campo Santo at different phases of their process, in the underpainting, or the first sketch upon the walls, and that nowhere else in Italy is there such a ' laboratory ' of mediaeval painting. The frescoes by Benozzo Gozzoli are thus mentioned. Of the fate of Traini's painting, *The Triumph of Death*,[1] no precise details have yet been given, and we must

---

[1] Attributed by Vasari to Andrea Orcagna, but now believed to be painted about 1350 by Francesco Traini, a Pisan master. It will be noted that we have attributed it ourselves, indifferently, to Orcagna or Traini, for the criterion of this great painting is that it is tremendous and anonymous.

presume it to have been totally or effectually destroyed. Even if it has been spared, and the fresco no worse than badly scorched or shaken, it will no longer have for neighbour in the Campo Santo the vines and cypresses of Benozzo upon his terraced hills, his young women in loose, rippling gowns with baskets of ripe grapes upon their heads, the treading of the wine, the bright painted birds and angel children, and the moral of this terrific mediaeval painting must be heightened after it has, in its own person, come face to face with destruction. How awe-inspiring must have been the spectacle of its approaching danger ! That would have been the night to hear the fanfare and the hunting calls, near and far, and to understand their meaning.

As now ; for they are lost, or in flight. Or have given their message and are no longer needed. There are ten of them, knights and countesses or princesses. But who are they ? And who can be the ladies ? In our excitement as to their identity and our anticipation of what is to come we cannot but recall the portrait of the last of the Greek Empresses left to us by the traveller Bertrandon de la Broquière, courtier to Duke Philip the Good of Burgundy. He had seen the Basilissa during a service in Santa Sophia, and waited all day without food or drink in order that he should see her again. She was the Palaeo-logina, Maria Comnena, sister of the Grand Comnenus Alexius IV of Trebizond, and wife of the Emperor John VI Palaeologus, member of a family famous for their good looks. He saw her mounting her saddle-mule from a bench, behind a cloak which was outstretched for screen. She wore a long cloak and a pointed hat, with three golden plumes, and long golden earrings set with jewels. Her face was painted, " of which she had no need, for she was young and fair ". She was attended by two ladies-in-waiting, some courtiers, and a corps of eunuchs. Nearly ten centuries before this, in the mosaic of San Vitale at Ravenna, the Christian Empress Theodora has eunuchs in her train. So

48

much for the continuity of Byzantine custom, while certainly in *The Triumph of Death*, this tremendous relic of the Middle Ages, which dates from about 1350, the period is so early that the conception is Byzantine as much as it is Gothic. The anchorite St Macarius, who stands above the hunting party in the fresco, to warn the knights and ladies of death and of the passing of human pleasures, is a saint or hermit of the Eastern church. His cell or sketa was in the Thebaid or Egyptian desert.

They are the knights and ladies of Orcagna's fresco, but we clothe them according to our fancy. The first to ride forward wears a long robe of blue, heavily marked with gold, and looking at his pointed shoe against the scarlet saddle-cloth, we see that he wears white stockings spotted with gold in a particular manner, like a leopard's spots, and that he has golden spurs. This knight rides with his back to us. Next to him comes a lady in a long robe of wild rose colour, with paler sleeves, and a white wimple.

Here are a knight and his lady riding pillion ; she in a blue gown with red sleeves, and a long white train which forms her saddle-cloth ; he in paler blue, with a wide-brimmed hat of straw, and a pair of falcons on his wrist. After him, a lady in a gown of lavender blue, with long white sleeves that hide her hands. Then a knight in a robe of lapis blue with a fur collar, but it is particoloured, for his shoulder and right side, and half his figure, are black to match his huge, shaggy hat of Burgundian fashion. The knight riding next to him is the most gorgeous of them all, for he is dressed in the Royal livery, in the King's colours, and it is probable that he is a prince of the blood. The livery is half red, and half black and white ; that is to say, the left side of his body is scarlet with a white sleeve, and his right side is black with an inner panel of white, and a white, flame-like border or edging into the black. He wears a black hat with white on the crown, and a long, white trailing end. One curious thing, that all of them, alike knights and ladies, are crowned or garlanded with leaves. The ladies have spring leaves in their hair or upon their starched white wimples, while those knights who are hatless wear garlands of spring leaves upon their heads.[1]

But riding in midst of them, in a row, one behind the other, come three young ladies dressed, all alike, in green. They have high bosoms, and their green robes seem immensely long, which is because their length is unbroken, and they trail down so low that they conceal the feet. Under the long lines of that garment we discern the shape of their knees as they sit riding, and again they have long trailing sleeves that hide their wrists and hands. They are dressed alike, except that two of them are bareheaded and have garlands of leaves entwined into their hair. But the young lady who is nearest to us wears sprays of leaves upon her white linen wimple, and a blue lining to her sleeves. She rides upon a milk-white *haquenée*, with plaited mane and tail, and a harness which is composed entirely of gilded ropes entwined and worked with leaves. They ride forward, all three of them, with that familiar ambling motion of women riding side-saddle, which is always, and inevitably, that of the queen or princess led along upon a leading rein. Their long green habits are " the livery of May ", made of that " gay green " cloth which the French King Charles VI gave to his friends and intimates at the beginning of each spring. A green that suggests the green leaves and boughs of spring, but does not attempt to copy what is impossible, the spring of the year being expressed in the young faces and youthful figures of the three princesses, a thing that cannot be taken from them except by death or illness, and that no one older in years can pretend to or assume.

They are the portraits of our three loves at the time when we

[1] Our costumes are taken from the *Très Riches Heures du Duc de Berri*. This most beautiful of illuminated manuscripts, with miniatures from the hand of Pol de Limbourg, is in the Musée Condé at Chantilly. It takes the form of a calendar of the twelve months, with the castles and familiar scenes of the Duc de Berri (*d.* 1416) in the background.

50

first saw them, or of one and the same person, as though, in our excitement of recognition as she rode forward out of the wood, we remembered her, a moment later, and for ever more, in as many different movements or phases of her first appearance. This much is certain, that the image of the person loved is never fixed and still. The static image is for persons of ordinary occurrence, or who have taken our interest in some other way. But, the stronger the force of the emotion, the more we remember it with all the other senses, but not with the eyes, to the extent that the limning or delineation of the particular person may escape us altogether and we remember, instead, many irrelevant details and the mood in general, but not the image in the eye. Of the immortal force of this first image, its fiery strength but misty outline, there are the three great instances in literature, with Dante and with Petrarch, but in humility we associate our image with the least of the three, and would recall that Boccaccio, on a visit to Naples, first saw Fiammetta on Holy Saturday, 30 March 1336, in the church of San Lorenzo. "This encounter", we read, "upset the whole of his existence and eventually inspired him to write *The Decameron*, after he had joined the whirl of Neapolitan society for several years in order to lead the same life as Fiammetta led, at the end of which time he returned in poverty to Florence", a situation which would find its modern parallel in living in London and returning to the country.

(viii)

Castles of Les Très Riches Heures

We will glance at the castles of the *Très Riches Heures*. The high square towers, scattered and wide apart, rising behind the winter trees like celestial skyscrapers at the back of a wood shaped as an amphitheatre, for they are killing the boar in a clearing of the forest of Vincennes. Or we see an immense brand-new château rising at the far side of a river behind a crenellated wall, and it is the old palace of the Louvre seen from across the Seine. There are towers at the corners and coupled towers in the centre of each wall, so that we imagine for ourselves the numbers of rooms on each of the two upper floors, and how many of them must have semicircular bays or window embrasures looking out over mediaeval Paris. Above, rise the turreted chimneys and high-pitched, leaded pinnacles and roofs. Promenaders are strolling along the river below the castle wall. But in the foreground a ploughed field is being sown with seed. A blue-smocked peasant scatters it in handfuls from his apron ; there is a scarecrow in the form of an archer drawing a bow ; bits of cloth are fluttering on the earth upon wires to scare the birds ; and painted magpies are hopping in the furrows.

Still more fantastic is the château of Saumur. It springs from a grassy bank high into the empty sky. Vineyards stretch right up to the foundations of its towers, and it is the grape-gathering. A two-wheeled ox-cart is pushed into the vines, and its pair of tubs or barrels are filling with the grapes, while donkeys with loaded *paniers* are waiting in the path.

But the castle takes our breath away. We see the huge pyramidal roof of the kitchen, like that of Glastonbury, detached from the main building. The castle has four towers, one at each corner, plain in their lower reaches, but ribbed where they rise high enough to be pierced with windows. The entrance is under a porch or portcullis which has a cluster of turrets and its own roof-line below the parapet of the main building. But the towers themselves are magnificent in their corbelling, and between them the lower roofs have high dormer windows, while the tall chimney-stacks and conical, pointed roofs make a spectacle of fantastic complexity and elaboration, and we can see the white stone lilies of France upon the battlements of the towers and the gilded fleurs-de-lis below the weathervanes.

Another miniature shows us the castle of Poitiers, built in the shape of a triangle between two rivers, and entered by a long wooden bridge into a wall that is blank and windowless up to the top storey. Blue-slated roofs upon the three long walls enclose its triangle, but we can see the enriched gables and dormers of the interior court. There is a tower at each corner, and their cappings turn from defence to pleasure with their turrets and their dormer windows. A stream with bulrushes and pollard willows flows through the foreground and divides the pasture from the cornfield. A shepherd and shepherdess are sheep-shearing, she in a hooded headdress and long blue kirtle ; while over the stream two men are reaping the harvest, and there are poppies and cornflowers growing in the ripe honeycomb of corn, shaped, too, like a comb of honey, for it is enclosed or boxed in by the willowed stream.

For the third month of the year the Château de Lusignan crowns its undulating hill. It has an outer wall low down upon the hill slope, an inner body or enceinte, towers with red caps, while the keep has blue-slated roofs and a great tower with pinnacles and dormer windows. Above the roofs, in the miniature, flies the fée Mélusine of the old legend. But it must be enough for us that Plantagenets were born here and that the name of Lusignan was carried to Jerusalem and Cyprus. For fields and vineyards run up the hillside, and a stone shrine stands at the intersection of four paths among the vines. A peasant with a team of oxen is tilling in the foreground, while behind low walls the husbandmen dress and trim the vines. It is one of the flinty soils and sun-drenched hills that make good wine, and although this is only March, the third month of the year, there is hard clear light, and air and wine tend to the Latin, not the Celt.

But we will end with the month of June. Again, there are a river and pollard willows. But above them rises nothing less than the Sainte-Chapelle and the immense blue roofs of the palace. There are the two gables, side by side, of the great hall ; an outer covered staircase and a garden with a long trellised walk, and a domed pavilion of trellis and green leaves. But a grass field runs up to our feet. Three men with rhythmic movement scythe the hay ; there is the darker colour of the uncut grass, the lighter of the new-mown, and the dark strips that each man is in the act of scything. Nearer still, two young girls are raking and gathering the new-mown hay. One is dressed in lighter, and one in darker blue. Both have white sleeves and white kerchiefs on their heads. The girl in dark blue has her dress folded up, in front, to show her white underskirt or petticoat. Her bodice, too, is more elaborate with its division or opening. She holds a wooden pitchfork, while her companion has a wooden rake. They are raking and throwing the new-mown hay into little heaps, and a line of their handiwork curves back towards the river. This familiar scene and the unfamiliar beauty and simplicity of their blue dresses are the last things that we remember of the *Très Riches Heures*.

(ix)

Fox-tossing

But we continue with our philosophy of the hunters and the hunted. It is, of course, a kind of mimic war. Need we, then, metamorphose the three princesses, the castles and the fée Mélusine, in order to meet them in the hotels and restaurants of modern London ? For that would be the parallel. Let us encounter, instead, the ghosts and emblems of this ancient warfare, and see where they will lead us. There could be no better beginning than with the art of falconry. It is, indeed, an art, a literature, and a language of its own ; an art, too, that was Oriental in its origins. A learned author, in his bibliography of ancient and modern works on falconry,[1] cites nearly four hundred printed books as well as many early manuscripts, including *De Arte Venandi cum Avibus* written by Frederick II *Stupor Mundi* early in the thirteenth century on his return from his Eastern travels, and he gives as well more than six hundred technical terms of falconry in the seven principal languages. We would start from the falcon mews in some old castle where, as still at some old manors in North Wales, these have been made into an architectural feature in the stable yard, and watch the hooded falcons, six in number, carried forth perched upon the cadge or brancard, which is a wooden frame, like a tray or door with slats of wood across it, carried strapped to the shoulders, with a man, the cadge-bearer, walking in the middle of it. We must learn to distinguish between the goshawk and peregrine, sparrow-hawk and tiercel, and that the costly white jerfalcons are caught on the sandy coasts of Lithuania, and as like as not have been sent as presents by the Grand Master of the Teutonic Order.[2] Two centuries later, the Kings of Denmark were in

---

[1] *Bibliotheca Accipitraria*, by J. E. Harting : London, Bernard Quaritch, 1891.

[2] Several ' convoys ' of the Baltic falcons were thus sent to Henry IV of England, together with the bodies of three aurochs captured in the Lithuanian forests, according to the *Tresslerbuch* or *Diarium* of daily expenses of Marienburg, the headquarters of the Teutonic Knights, 1399–1409, published by Dr. Erich Joachim, cf. *Sport in Art*, by W. A. Baillie-Grohman : London, Ballantyne & Co., 1913. The aurochs is mentioned by Caesar in his account of Gaul, and a famous aurochs hunt was held by Charlemagne in the Hercynian woods in honour of the ambassadors of Haroun-al-Raschid, an occasion described by the monk Eginhard of St Gall, and beyond doubt one of the most picturesque incidents in all history. Having attempted in another place a description of the hunting of the great elk, *Cervus giganteus*, in primitive Ireland, my imagination is unable to conceive of a theme more inspiring and romantic, or more suited to my own personal tastes and aptitudes. This fabulous occasion, of which we may hear, whenever we will, the echo of the ivory olifants and the storming hooves, and see in imagination the turbans

the custom of sending expert huntsmen from Norway to snare
the Iceland falcons, which were to be found only among the
most inaccessible crags of basalt and lava, near the volcanic
fires, or overhanging a tarn in the mountains, or the frightful
sea. The Iceland falcons, again, were sent far and wide as presents;
and it was this bird, more particularly, that was trained and
worked during many generations, until recent times, by the
Dutch falconers of Valkenswaard, near Bois-le-Duc.[1] Another
race of falcons was procured during the Middle Ages from
Albania, whence were supplied, in large part, the mews of the
Sforza and Visconti and of the Kings of Aragon ; and another
from the Isola di San Pietro, ' Insula Accipitrum ' of the Romans,
off the southern coast of Sardinia. It is an art which, visually,
and for good reason, has Persian or Moghul affinities so that the
peregrine in its hood, shaking its gold or silver bells as it darts
its masked head from side to side, whether, as in particular
instances, by Jan van Eyck or by Gentile Bellini, always suggests
a Persian miniature, and this holds true of every detail in which
the art of falconry is represented, be it in tapestry or painting.
But the fullest portrayal of this forgotten art is, probably, in the
large and unnoticed paintings by a Dutchman in one of the rooms

and scimitars of the guests from the Orient lighting the long galleries and darkening
forest glades, to thickets where the great aurochs stands at bay and hunters and hunted are
lost together in the dusk of time, the wild hunt and ensuing banquet, this, indeed, could
be an interpretation of the Oriental and Occidental worlds as those are mingled in the
sculptures of Moissac and Santo Domingo de Silos. Gold- or silver-mounted aurochs'
horns were favourite presents from the Teutonic Knights. At that date the Lithuanians
were still pagan and had, like the ancient Gauls, Druids and aurochs in their forests. The
last aurochs died in Poland in 1627, and it is the European bison, distinguished from the
aurochs by its additional or fourteenth pair of ribs, that used to be hunted by the Russian
Tsars in the Polish forest of Bialowieza, but has probably been finally exterminated
during the war.

[1] The *Traité de Fauconnerie*, by H. Schlegel and A. Wulverhorst (1843–1854), a work
with twelve magnificent coloured plates of the different breeds of falcons drawn by
Joseph Wolf, gives many details of the annual supply of falcons from Iceland to the
Danish Court. A special vessel was despatched every year from Denmark to Bessestaed,
the old capital of Iceland. The Royal Mews at Copenhagen were discontinued in 1803,
owing to the Napoleonic wars.

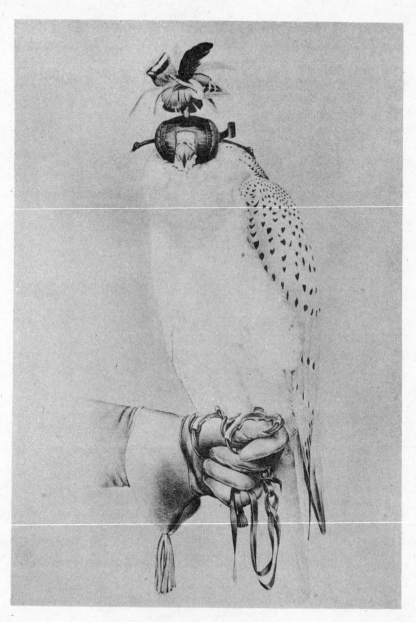

WHITE GREENLAND FALCON

of Herrenhausen, outside Hanover, which have for subject the
falcons and hunting exploits of the first Elector of Hanover,
Ernest Augustus, father of our George I.

The great stag-hunts in the Saxon and Thuringian forests
are recalled in paintings by Lucas Cranach and his son. The
crossbow was last used at these court hunts, and the Emperor
Charles V, easily recognised by his Habsburg features, was
guest of honour and is to be seen, crossbow in hand, loosing at
the stag-antlered river, for the Elbe runs in between. In every
one of the Cranach paintings innumerable stags are struggling
in the water, and it must be a remembrance of the naked nymphs
of the same painter with their flaxen, Saxon features and quaint
waists that gives a mythological meaning and puts an imaginary
Diana and an Actaeon into every hunt. In the background,
and so different from the châteaux of the *Très Belles Heures*
that it is another world, are the brand-new castles of Hartenfels
or the Moritzburg, the last standing on an island in a lake and
full, to this day, of antlered heads and forgotten paintings of the
chase. The Moritzburg remains, indeed, to all who have crossed
the drawbridge into its endless rooms, the capital and metropolis
of the mimic war against the stags.

So vast was the slaughter at the court hunts that it must be
assumed the deer population of the forests was ten times what it
is now. The two Electors of Saxony, John George I and John
George II, during the seventy years of their combined reigns
(1611–1688) killed 110,530 deer and 52,400 wild boars, besides
wolves and bears. This father and son must qualify as the
greatest slaughterers of wild animals of all time.[1] Their relative,
Duke John Casimir of Saxe-Coburg, was not less indefatigable
and left, as memorial, the Coburg Hunting Chronicle, a set of

[1] Only, however, so far as larger game are concerned, for Toudouze, *lieutenant de la
Vénerie* to the Prince de Condé, at Chantilly, states that in the space of thirty-one years
he had seen killed 924,717 birds and animals, large and small, in the forest. Cf. *La
Chasse à travers les âges*, p. 216, by Comte de Chabot : Paris, 1898.

paintings done in gouache by Wolff Pirkner. These depict in detail every stage and kind of hunting. Early in the series, John Casimir is ordering the unfolding and erection of the canvas screens which were put up, mile after mile, through the forest in order to surround and hem in the deer, a task performed by hundreds of peasants, men and women, as forced labour. Later, we see him shooting at the driven deer from the inner ring of a great canvas circle within which the hunt breakfast is laid out under the fir trees, and already a hecatomb is rising of the slain. The court dwarfs are in attendance, headed by Claus the jester, who was no taller than a boar-hound. In another painting we can participate, in twenty-one separate scenes on the same canvas, at the undoing of the stags, and see these noble and pathetic animals converted from dead bodies into mere skin and bone. The *curée* is, perhaps, the most fantastic of these scenes, for the hounds are held back on leashes while a whole corps of huntsmen sound the different signals on short hunting horns, and the procedure is as elaborate as at a state ceremony. Eventually, we have the return home of the whole hunting train, winding up and down over the hills : first of all, many horses and the Duke's six-horsed coach or litter ; at the tail of the procession the ordinary hounds led in threes by women ; and climbing the rocky path in the foreground, and therefore more conspicuous, the enormous boar-hounds, led singly, for they were the size of yearling steers.

During the latter part of the seventeenth century, and the early years of the eighteenth, the court hunts tended, more and more, towards a ceremonial or mass slaughter of the innocents. They took on the character of a *carrousel* or state ceremony, and the taste of the period caused trophies of the chase to be collected with something of that fervour bestowed more often upon relics of the saints. With that went also a craze for the curious and abnormal. Typical of this was the cult for piebald or speckled horses, to which we shall return later, or such eccentricities as the hunting leopard of the Emperor Leopold I, *en croupe* behind that monarch when he went riding. But the antler mania reached its climax in the *Wundersamste Hirsche*, the 'Most Wonderful Stags', of J. E. Ridinger (1698–1767), a series of a hundred engravings. We can see the sixty-six-tined antlers of the stag shot by the King of Prussia and exchanged by him with the Elector of Saxony for a company of tall grenadiers.[1] There are other stags with antlers like the forked lightning, or malformed and twisted specimens, some with a third antler, and the portrait of a poor stag which, fleeing, jumped a twelve-foot wall but was shot or 'grassed' before the year was ended. Nevertheless, there is a strange and wild magnificence to these stags, and some of the heads are noble and romantic to the last degree. The spotted red deer of Württemberg are depicted. One of them is shown leaping a forest stream, from bank to bank of which are strung bunches of feathers, tied upon strings, and a pair of lines as well, upon which flags of different coloured cloths are fluttering, devices the purpose of which was to frighten the stags and force them within the limits of the drive ; but the learned authority from whom we quote points to the curious details of the grand-ducal monograms and coats-of-arms upon the flags and adds the information that the manufacture of the bunches of feathers was a form of home-work imposed upon the Jews, who had to furnish, individually, a thousand such bunches in the year. One ghost is missing : a white stag to be seen flitting through the dank thickets. But here it is : a white stag of the race of Hesse-Darmstadt. The Landgrave had his great deer parks stocked with these, but they died out towards the end of the century and the last twelve of them, sent as a present to the Elector of Saxony, made a belated appearance during a carnival

[1] This pair of antlers still hangs in the Moritzburg, the hunting castle of the Kings of Saxony. Ridinger, a native of Ulm, spent most of his life at Augsburg.

procession in the streets of Dresden, after the French Revolution, drawing a triumphal car on which was enthroned one of the princesses in the garb of Diana.

Fox-tossing was the most curious and far-fetched of all such ceremonials. This was practised either in the woods, within one of the circles made of canvas screens, or in the court-yard of some palace. The foxes were released from traps or boxes, and the sport consisted in tossing them into the air as they ran past by means of a tossing-sling of cord-work or webbing, the centre of which lay waiting ready on the ground while the two ends were held up by a pair of partners, generally a lady and a gentleman. Sometimes there were as many as three lanes of slings down which the wretched animals had to run the gauntlet. The jerking or tautening of the slings had to be done as strongly as possible so that the foxes were hurled high into the air, while the ground was strewn with sand or sawdust in order to prolong the agony and not kill at the first throw. Full-grown foxes were tossed in this manner twenty-four feet into the air. Augustus the Strong of Saxony, whose love for this sport is not less remarkable when we remember him as patron of the fragile Meissen china, would hold his end of the sling with one finger against the two strongest men to be picked out of the company. Nor was he content with foxes ; he let wild boars and wolves into the ring, and at one contest 687 foxes, 533 hares, 34 badgers, 21 wild cats, 34 wild boars, and 3 wolves were sacrificed.

It became more fantastic still when masked fox-tossing was introduced at the court of Brunswick, for not only the hunters but the hunted played their parts in masks. The gentlemen were heroes, Roman warriors, satyrs, centaurs, or buffoons, while the ladies disguised themselves as nymphs, or goddesses, or the nine Muses. Foxes, and hares more particularly, were " dressed up in bits of cardboard, gaudy cloth, and tinsel ", sometimes as caricatures of well-known characters, in public or in private, and the proceedings would end with a performance in an open-air theatre, or a torchlight masquerade through the park. And these exceedingly curious ceremonies can be concluded with mention of a royal stag-hunt on the Starnberger See, near Munich, a contemporary painting of which event hangs, or used to hang, in the Nymphenburg. A great stag was forced to soil or take to the water close to where the great state barge, a copy of the Bucintoro of Venice, rowed by one hundred and ten oarsmen, was lying ready. Other curious craft were waiting near by, one of them with a huge mast and furled, emblazoned sail, and this and the others as richly carved and painted, with as much gilding, as the dragon barges of the Kings of Burma or Siam. Cannon are firing, trumpeters are sounding a fanfare from the flagged roof of the mock-Bucintoro, and could we defy time and wait but a few moments longer we would see the fourteen-tined stag dragged on board and killed at the feet of the Duchess, who will be given the poor animal's right foreleg, cut off at the knee joint with a hunting knife.

(x)

Apeloosas

We have written of the cult for piebald or speckled horses, and that this was carried to extraordinary lengths. In the many prints after J. E. Ridinger that have horsemanship and the *haute école* for subject this is clearly seen. In each of the half-dozen plates of " The Large Riding School " there are horses so curiously marked that, but for his accuracy in other matters, we might not be willing to believe him. The scene is an outdoor riding school overlooked by a balcony that descends from a formal garden ; or it is the *manège* itself with boxes and tribunes, and their balustrades support groups of cupids who hold tilting lances, or are trying plumed helms upon their heads. Other prints show an outdoor yard or arena crossed by a gallery upon high arches, under a series of vaulted roofs, a reminiscence, surely, of the Roman prints of Piranesi, but influenced, too, by the Spanish or Winter Riding School of Fischer von Erlach in Vienna. The spangled horses that occur in these prints are similar to, or of the same race as, the circus horses still to be seen, which are of Eastern origin, being, in fact, Apeloosas, white horses speckled with black like leopards, and quite different in marking from the piebald or the skewbald. They are, it would appear, an Oriental race or strain, perhaps Turkish or Tunisian in the first place, much esteemed at the time of which we are writing, in Central Europe, but now relegated to the circus tent.[1]

But those curious animals have, in particular, their own painter. His name is Philip Ferdinand von Hammilton, as he

---

[1] It was a craze not confined to Central Europe. Toudouze, *lieutenant de la Vénerie de Chantilly*, gives this account of a hunt with his master, the Prince de Condé : " 5 August 1777, the King (Louis XVI) hunted the wild boar with the hounds of M. de Duc. He drove to the meet 'avec un attelage de chevaux tigrés, dont la robe est fort belle '." It may be remarked that in one of the tapestries of the *Chasses du Roi*, after Oudry, Louis XV is mounted on a *cheval tigré*. To the same category belong the German Tiger Dogs which are, in fact, a variety of the Harlequin Great Danes. A German author describes them as " like a Tiger horse, which is white with small dark spots, as distinguished from the piebald horse ", and adds that in his time they were to be met with in Hamburg, which is near to Denmark. Writing in 1880 he says that, about fifty years before, these dogs were much in fashion, and that they had generally one or two blue or glassy eyes, which gave them an unusual appearance. They were carriage dogs, like the old Dalmatians. Sydenham Edwards in *Cynographia Britannica*, writing in 1803, says : " I certainly think that no equipage can have arrived at its acme of grandeur until a couple of Harlequin Danes precede the pomp ". This ' tiger ' fashion, perhaps originally of Danish origin, is further illustrated in the Danish Tumbler pigeons, the most highly prized of which had red heads and tails, with white bodies and red tiger markings, and in various other German breeds of ' tigered ' pigeons. Cf. *Die Mustertaubenbuch*, by O. Wittig : Berlin, 1925. While dealing with this curious subject mention should, perhaps, be made of the remarkable leopard-spotted horses or ponies seen by the travellers in the summer villa of the Dalai Lama, outside Lhasa.

liked to write his name, a member of a prolific family of painters, sons of a Jacobite Scot who fled from his country in the time of Cromwell. His four sons and a grandson were all painters, but Philip Ferdinand (1664–1750) was the most talented. He was the favourite painter of the Emperor Charles VI, the last male Habsburg, by whom he was ennobled, and his works are to be seen, fascinatingly neglected, in many odd corners of the old Austrian Empire. He is the Stubbs or Ben Marshall of their formal hunting parties and preposterous steeds, qualities which have brought it about that he is entirely neglected both in serious and sporting criticism. He corresponds more nearly to Wootton than to any other sporting painter, but his horses are huge and Michelangelesque, in the circus canon, with flowing manes and tails, on their way, we might surmise, to or from some frescoed Battle of the Giants. There is a room hung with his pictures at Schönbrunn, but he is better seen elsewhere. Was it this painter, or another of his family, who worked at Pommersfelden, in Franconia, and frescoed a painted hall in the great stables, the main panels having for subject horses of different breeds led along by grooms and Orientals to show off their paces? His paintings are to be seen, also, at Nikolsburg, in the entrance to the castle, an apartment of irregular shape contrived into the old bastions in such fashion that it is a huge, bare, narrow hall and the high, dilapidated paintings seem to be relics from a remote and curious past. It is, indeed, like half a day spent in another age to leave Nikolsburg on a morning of pouring rain, to come out through that hall of giant horses, half remembered, and flounder, mile after mile, through Moravian villages of whitewashed cabins, axle-deep in mud, where the language is unintelligible, and the geese in their white cohorts are the only ordered activity of the teeming hours. Such is a personal memory of the spotted or leopard-marked horses, of the Apeloosas; but it is probable that in order to know them in their greatest array it is necessary to have seen the pictures at Hluboká, the Bohemian castle of Prince Liechtenstein, near Budweis, and not only in the sham Gothic castle but at the hunting lodge near by, an early eighteenth-century building, where there are ten huge canvases of hunting scenes and groups of horses in the hunting hall.

Other survivals of this period of taste were the cream Hanoverian ponies brought over by George I that, till lately, drew the coronation coach. In their native place at Herrenhausen, outside Hanover, they were known more correctly as Isabellas. And there are the white Lippiza stallions of the Winter Riding School, of noble Neapolitan or Spanish strain, the ' selfs ', if we may speak in the language of fancy pigeons and auriculas, of this world of particoloured or spangled horses. The Lippizas, though of different colour, are the living embodiment of the Spanish horses of Velasquez, and they are trained to the same attitudes, according to the old rules. These are the set figures of the *haute école*, exactly as they are to be seen in the Cavalier Duke of Newcastle's book of horsemanship.[1] That is a treatise, nothing less, on equine choreography, an art or religion with a language of its own, and so curious are its illustrations that the hypothetical Indian or New Zealand native of literary comparisons might imagine, on turning its huge pages, that he was beholding the worship of the horse. In one engraving, in particular, the author wearing Cavalier costume and plumed hat bestrides a winged Pegasus which executes the *grande capriole* against the background of a cloud; the classical gods and goddesses are looking on from Olympus, while, below, eleven great horses in a semicircle are reared up on their haunches, but seated on the ground their forelegs pawing the air, and their flowing tails and, alternately, loose or plaited manes and the

---

[1] Abraham van Diepenbeeck (*b.* Bois-le-Duc, 1599; *d.* Antwerp, 1675) was author of these engravings. He was a pupil of Rubens, painted altar-pieces and glass windows at Antwerp, and came to England in the reign of Charles I.

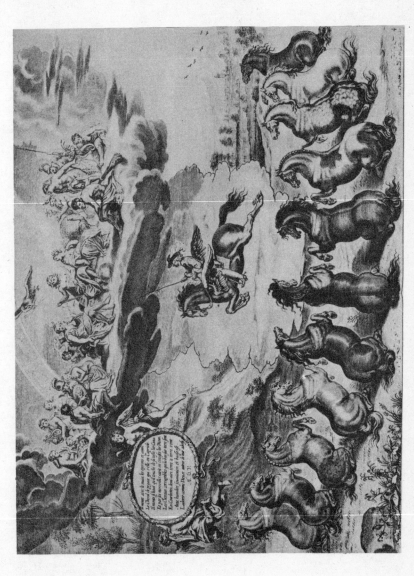

PLATE FROM THE CAVALIER DUKE OF NEWCASTLE'S BOOK OF HORSEMANSHIP

curve of their necks and backs give them the air of sea monsters praying to a god made in their likeness and mounted by a man.

With regard to the great horses of parade and state, an equine authoress, of the United States,[1] remarks that " it gives one a shock to be confronted by Tiepolo's enormous animals. In all his works ", she continues, " Tiepolo reflected the polished elegance, as well as the measureless arrogance that radiated from the Court of Spain. Over-elaborate, over-finished, they become the perfect accompaniment of the Rococo period. . . . But it is the flowing mane and tail which hold our attention. They are the forerunners of the long manes and tails we associate with the horses of Velasquez and Van Dyck." This is, of course, an anachronism, for Tiepolo lived a hundred years later than Velasquez or Van Dyck ; nevertheless, she is correct in her assumption, only it works in the other direction, for the white horses upon Tiepolo's ceilings are the idealised steeds of state processions lifted into the skies, and this is the end, not the beginning, of the reign of flowing manes and tails. The white horses of Tiepolo occur in so many of his frescoes. There are white horses in his ceiling painting of the Courses of the Sun at the Palazzo Clerici in Milan, while the loveliest of all, perhaps, adorn his ceiling at the Palazzo Rezzonico at Venice. The cloud horses are a genre to themselves, like garden statues, and it is not to be expected of them that they should conform to the points of the stables and the show ring. A race apart, but of similar derivation to the white Lippizas and leopard-spotted Apeloosas.

They have, certainly, some descent or affinity with the Arabian. The white Lippizas are a cross between the Neapolitan horse, the Arab, and the Spanish genet. If, in the course of ages, they have kept something of the coat and colour, they have lost the swiftness and the line of beauty of the Arabian. They have

[1] Lida L. Fleitmann (Mrs. J. V. S. Bloodgood), M.F.H., in *The Horse in Art*, pp. 158 *et seq.*: London, The Medici Society Ltd., 1931.

preserved the flowing mane and tail of their desert ancestor while losing the small head and bones. It is because a different physical type of breeding and aristocratic descent has been aimed at. The Bedouin of the burning rocks and sands has been cross-bred for the Spanish stables and the Winter Riding School. Rarer still is the Arabian in his own home. A writer, who has spent nearly twenty years of his life travelling and studying the breeding of Arabian horses, and who learnt to read and write Arabic for this purpose, distinguishes twenty strains and more than 230 sub-strains and families, but adds that not more than eight hundred first-class desert horses are left in all Arabia, with fifty on the continent of Europe, about a hundred in England, as many in the United States, and perhaps another three hundred elsewhere, between a thousand and fifteen hundred in all, and ends with the exhortation to " comb Arabia for the last time, before it is too late " (and it becomes an oilfield), " and secure a dozen or fifteen of the very choicest animals from the Bedouins of Nejd ".[1] The racehorse, of distant Arab blood, will continue, but the parade horse is doomed to disappear. Never again can there be such a spectacle as the golden coaches of Belém drawn by piebald horses with long manes and tails, and trained to such a short, close gallop that they kept pace with the footmen walking at their side.

(xi)

Les Belles Chasses de Maximilien

But a more melancholy and subtle music breaks upon the ear. We are listening to the horns of Les Belles Chasses de Maxi-

[1] Carl A. Raswan, in an article on "Horses of Arabia" in *Country Life* for 15 December 1934. Among his illustrations, that of the white Saglawi type, the ideal show or parade horse, approximates to what must have been the Arabian ancestor of the white Lippiza.

milien in the forest of Soignes, near Brussels. The hunting horns are semicircular in form ; some, indeed, are still the horns of animals, or they are made of metal in that shape, and they can only blow upon one note. There are, also, ivory horns or olifants, but most of the horns are of metal. These twelve panels of Brussels tapestry were designed by Bernard van Orley, a Flemish painter who had worked in Rome and been a friend of Raphael. They were executed some years after the death of the Emperor Maximilian to the order of his daughter, the Arch-duchess Margaret, Regent of the Netherlands, and of Mary, Queen of Hungary, who was his granddaughter. The two ladies must have given the painter every opportunity to interview the huntsmen and foresters, for the tapestries are most copious and accurate in detail, and both were great and famous huntresses themselves. The *limier* is holding back the hounds on leash, while they droop their heads to get the scent and their long ears fall forward, and we see their wrinkled foreheads and bloodshot eyes, and the huntsmen are all bearded, like German or Swiss *landsknechts* with slashed doublets and trunk hose and little caps. The hunt breakfast is in a clearing of the forest. It is an October or November morning, and many of the trees have shed their leaves. Maximilian in his winter hunting hood is eating at a trestle table, but he appears in this panel of tapestry three times at once, warming himself at the fire, and listening to the chief huntsman. The slanting halberds of the spearmen make a beautiful diagonal across half of the tapestry, and the whole clearing is alive and bustling with the figures of the hunt. In another panel, the party are riding to the chase. They are coming out under some trees and passing by a Flemish village of high gabled houses. The village well is in the middle ; but a lady ambling along, riding side-saddle with her back to us on a richly caparisoned horse, talks to a bearded gentleman, while, immediately following them, two young children in feathered hats are so entirely the children of their time that we feel we know them by their names. *Les Belles Chasses de Maximilien* are a ballet or fairy story of the remote past. In another of the tapestries a great stag has taken to the water and a huntsman is wrestling with it, having hold of it by the antlers ; there is furious blowing of horns upon the banks, hounds are pulling at the leash, horsemen are reining in their horses, and all the time it is a placid moat or pool beside a castle ; or it is the boar hunt, the beast is killed from horseback, and, later, we see the singeing of the boar before it is roasted whole, while at the back there is skating on a frozen lake below another castle wall.[1]

This set of hunting scenes represents the art of tapestry in its ultimate perfection. The panels are not as crowded as the Gothic tapestries, while such details as the hands and faces of the figures, and the leaves and grasses of the foreground, are incomparable in execution. But their romantic qualities are of a particular derivation. Though woven in Brussels after 1530, their subject is the hunting exploits of the Emperor Maximilian, who died in 1519 ; and in some of them his first wife Mary of Burgundy is shown, who was killed in a hunting accident, while hawking, in 1482. The costumes of fifty years before are not attempted, except in the case of the hunting dress of Maximilian, but yet these tapestries are poetical and romantic. The other contemporary sets of tapestries, *The Battle of Pavia* and *The Conquest of Tunis*, which are the masterpieces of their age, are superb by reason of their curious realism.[2] But, here, it is not battle but the mimic war of hunting, and the hero is the Holy Roman Emperor who was already legendary as a hunter. His actual hunts cannot, in fact, have resembled the tapestries that

---

[1] In another panel there is a wonderful distant view of Brussels, to be known by its chief buildings.

[2] The tapestries of *The Conquest of Tunis* are fully described in my *Splendours and Miseries*, pp. 62-64. The set of *The Battle of Pavia*, in seven panels after designs by Bernard van Orley, hangs in the Naples Museum.

we are admiring, for this is the early Renaissance and that was the late Gothic.

Of its true visual appearance, condensed or crystallised in naïf terms, there is evidence in the *Hunting* and *Fishing Books* of the Emperor Maximilian, records written down at the dictation of the Habsburg and illuminated with paintings by Jörg Kölderer. The scene is the Tyrol, and the painter was a Tyrolese. The *Hunting Book* of Maximilian is concerned principally with chamois hunting, and opens with the report of his chief huntsmen upon the two hundred beats in which the chamois were to be found. In one of the illuminations the scene is a high mountain valley in the Tyrol with the topmost pine trees half into the snow. A stag is standing at bay at the edge of a wood with his does behind him. Lower down, a mountain stream of a vivid blueness runs swiftly over the shingle, and a great stag is swimming in the deeper current. Maximilian on his white horse, between two halberdiers, fires his crossbow. The whole scene is naïvely, and delightfully, Alpine. Or again, it is a snowy defile from whence there is no escape and the chamois, in silhouette, with hounds at their heels, are leaping like capricorns upon the snowy sides.

The *Fishing Book* is more enchanting still, in naïveté, by reason of its lakes and mountain pools. There is a scene in the Long Meadow, outside Innsbruck, with the fir-clad hillsides, a stag pursued by Maximilian on horseback, birds on the wing, fishing in progress on a square dam, and a wooden house near by, with a pair of antlers fixed upon the gable. Another picture shows fishing on the Achen See with stags and capricorns leaping on the banks, and a crowd of persons including mounted knights with profusely feathered hats, in red and white, in the manner of Altdorfer, and a fishing lodge with wooden balconies and wooden-slatted roof. One of the most delightful of the drawings depicts trout fishing in a little pool banked in by huge boulders. Chamois, again, are leaping upon the mountainside, while the particular kind of trout for which the lake was famous are shown by the bright red spots upon the three or four solitary fishes that are swimming in the waters. There is a scene of crayfishing, by torchlight, under a castle on a crag, with a four-horsed waggon carrying an immense barrel waiting for the crayfish. Yet another subject is shooting and fishing on the Plan See, one of the mountain lakes, but, in the foreground, Maximilian and his courtiers are tasting the freshly caught trout, and huntsmen and peasants are dancing to the music of a rustic band. Of Jörg Kölderer, an enchantingly minor artist, little enough is known. He was architect as well, but did not disdain the painting of a sledge for Maximilian in oil colours. The world of this Alpine primitive had its capital at Innsbruck where the mountains stand half into the sky at the end of every street. He is the painter of trout streams and chamois crags, of deer forests and mountain pools. Maximilian, the paladin of this total war against the animals, was progenitor of the Habsburgs and Bourbons, to whom he bequeathed his familiar features, his prominent nose and Habsburg jaw. His painter, Jörg Kölderer, is not far removed in spirit from Wolff Pirkner, the painter of the Coburg Hunting Chronicle. The one worked in the Tyrol and the other in the Thuringian forest. However, in the time of John Casimir, the hecatombs of animals had begun. But Maximilian hunted in the manner of a mediaeval knight. The deer were not driven past for him to slaughter in a canvas ring. He sought them out, for himself, in the high fastnesses. *Les Belles Chasses de Maximilien* depict his hunting exploits in the plain, in the forest of Soignes whence the boars run into Picardy and the wooded banks of Seine.

(xii)

Chasse du Jeune Henri

The Kings of France hunted in the forests of Fontainebleau and Compiègne, and in drawing nearer to them we are assisting at a spectacle which resembles nothing so much as the casting of the spell, and the awakening in *La Belle au Bois Dormant*. The more so because our early scenes take place under the Valois Kings and we end with the hunts of Louis XV. The Bourbon of Bourbons, François I, for he was that in physical appearance if not in name, set forth hunting in the same manner as if he was proceeding to the wars. He kept many packs of hounds of the different races, and there were three hundred falcons in the mews. But Henri II, who was not so vain of himself as a soldier and suffered, therefore, no defeat and capture of Pavia, distinguished himself like his predecessor, in venery, and as much or more in pursuit of Venus. The Château d'Anet, built by Philibert Delorme, was his hunting castle, and living here with Diane de Poitiers, his mistress, he was in the midst of the mews for his falcons and the stables for his horses, with the kennels for the hounds and the cages for his hunting leopards near by. The beautiful Diane de Poitiers herself appears in the well-known bas-relief of Diana and the Stag by Jean Goujon, and the same sculptor carved the famous white hounds, the Chiens Blancs du Roi, in another panel. The hunt of Henri II must have been a wonderful and poetical experience with his hundred and twenty huntsmen blowing their calls, near and far, in the autumn woods. Brantôme compares the queen, Catherine de Medicis, riding with her forty or fifty ladies to the hunt during the time of her regency, to the hunt of Queen Dido as described by Virgil.

71

The second of their sons, Charles IX, dying young, left unprinted his *Chasse Royale*, which is the chief authority for the different breeds of hounds. He gives the four Royal races, Chien de Saint Hubert, Chien Blanc du Roi, Chien Gris de Saint Louis, and Chien Fauve de Bretagne. The first were bred for many centuries at the hunting abbey of Saint Hubert in the Ardennes, founded on the spot where, according to legend, the stag appeared with the Cross between its horns to Saint Hubert, an impious prince who went hunting on Good Friday. The abbots were famous huntsmen, and every year, down to the French Revolution, they sent three pairs of their hounds to the Kings of France. Much may be legend, but it is certain that they kept a famous breed of hounds and that they hunted for centuries in the forests of the Ardennes. The blood of their hounds persists in dilution, even to this day, but there is argument as to their colour. They have been confused by some authors with the Chiens Blancs du Roi, for these were white, as their name implies, while the Chiens de Saint Hubert were black-and-tan bloodhounds, but without wrinkled heads. There were, however, both black and white Saint Huberts, but the black, with red feet and eyebrows, were more numerous, the white being only used for deer-hunting. The Chiens Blancs or Chiens Greffiers du Roi were the favourite hounds of Charles IX, and none but white or white and fawn were allowed by him into his pack.[1] The Chiens Gris de Saint Louis are said to have been brought back from the Crusades, and became extinct with the pack of the Comte de Soissons in the reign of Henri IV. The packs of the Kings of France were composed of these grizzled red hounds for some centuries until the Chiens Blancs du Roi came in, about 1470. The Chien Fauve de Bretagne was a rough-coated

[1] A white hound called Souillard was given to Louis XI by a gentleman in Poitou. Later, under Louis XII, another cross was introduced by one of the King's secretaries or *greffiers*, and later still Barraud, a white hound bred in Scotland, was given to François II by Mary Queen of Scots.

hound adapted by many generations of breeding to the rude climate and the rocks of Brittany, but of origin in the British Isles and taken over to Brittany in the Middle Ages.

The romantic history of these French breeds of hounds will come as a revelation to those persons who can think only of the English foxhound. But France is the classical land for hunting with packs of hounds, and it is France which has the greatest traditions of the chase. There are, or were till recently, French families living in the provinces with small packs of hounds of unbroken blood since the reign of Henri IV. It was Henri IV who sent James I, not only French hounds, but his *valets de chiens* or kennelmen and important officers of his hunt. The Royal pack of white buck-hounds which was maintained at Windsor until early in Queen Victoria's reign was probably descended from these importations of the Chiens Blancs du Roi. But, more curious still, the rough-coated Welsh hound, which survives in Wales, has been traced back to the hounds kept by the abbots of Margam Abbey, which, in their turn, had been sent over as presents from the abbots of Saint Hubert in the Middle Ages.[1] Another survival is the Kerry Beagle, the Scarteen pack in Limerick having been kept from 1735 until present times by the Ryan family. Originally they were imported from France and were of Gascon or Gascon-Ariégeois blood, related therefore, remotely, to the Chiens de Saint Hubert.

In France itself the survival of these ancient breeds of hounds through the Revolution is the occasion for many touching and romantic stories. More than one country gentleman on his return home after a quarter of a century of exile found there was a hound or two still left, descendants of those he had hunted during the last years of the eighteenth century. One nobleman, the Comte de Vaugiraud, preserved in this manner a drop or

---

[1] After the dissolution of the monasteries the hounds were kept by the lay owners of Margam Abbey till about 1800, when their blood was dispersed into various Welsh packs.

two of the precious blood of the Chiens Blancs du Roi, a breed which as we have seen was celebrated under Charles IX, giving one of his best dogs before he emigrated from the Vendée into the care of a farmer, but only after having cut off its tail and ears so that it had the appearance of a common mongrel. Another nobleman, the Vicomte de Larye, who perished in the Revolution, had a famous strain of hounds, the Chiens Bleus de Foudras, which had been at his Château de Berge, in Haut-Poitou, since the sixteenth century. He had given some of his hounds to two neighbours with the result that members of this race, too, survived the Revolution. The Chiens de Poitou, Chiens Normands, and Chiens d'Artois preserve, then, some vestiges of this ancient descent from the Royal race of the Chiens Blancs du Roi. There are also five races of smaller hounds or Briquets, three smooth-coated and two rough or wire-haired, and including the charming, smooth-coated Porcelaines with fawn-like spots and dapplings.

But there are also the four races or families of Basset hounds, animals so quaint and curious that mention of them must not be omitted before our attendance at the *Chasse Royale*. They are of such antiquity that they are illustrated in du Fouilloux's *Vénerie*, in 1561 ; the Basset hounds are, of course, nearly related in type to Dachshunds and may dispute with them that historical argument as to what is Frank, or what is Teuton, in their origins. This dispute, which centres round the giant figure of Charlemagne, finds a dwarfed and canine parallel in the Bassets and the Dachshunds, for although both are identical in type and descended from a common ancestor, nothing could be more Gallic than the one, or more Teutonic than the other. There are the smooth-coated and the wire-haired Bassets, the latter coming from the Vendée, and usually white with lemon markings or a shaggy grey. But the most quaint and fascinating are the smooth, tricolour Bassets d'Artois, a breed whose continued existence is due entirely to Comte le Couteulx de Chantaleu, a sportsman

74

of the latter part of the last century, who spared neither trouble nor expense in his purpose.[1] "The breed was not revived," we quote from an old book on dogs, "it had never died out, but it was necessary to search all over the Basset districts to find in sportsmen's kennels the few and typical specimens, and to breed from them alone." And the same author gives the following passage in which the Basset hound is described by Shakespeare :

> My hounds are bred out of the Spartan kind,
> So flewed, so sanded ; and their heads are hung
> With ears that sweep away the morning dew,
> Crook-kneed and dew-lapped like Thessalian bulls,
> Slow in pursuit, but matched in mouth like bells,
> Each unto each.[2]

In corroboration, their music is described as particularly melodious by all who have had experience of them, and only inferior to the Chiens de Poitou, which are the most musical of all. But the fascination of the Bassets d'Artois is their mediaeval shape and brilliant colouring. They are the hounds of the Middle Ages, and there could be no better view of the difference between the centuries than to hear the music of a pack of Basset hounds and see them moving slowly through a wood with their peculiar, crooked gait, and to meet, by contrast, the hounds of Augustus III of Saxony and to see their coats branded with the mark of the crossed swords, which is the same as that upon the porcelain of Meissen.

We may be hearing, in imagination, the *hallali* of the *Chasse du Jeune Henri*, an overture to an opera composed by Méhul

---

[1] For the history of these various breeds of French hounds consult *The Book of the Dog*, by Vero Shaw : Cassell & Co., 1880. But the modern authority is Sir John Buchanan-Jardine in *Hounds of the World* : London, Methuen & Co., 1937.

[2] Other authors refer this quotation to the Otter hound descending, in its turn, from the old Southern hound. Comte le Couteulx de Chantalau says that the Lancashire otter hounds of his time were a degenerate form of the Griffon de Bresse, a shaggy, rough-haired breed of hounds with a history going back to ancient Gaul.

during the most sanguinary years of the French Revolution. This *ouverture de chasse*, which had to be given three times over at the first performance, depicts Henri IV hunting in the forest of Fontainebleau. The popularity of this piece of Romantic and Royalist music at that time is a social phenomenon which it is difficult to explain, more so still when we consider that Méhul was a composer of Republican tendency. Cast, as to the first half of it, in the conventional forms of the late eighteenth century, it becomes later one succession of hunting calls and signals, the exact meaning of which, from find to kill, can be understood by all followers of the French *chasse du cerf*. This latter half of Méhul's overture, in spirit, could be music of the French *Restauration*. It is like the Royalist songs called for at the theatre, under Charles X, when the Ducs de Berri and d'Angoulême were in their boxes. It harks back, that is to say, to Henri IV, the Romantic hero of the epoch. Of the hunts of that monarch we have not space to tell, nor of his ghostly encounter with the huge black huntsman in the forest, not long before Ravaillac murdered him. But in Méhul we hear some echo of the French hunting music, the most beautiful in Europe. The language of French hunting had not changed since the fourteenth century. Their fanfares and hunting calls had been greatly improved under Louis XIV and since his time. If, then, we want to see and hear the *Chasse Royale*, our opportunity will come in the reign of Louis XV.

The hunting horns are no longer the traditional horn, shaped like that of an animal. They have become horns of bronze or copper, with one and a half or even two and a half complete turns round the body. The purpose of this improved music was to be brilliant and gay. A French writer on this subject contrasts it with the *cornet aigu* of the English which he accuses of sadness and monotony, and the English hunting horn is, in fact, thin and metallic, and has no music, when the fanfares of the French hunt are compared with it. The genius of this

special kind of music was the Marquis de Dampierre, " gentil-
homme des Chasses et Plaisirs de Sa Majesté ", whose *Recueil
de fanfares pour la chasse* was published in 1770.[1] Many of
Dampierre's fanfares are exceedingly beautiful, and our authority
quotes as the best of many, La Reine, La Discrète, La Dauphine,
La Royalle, and La petite Royalle, titles which recall the names
of harpsichord pieces by Couperin and lesser French composers
of the eighteenth century. Such are the calls to be heard ringing
down the formal rides cut through the woods, and down the
newly planted avenues.

The hunting liveries were not less gay and splendid. They
had developed into a greater fantasy than the red coats and black
velvet caps of the English, only relieved in this island by the blue
and buff of the Beaufort, the yellow velvet of the Old Berkeley,
and the dark green of our harriers. The French hunt was
altogether upon a scale of greater beauty and magnificence,
whether we consider their music, their costumes, or the greater
variety of their breeds of hounds. This was, above all, because
the different Royal Princes, descendants of Louis XIV or his
generation, had the Bourbon passion for the chase. This was
particularly strong in the Condé, as may be seen in the splendid
stables of Chantilly, built by Germain Boffrand, to hold 240
horses and as many hounds. The livery of the Condé was the
famous *ventre de biche*, the soft colour of a hind or roe deer's
belly ; while that of the Prince de Conti, grandnephew of the
grand Condé, was of a paler fawn or yellow, called *chamois
Conti*, laced or galooned with silver, and with facings of blue

---

[1] *Recueil de fanfares pour la chasse à une et à deux trompes* consists of engraved title
portrait of the author in elaborate hunting costume, 52 pages of music, and 9 plates of
hunting scenes engraved by Henriquez after Breton : Paris, c. 1770. Cf. *La Chasse
à travers les âges*, by Le Comte de Chabot (Paris, 1898), a work of learning to which
we are much, or nearly totally, indebted. Two piqueurs belonging to a boar hunt that
was famous in France before the war, told the present writer, in conversation, that they
knew twelve hundred fanfares and hunting calls, most of which dated back for many
centuries

velvet. The livery of the Orleans family was scarlet, blue, and silver; that of the Comte de Toulouse was red and gold; and the hunt of the Grand Dauphin wore long coats of blue cloth, trimmed with gold and silver lace, spotted or tabbied with black and carnation, a very rich jacket with a red ground, gloves with gold fringes, a gold-trimmed hat with a white plume, and a hunting knife, a belt, and a horse-cloth.

The authority for the *Chasse Royale* consists in the Gobelins tapestries designed by Oudry. There are nine of these hangings, and sets of them are to be seen at Fontainebleau, and in better state and colouring at Florence, in the Bargello. They depict Louis XV stag-hunting in the forests of Fontainebleau and Compiègne. Perhaps the ceremony attendant on these hunts had diminished somewhat since the latter part of the seventeenth century, when Louis XIV went to the mimic wars. They must have remained, nevertheless, a spectacle of extreme beauty and magnificence down till the French Revolution, as can be judged by the account of Chateaubriand, who attended the hunt with Louis XVI in the forest of Saint-Germain in February 1787, and who says that when the presumed body of Marie-Antoinette was exhumed, after the Restoration, he remembered and recognised the smile on her poor, shrivelled head from her dazzling and graceful smile, thirty years before, when she was a beautiful young woman at Versailles and in the forest of Saint-Germain. The Royal hunts continued with much of the same character from 1660 until 1790. Their chief personages, at least, were so alike physically as to be unmistakable, and it may be that the main distinction to be drawn would be between the favourites of *Le Roi Soleil* in their shaded litters, and then lifted perilously upon horseback while the ageing Apollo followed in an open carriage; the four daughters of Louis Quinze, Mmes Adélaïde, Victoire, Sophie, and Louise, as 'Amazones vertes', deer hunting with their own pack under Dampierre and his music; and the later hunts which, among sixty or seventy ladies, Mme du Barri would attend. Portraits of the favourite hounds of Louis XIV, painted by Desportes, hang in the Louvre. Ponne, Nonne, and Bonne, Mite, Faune, and Zette, were their names, and their portraits hung originally in his private apartments at Marly. White is dominant in their coats and they have liver or dark-brown ears and markings. Their tails are shaved but for a tuft of hairs at the end. They are true spaniels, of Spanish ancestry, but of the small type known as 'braques' or 'bracquets'. Somehow, the monosyllables of their names, Ponne, Nonne, and Bonne, bring us closer than ever before to the *grand monarque*.

(xiii)

Chasse Royale de Louis Quinze

But another human generation has risen up, and none but the old can remember *Le Roi Soleil*. It is the middle of the eighteenth century, and for our present purposes we must accept the opinion of Talleyrand that no one who had not lived at that time would ever again know how pleasant life could be. As upon this spring morning, for they hunted till April, and the scene being France and in the environs of Paris, we must have it that the leaves are green. In no other land are they so green. Once again, and every year, it is the 'livery of May'. In a few days, even to-morrow ; but meanwhile the foliage is so fresh that it is without the blue shadows loved by Fragonard, those shadows that in such paintings as *L'Escarpolette* are like the blue shadows under the eyes of the young girl in the swing, who kicks off her slipper towards her lover as the swing carries her into the air, and we know that the year has advanced, it is no longer innocent, but will be a faunal, summer night among the statues and the fountains. A spring morning, the air sparkles and exhales, and we are at the rendezvous before anyone else has arrived. So much so that we feel we have mistaken it. But there can be no doubt. It is the *puits-du-Roi*.

An open space in the forest which is at the start or meeting of three avenues. A favourite spot at Compiègne that is often chosen for the rendezvous. But no one has come yet. It is so early that there is time to look around. There are bars across the opening of the avenues, and a light railing, as though for Rotten Row. We are in the middle of a circle from which the avenues are planted in the form of a *patte d'oie* or goose's foot, but the trees are not full grown. We behold them in their youth, and the green flame of the leaves is nearly indescribable as they tremble away into the distance. They are purring and flickering in the gentle heat. But we look down the avenues and see no one, and there is not a sound.

We turn in the other direction, but still there is no one. However, while our backs are turned and we are looking inwards into the circle, two men, carrying something in a sack, must have come up behind us, and walked out through the trees. They keep in a patch of shadow, some distance away, so that we do not see them distinctly, but they are waiting. They are the first to arrive. And they are early. Half or three-quarters of an hour goes by while nothing happens. But we hear galloping hooves. A man, mounted upon a black horse, rides across to talk to the two men who are hidden in the shadow. We hear their voices, and our own footsteps apart, it is the first sound of the morning. Another wait, and time to wonder what we are about to see, and whether it will be worth the trouble and the long delay. Then the sound of more hooves, but walking not galloping. Hooves that take a false step, or strike upon a stone, and a horseman appears, leading another horse, and they take up position just in the sunlight, but stand quite still, except when either of the horses makes a sudden movement. And two more men, and an old woman, have come to watch. But as yet there is no general stir, and spectators are only arriving in twos and threes, and standing back behind the wooden barriers.

Now, looking from one avenue to another, something is approaching down the left-hand tunnel or canal, for whatever it be, the pace is as slow as if it were being towed along the water. It is coming at a walking pace. For a whole moment it does not seem to move at all. Then it is a dappled, confused mass, inwardly agitating, and never still ; and at last a mass or body with several men walking in midst of it. First come the lymers or track hounds, led along in fours, and then the *valets de chiens* or berners with the hunting hounds. So many red tongues hanging, and the waving of so many tails, and all straining, and trying for the scent, and struggling to be free, for one kennelman has a *harde* of as many as six or eight hounds upon the lead. Such a multitude of dappled coats and markings ; but the kennel-men in their *tricornes* have liveries to match, for their long coats or *justaucorps*, which we will find are different from those of the huntsmen, have a flecked or tigered edging down the front, upon the pockets, and along the sleeves. It is a long leash that they hold, and it divides into other leading ropes, and we hear them talking to the hounds and calling them by name.

Behind them come the huntsmen riding down the avenue, twenty or more *piqueurs* splendidly mounted, with their horns slung on their left shoulders, encircling their bodies, and wearing the magnificent uniform of the *Chasse Royale* : *justaucorps* or surcoat of turquoise blue lined with red, the stripe or edging formed of a line of silver between two lines of gold, laced hat, red breeches and red undercoat, and long boots polished *à chaudron* or kettle-black, their powdered hair tied behind into a pigtail and a ribbon ; a uniform the more sumptuous because of its embroidered facings, its cuffs and pockets, all red on turquoise blue, and the fine coat-tails laid back along the horses' flanks. They ride along in a body, their hunting horns, polished and shining, encircling their bodies, and they form into two or three knots or groups in the shadows of the trees, where again they stand quite still except when a horse kicks or makes a sudden movement.

More and more spectators are arriving, and the huntsmen are joined by other grooms and horsemen. There is not long to wait. Down the middle avenue, and filling all its width, the cavalcade approaches slowly, in silence, at a walking pace, sixty or seventy ladies and gentlemen and high officers of the hunt, and when they reach a certain point down the avenue and we can see a moving object in their midst, two of the *piqueurs* sling their horns, lift wide their right arms, and sound a flourish. It is the signal. The crowd uncover. That swaying object is a high, open coach, wheels set wide apart, but with a high roof and back, a coach and pair driven by a coachman. It proceeds into the middle of the open space, and stops. We do not clearly see the King descend, but in another moment he is standing in his hat and hunting coat, taller than those around him, while his chief valet pulls on his riding boots and two valets stand behind him in the red and blue livery of the Kings of France. The master of the hunt, hat in hand, has ridden up, and awaits command. He gives the news of the day ; and now the two men who were first to arrive in the dewy morning, and whom we noticed carrying a sack, come forward, and upon bended knee present the fewmets or stag's droppings upon a platter of green leaves, to prove the size of the animal and its good condition. Just in front of us are the two led horses that the King will choose from, and he makes choice of the lighter of the pair, and leaning on a groom, is helped into the saddle.[1]

[1] Louis XV, when hunting, was generally mounted upon *courtauds*, or horses with docked tails that were imported from Suffolk.

The hunt moves off. The huntsmen, and the ladies and gentlemen of the court, take up their places. The kennelmen lead along the hounds. They march down another of the avenues to the place chosen to give battle, which lies at a corner of the deep forest, and here they leave the avenue and strike into the trees. In a few moments that straight tunnel or green canal is empty as when we saw it in the early morning. We will walk up and down and listen, for we have to wait till something happens. We hear the quickening pace of the horses. The hounds have been let off the leashes. The first beginnings of their music come from the forest. But all are moving, parallel to the avenue, and lost to sight. It is like a ghostly battle, invisible, but near at hand. At present only the galloping hooves in pursuit or flight, for it could be either, down the haunted woods, and soon we are lost ourselves in the long rides and take one and then another direction as we follow the *Chasse Royale*.

In a little time the voices of the pack become louder and more confident. They have found the scent. It is a deep and continual belling, rising and falling, an ancient music old as the Molossian choir of Queen Dido in the Libyan wood, on the day when she hunted with Aeneas and they were lost in the storm of thunder and lightning and had to seek refuge in the cave. But here is no rain, nor wind. Instead, there is the green flame of spring which is like the trembling of a million bells, the flickering of a million tongues. Nor the mournful horns of the ancient hunt. They are in full cry. And, suddenly, the first gay and brilliant fanfare upon two or four horns, in unison, and not far away, and the cry of *Tahou*, *Tayou*, or *Tahillaud*. There the forest is treeless and rises into some shelving rocks and we see the entire hunt, at full gallop, but the first horsemen drawing rein. The stag is viewed and has broken covert. The King rides past, immediately in front of us, upon his white horse, in the centre of a group of horsemen. The hounds are running up into the rocks, and some of the men have dismounted and are calling the hounds and looking into the crevices where the stag may have hidden. Their music has died down while they search for the scent, and run hither and thither, nose to ground, and all at once have found it and are off again.

When we come up with them the stag has soiled or taken to the water. The fewterers, men who hold back the hounds in couples, are uncoupling them at the edge of the water, and in the corner running out of the trees a whole *relais volant* or reserve of hounds plunges into the pool. From the two sides men are pushing out in boats, while, out in the middle, with the hounds at his neck and throat, we see the ghost or phantom of the stag, his antlers rising like boughs of a tree, waterlogged, and carried down the river to where they catch in the weeds and stop the current. But these are swimming antlers with the living head attached. This is a sight that, first seen, seems familiar from instinct. There are immediately tremendous flourishes or fanfares. We hear *La Reine*, a beautiful hunting melody, for we could call it nothing else, blown on the horns which have to be unslung from the left shoulder, over the head, and held out at full arm's length in the right hand, holding the copper hoop or circle at its far circumference, and with the mouth of the horn pointing backwards. It is a peculiar and characteristic sight, when the huntsmen blow their horns, for the instrument is as circular as a circus hoop, it shines and glitters, and has to be lifted and held horizontally in the air at shoulder level. A moment later it is the *mort*, to the cry of *Hallihi, Hallali,* and the dying Actaeon is dragged out of the water.

We do not wait for the humiliation of his end. The horns are blowing again. The hounds have found another scent and more than one stag is to be battered down and meet his death to-day. But it is afternoon, and the scent is lost. Most of the hunt, the King included, dismount and try to track it with the lymers. We see them leading the great hounds, starting every way and changing their direction, not stopping to scratch up the earth, so that we have the sensation that it is not buried treasure but some object or talisman left, uncovered, at the tree foot. All but the King are hatless, and suffering themselves to be dragged this way and that, but the lymers pick up the scent and we hear the wonderful call again, and the cry of *Tahou, Tahillaud*. In a moment they are gone like a dream.

There ensues a long pause while we see nothing and only hear the music of the *meute* or pack of hounds. The *Chasse Royale* was late in starting and it is chill in the long afternoon. We smell the damp forest. Boots are wet and sodden by the cold grasses. The long ride is golden, one side, by the slanting sun but its other edge is in deep shadow. Now, suddenly, and for a last magical few moments we hear the horns calling from first one and then another corner of the forest. They have found a *seize mal seme* or stag of sixteen points. The *seconde vielle* or relay of hounds is cast off. Beautiful calls are blown in such quick succession that it is difficult to remember them, but all have meaning and proclaim the different stages of the hunt. Some are simple commands ; or a voice will break in, apparently in shrill ornament ; some are comments ; or announce the technical stages of the chase, and that the stag is by that much nearer to his death, or that he is taking to covert, is soiling, or is across the wind. There are answering calls that respond to each other and give news from the flanks ; there are the body of horns accompanying the master of the hunt, where the King rides in the middle ; horns that personify the ladies of the court, and are feminine in sound, as though blown by the lips of Amazons ; others that are quasi-military in intention till we remember this is mimic war ; some that are mournful and melancholy as though, in metamorphosis, the stag's own music as he runs towards his end ; others that are a riddle or an aphorism and will remind us of the muezzin's call ; and, all at once, from somewhere near, but hidden, one that is gay and brilliant, taking up and repeating itself, higher, then descending or climbing down, and silent, and we hear the echo of its second syllables repeated, far away, by another horn in answer, and the galloping hooves of the whole hunt, and then the *mort* and *Hallihi, Hallali* under the near-by trees.

The stag is to be undone here and now, and there is to be *curée chaude*.[1] He is to be brittled or broken up at the exact spot where he died. First of all, the right front leg of the deer is cut off at the knee joint and offered to the King by the master of the hunt who kneels before him. Then the dead stag is placed lying on its back, and flayed. We see every stage of the pitiful disintegration of its noble corpse, the knife entering its body, the disembowelling, after which the head is cabbaged and the antlers are cut off, a moment which is humiliating and terrible in symbol, for it amounts to the taking-off of the crown of the dead King while his body is desecrated. This act is accomplished by cutting through the brain-pan across the orbital cavity, after which the antlers are given to the lymer or track hound who brought him down, and he is allowed to lick them. Next, the hide or skin is placed, flesh side upward, on the grass and upon it is poured the mess of blood mixed with bread or flour. While this is doing, choice morsels of the deer are held up out of reach upon a long wooden fork. The lymers are fed first ; and when they have finished, there comes a moment when the decapitated head and antlers are lifted away from the dogs, and another huntsman takes up and folds the skin of the deer, still with its rudimentary limbs, but boneless and licked clean, and holding it by the corners, creases it, and gives it to a man to take away. In the meantime, the horns are blowing a gay music.

---

[1] The *curée froide*, so called, was when this same ceremony was transferred with the stag's dead body to the courtyard of the château. Often it took place by torchlight.

But now, the lymers fed, comes the feeding of the other hounds. It is the *forhu*. The pieces are shaken from the fork, while the hounds rush in frenzy upon the stag's head which a huntsman holds firmly by the antlers, and devour the mess of blood and flour upon the ground. Such is the *curée chaude*, the reward of the dogs, and in a moment they would be fighting and killing each other to get more. The horns blow, gaily and furiously, and the King and the ladies and gentlemen are looking on. The huntsmen in their livery of scarlet and turquoise blue, their *habit bleu à la Bourgogne* and their gold and silver, are nearly indistinguishable in the deepening gloom. The evening darkens, and to the music of the horns they ride slowly home. The hunt is over, and all that is left of this king of the sylvan glade is his hide and flesh and his branching antlers.

ENTR'ACTE

Bohemian Polka à la Smetana

THE poetry of bleating flocks and creaking ox-carts, or of oxen that draw the plough, it may be, over the stones and sherds of ancient cities, will always recall the pastoral reign, wherever it be ; whether it is the milk-white oxen coming down with the tumbril among the Tuscan vines ; or the buffaloes of the Maremma, and of the plain of asphodels that spreads to Paestum and its temples ; the races of cattle in a landscape so immense and endless in extent that about noon, in July or August, the Fata Morgana may be seen above the reed huts of the shepherds ; or the sacred herds of the Hindus tended by gopis or milkmaids and sacred dancing-girls. The hump-backed cattle are somewhat Indian in appearance, and Pales the goddess of herds and sheepfolds has assigned them to distant lands, great heats, and marshy plains. The pastoral gods and goddesses, this is our meaning, preside in our imagination, in whatever garb or clime ; with the Kyloes or Gaelic cattle, shaggy-headed, grazing in the cotton grass which is the asphodel of their quaking peat bog ; or in mountain valleys where particular breeds of cattle have been evolved, as with the dappled herds and piebald horses of the Ziller-Tal. The milking, the homecoming, the penning of the flocks and herds, these are scenes in the pastoral drama ; as when, with night falling, they wend back slowly to the villages and their enemy is the wolf that scours the Transylvanian plain, under Sirius the dog-star, presaging great winter snows but summer heats to music of the Ciganje dulcimer and violin. It is then that the cattle have garlands upon their horns and wreaths of flowers upon their necks and dewlaps.

But let us look around ! In another land, near by, it is the country of the Kraslice or painted Easter eggs. We see silver and gold embroidery on white linen caps and large puffed sleeves from Piešt'any. We see broad-brimmed hats of the Chod clansmen and black or scarlet women's headkerchiefs at Domažlice, close to the Bavarian frontier ; and at Oujezd, the next village, blue cloth coats, striped skirts, and men with bagpipes that have two curving horns tipped with silver. The broad-brimmed hats are overwhelmingly Spanish, but their edges flop and fold over like blackened mushrooms. This is not the Thessalian hat of the gruff picador. At Liptovský St Mikuláš, in the High Tatra, there are men in white woollen suits with long curving cocks' feathers in their hats. They are akin to the Polish mountaineers of Zakopane. There are Slovak dancers of Čičmany in white accordion-pleated skirts, white aprons, and white headdresses with red embroidery ; and others, like peasant ballerinas, who are wearing as many as sixteen or seventeen petticoats of different colours under their short skirts and low, slipper-like dancing shoes. The women and girls in one village wear blue and silver dresses and stockings worked with red roses and green leaves, while the men and boys are in dark blue with brass buttons, and yellow shirts and ribbons. We should find at Jasiňa, in Subcarpathian Russia, that the Hucul tribesmen wear beribboned 'Harrow' straw hats ; and at Detva, in Slovakia, where is a strong admixture of Balkan blood, and whence both Liszt and Brahms derived many of their 'Hungarian' tunes, that the men dancers wear a black apron in front of their trousers, crimson leather waistcoats, Wellington boots, and artificial flowers and silver tinsel in their hats.

All worn for markets and holidays. And crossing into Hungary, we would find at Géderlak the patterns of embroideries that were originally flowers to paint upon the walls of houses, and at Varaljá head ornaments of pearls and artificial flowers.

Red kerchiefs and red top-boots of Egerboés, high caps of Kajar, hats of astrakhan at Szany, and velvet stitched shoes of Hacszuhéteny. Perforated embroideries and wedding cocks and hens of caramel sugar and hazel-nut or walnut at Boldog. But the Magyar accent is upon dancing. Men's sleeves of Mezökövesd contrived especially for the whirling csárdás, and peasant ballerinas in their short skirts at Buják. But the climax comes at Erzeksánad, a big country village. Here the women and girls wear dresses which are distinctly Eastern, and have veils turned over their caps and down their shoulders. Moreover, and this is unique and to be found nowhere else except upon the stage, the heels of their red top-boots have a little gadget formed of metal plates to make a clinking noise as they walk or dance. These are called ' musical heels ' in the local dialect of Hungarian.

The men are dancing alone, in spurs, to the music of a Tzigane band. But, after it is done, men and women together begin dancing a very quick measure preliminary to walking to the wedding ; or, better said, instead of walking, they come forward through the village, leaping, whirling, and dancing to the tune. It is now, in this curious progress, half walking, half dancing, that we hear the clinking of the metal heels upon the red top-boots. There is a fiery and indescribable excitement in their movements. But every couple ends and stands ready for the polka. There are the two positions : the left foot forward, resting on its heel, both arms clasped upon the man's right shoulder, and the backs of his hands folded behind him, upon his hips ; or both dancers look down, she has her right foot pointed, her hand is on his right shoulder, and she holds his other hand. Their arms, therefore, form a circle. One foot is posed ready then, with its heel upon the ground, and each dancer has clasped both hands upon her partner's shoulder while he has his hands folded behind him, upon his hips. Such is their pose while they are waiting for the music to start.

And the polka begins. It starts off with three ascending notes, like a gulping or an indrawn breath, then a pause of a second ; they lift their joined hands, or another couple leap high into the air, and the vertiginous polka has begun with deft and pointed triplets, pointed by the toes, and given accent by their clinking heels, danced with a dazzling speed until the changing of the rhythm, when they all sway together in the three-two time. But it returns again, the former rhythm slipping in neatly upon the other, with many pointed steps, high leaps, and the clinking of the metal heels, till the whirling clension when all the couples spin round together. The long sleeves of some of the men dancers give a Magyar accent, for the long sleeve is their emblem, it is the fire and character of their nation to be dancing in long sleeves ; but all move into their last positions, the chief dancers come forward, leaping, and the polka ends *fortissimo* with long-drawn notes.

BOOK 2

A RAG AND A BONE
AND A HANK OF HAIR

A RAG AND A BONE
AND A HANK OF HAIR

(i)

Époque Bleu : Époque Rose

A CLOUD or haze of dust hangs over London, raised by the trampling of many thousand pairs of feet. What we are witnessing is the parliament of tramps. They sleep under the colonnades and in the open spaces. We see young men who are like bearded explorers come out of the desert, or shipwrecked sailors, and individuals who resemble the eccentric of the town, a person seen walking the streets and of so peculiar a physiognomy that we enquire who he can be and all we discover is that he is not as other men. But there are those as well who have the unforgettable appearance of the one tramp among ten thousand tramps, of the princes of the beggars. To-day there are tramps on the streets of London who in demeanour and appearance could be holy men. To-night, in this fiery sunset, there are tumult and frenzy in the motes of dust.

To judge from their several suits of rags, and sordid packages, it is as though the tramps and beggars had made ready for a winter expedition, to cross the snows and come down upon the land of opportunity. Their creed is poverty, hunger, fasting, and abstinence. They are assembled, unarmed, but they will take up sticks and stones. They are as dangerous as the rabble of the slums. Their will is to destroy and to begin anew. It is a revolutionary fervour, believing in miracles, and there can be little doubt, achieving them. Where miraculous cures are effected there, also, the disbeliever can be struck down dead. As we regard them, they are imbued even with a hopeless and appalling poetry, akin to that which stalked the streets of Calcutta in the famine of 1943. It is related that during that time an English-woman, the wife of an official, was jostled in the streets by a hooded figure which had the folds of its garments round its head. She remonstrated with it, upon which the beggar removed his hood or mask and showed his face, at sight of which the Englishwoman fell down in a dead faint.

How are we to indicate this famished kind of poetry except by saying that it corresponds to the paintings of the ' blue ' and ' rose ' periods of Picasso. There is, perhaps, no other group of paintings with their nostalgic quality. But what was their origin ? Where did he find his inspiration ? To anybody who has been to Barcelona, where Picasso spent much of his youth, it would appear certain that they are a reminiscence of the open-air theatres and booths along the Paseo de Gracia in that city. Along the whole extent of that wide boulevard, planted with plane trees, there are entertainments descending from the expensive zarzuelas and operettas to the most fantastic spectacles of poverty and misery at the far end. Many of Picasso's canvases of his ' blue ' and ' rose ' periods, which would include his numerous harlequins and his subjects of thin and starving persons, must be of this or similar experience in the smaller towns of Catalonia. They are actors and dancers of the itinerant theatre partaking, directly, of the Spanish booths. There are even photographers along the Paseo de Gracia, in and among the little theatres, whose painted backgrounds are precisely of this style and manner. You can be photographed, that is to say, upon the back of a charging bull ; in other predicaments which are intended to be funny ; or seated upon an equivocal throne of which the attendant chains and water tanks are rendered in nightmare fantasy worthy, nearly, of the name of genius. The same itinerant painters, if they are still alive, could do a portentous painting of a person in a gas-mask. One and all, they are prophecies of *Guernica*. The weeping women of *Guernica*, tears streaming from their eyes, choked with sobs, are the comic aunts of this brute spectacle, hardly redeemed by their humanity from the wretched nags that are driven, blindfold, to be impaled upon the bull's horns.

We may find a beggar sitting barefoot on a bench with his dog beside him, dressed in rags, but wearing the beret of the Spaniard, and drinking from a bowl of soup, while two children, hands hidden under their rags, watch him and peer forward to look into the beggar's bowl. We may be reminded, too, of *L'Aveugle*, an early etching, in which the blind man sits with his companion before a crumpled cloth, upon which are a bowl, a crust of bread, and a wine bottle, but we know the bottle holds not wine but water.

His sightless eyes are turned away from us. He sits, half in profile, in his bowler hat, his hand upon the woman's shoulder, and his other hand touching on her arm. She rests her elbow on one hand, and her chin rests on her other hand. Both of them are young. Poverty and semi-starvation are expressed as much in the drawing of his ear and neck as in the thinness of his features. She looks at us out of the etching. It is implied that she takes him out and leads him along the streets. There must be a place in which they sleep. There can be little to talk about. Poverty and silence must be the rules of their strange lives, but she has the gift of sight. Where can the artist have met with them? For they are observed. They are the white brother and sister — or are they lovers? — of the Hindus who starved, only last winter, among the shops and trams.

All these are beggars. But let us continue with the nomads, the showmen of the road, who live, like the Gypsies, in tents and caravans. *Les Saltimbanques*, one of the masterpieces of this period, is the entire epitome of the travelling theatre. This picture is even painted on the canvas over and above two other compositions of equal importance. Such was the painter's fecundity of invention, and he was too poor then to afford another canvas. *Les Saltimbanques* may have taken him no more than a day to paint, so rapid was his execution. Gertrude Stein tells us this anecdote : " Later one day when Picasso and I were discussing the dates of his pictures and I was saying to him that all that could not have been painted during a year, Picasso answered, you forget we were young and we did a great deal in a year ".[1] In the painting we are describing, the itin'erant players seem to have but just arrived, and to be looking round for a suitable spot to pitch their tent. It is in the open, bare landscape outside a town.

One of the harlequins, Spaniard-like, has his muffler round his neck. He leads by the hand a little girl in a dancer's skirt, who holds a long-handled flower-basket, a *panier*, of the sort in which flowers are sent up on to the stage, in her other hand. An older man, in a clown's or jester's hat, carries his sack upon his shoulder. A beautiful and enigmatic young woman sits on a bank in the foreground ; but the central figure in the painting, close to a boy acrobat in tights who must be the elder brother and who holds a drum upon one shoulder, is a pitiful and appalling little boy, about ten or twelve years old, with close-shaved head and wearing dancing shoes, in a cast-off suit many sizes too big for him. He is the same child to be recognised in other of Picasso's paintings, and his attitude with hands and arms held straight down to his sides is that of the ragamuffin who at any moment will turn a cartwheel, or walk upon his hands.

The same young boy, against a background of a glowing terracotta, as of the light of a caravan or tent fire, stands naked with his infant brother on his back, while in the foreground of the painting there is a huge drum, and a jug with flowers in it.

[1] *Picasso*, pp. 20, 21, by Gertrude Stein : B. T. Batsford, Ltd., London, 1938.

Or we have, for companion, *The Little Girl with a Basket of Flowers*, belonging to the ' rose ' period, a little naked girl with black hair and a face older than her years, holding the identical basket or *panier* of *Les Saltimbanques*, and standing against a blue background. In another painting, *La Fillette sur la Boule*, the little girl practises upon her pushball, an athlete sitting on a packing-case is looking on, a woman and children are in the background, and we see the white horse that draws the caravan grazing not far away.

A prodigious number of canvases was painted in this short period, 1904 to 1906. A child harlequin in one of them, with his little acrobat brother who has his hand upon a dog, stands in an empty background of a mean house and nothing more. He is carrying a meagre sack or bundle on his back, and the ends of the string twist round his chest and emerge into his other hand. His features express a sullen, downcast misery. Or again, this, or another small boy belonging to the troupe, for he is not particularised, leads a horse along, naked, as though it is early morning and he has been sent out of the tent to bring the horses in, against a background that consists of nothing but a line of hills.

In the more famous *Famille d'Arlequin au Singe* we have what is evidently the interior of the tent. The central figure is that beautiful young woman of *Les Saltimbanques*, her hair done, curiously, in the vague suggestion of the time — it was painted in the spring of 1905 — her babe is on her lap, and her harlequin husband sits beside her, and turns towards her and her child. He is thin and emaciate, with wasted chest and shoulders, wearing his harlequin's hat, a limp ruff, a plain suit of tights, without the chequers, and the characteristic and eternal dancing shoes. The other human being in the picture is the monkey sitting on the floor, who looks up tenderly and lovingly at the little babe lying in its mother's lap, the humanity in the ape being expressed, too, in its feet and hands. It has even a more animal and enduring warmth than that of the thin and ill father, a ghostly parent, for he will not live long. But we are drawn back to the beautiful head of the young woman, her lovely nose and forehead, and dark-lidded eye.

The same couple appear also in another picture in which the young woman stands naked above a basin of water, upon a packing-case, to look in a square of mirror and arrange her hair. We see now that she is not so beautiful, undressed. She is, indeed, misshapen. She has short legs and thick, clumsy hips, misformed by her hard profession and by bearing children. Her husband stands with his back to us, and looks at her. He holds the baby, and we can see its head above his shoulder. He is, on this occasion, wearing his harlequin suit. His legs are perfectly straight and thin, with no muscle, and his whole figure is wooden, in the primary sense that his bones are like matchsticks. A painting of another order, and a different subject as to persons, is the head of a young harlequin, hatless, with only his sensitive features, his ruff, and the chequers on his shoulders. This has a quality and an impasto of its own, and could have been the forerunner of a whole set of paintings. It is often thus with Picasso. Or there is a clown on horseback, but a very thin and agile clown, wearing, however, the classical peaked hat or mitre of the clown ; but no more than a sketch in oils and accomplished, probably, in the night hours on returning from the theatre.

They are all actors and dancers of the itinerant theatre, and now we come to a picture in which their painted scenery, such as it is, has been his model. This is one of two paintings, now separated, each with a pair of child harlequins in similar attitudes, and each with a great stone vase of flowers in the background. In this instance, for it would be redundant to describe both canvases, the taller of the children wears the clown's mitre, or it is, in fact, a dunce's cap, the hat of *Le Roi d'Yvetot* in the early etching, or of the strong man in *Les Saltimbanques*. His ruff is in the form of a wide linen collar and he has peculiar peaked shoulders. He is wearing tights and his jacket, which is a separate garment, has a belt at the waist and ends in a scalloped edging. The tights are pulled on over his feet, but it would appear that he is wearing shoes beneath them. This enigmatic figure, for his features are quite blank and without expression, holds a rapier in his right hand, hilt downwards, so that he grasps it by the blade, below the handle. His other hand rests on the shoulder of his brother, an infant harlequin of five or six years old, the top of whose cocked hat only reaches to half-way between his elbow and his shoulder. This child is clothed as the complete harlequin, in lozenges of three colours, with little ruffs at the neck and wrists, a little belt, and the white socks and black shoes of his calling. His head is too big for his body. Behind them is that high stone vase of flowers, like the old photographer's painted background.

The interest of this painting is that it is apart from the other harlequins of the 'blue' period. Picasso, then a young genius of twenty-four, seems to have set out to challenge Watteau with his pair of comedians posed against the cheapest form of painted backcloth. The intention is even half excused because his harlequins are children. The elder child, in the clown's hat, is not entirely a young boy dressed up in studio clothes and posed for a painting. But neither is he painted directly from memory. We are not to believe that he belongs to the travelling company of all the others. He is the personal vision or interposition of the painter, something which he has imagined and which, almost certainly, he would be unable to explain.

His ruff and neck and peaked headdress are of an intense fantasy and complication ; he is inordinately tall and thin ; and his thin, pale hand holding the sword, from the ruff, wrist downwards, is in the noble and beautiful convention of Van Dyck's hands. He is the young prince of the sonnet ; and this, from his

fantastic headdress and from his hand that holds the rapier, becomes the more extraordinary and inexplicable when we look at
his woollen tights. But, as an adolescent, his future lies not in the
world but only in the imagination. This painting, even, would
have been less poetical had he worn, like the smaller boy, the
conventional colours of the harlequin. Instead, he is dressed
as we have read so often in history books, inconspicuously, and
like the meanest of his subjects. What can be his kingdom?
It is different from that of Watteau with his silks and satins.
Its illuminations are the Bengal lights, which cast a reddish glare
like that of the town seen from its mean suburbs. He is condemned to the tent or caravan that is pitched on the waste land
outside the town. He is for ever laying siege to the great city
and will never enter it, except furtively, and in his ordinary
clothes. Again it is a canvas painted in a day or two at most,
while the mood lasted. We are to consider it as a state portrait,
the *Don Juan* or *Don Balthasar Carlos* of the itinerant theatre.
For it has those echoes. Indeed, it is both of these personages,
together on the same canvas. But the rapier held by the harlequin
is for a duel upon the stage. Velasquez painted the Infantes
with a dog and gun standing under a tree, and the snowy Guadar-
rama in the background. But why is the elder harlequin staring
so curiously out of the picture? He is looking at nothing at all ;
and the smaller child, standing awkwardly, turns his eyes away.
The future holds nothing for them. If still living — if, indeed,
they were ever living persons — do they remember that their
portrait was painted forty years ago?

From such subjects Picasso plunged directly into his negro
and his cubist phases, but the ' blue ' and ' rose ' periods returned
again, ten years later, between 1916 and 1924. Naturally there
have been changes in the interval. No one can hope to return
to his old loves after ten years and find them the same. Since

1906 the motor-car and cinema have come in. Certainly, once the four-years war is over, and cheap cars are on the market, they will no longer be travelling the roads at the pace of a barge on a canal. We are getting to the years when beggars will wear shoes made out of old rubber tyres. We are nearing the town of petrol tins. We are between two wars. The harlequin who appeared in so many paintings we surmise has long been dead. We meet him no more. He must have died during the lean years when there were such riches. Neither do we find the child harlequins. And the beautiful and enigmatic young woman, too, is but a memory.

But a great many drawings of harlequins date from this second 'rose' period ; they are the most accomplished and perfect of his line drawings, and this phase which lasted for a few years, until about 1924, includes the superb portrait of himself, in oils, seated, dressed as a harlequin with clasped hands, and the portrait of his little son, as a harlequin, standing by a chair. Both pictures were painted in 1923 ; but from 1917 dates the portrait of a harlequin given by the artist to the museum of Barcelona in permanent memory, as it were, of the open-air theatres and booths of the Paseo de Gracia. In this painting, the figure, hat in hand, leans his elbow on a balustrade. His suit, which is in large chequers, has a collar of dark material and little suggestion of a ruff, while this, and the braiding on his shoulders, which makes his sleeves separate and like the sleeves of a chorister in a surplice, gives the suggestion that his whole dress is a vestment. He is acolyte more than actor ; and hat in hand he poses for the picture, which yet is not a portrait. Nevertheless this picture, after its fashion, is the *Grand Gilles* — of Barcelona.

The curtain or drop scene for *Parade*,[1] painted in the same year, 1917, at Picasso's best period, is the aftermath of the travelling

[1] *Parade*, produced by Diaghilew, had music by Erik Satie, a book by Jean Cocteau, and scenery and costumes by Picasso.

theatre. At the moment we see the comedians, on the painted curtain, they are at their supper. The whole left-hand half of the drop scene is taken up by a winged white mare who turns her long neck to lick the little foal beside her. It is implicit in the drawing of her forelegs and neck that this is the circus mare, the performing mare of the circus ring, and there is the suggestion that it is a pantomime horse with two men inside it. A huge pushball, painted like a globe with stars upon it, lies motionless in the foreground, and is an important part, evidently, of the stage properties. Upon the mare's back a little girl in a ballet skirt, with wings upon her shoulders, turns to play with a monkey that is climbing a ladder. The rungs of this ladder disappear into the folds of a curtain that forms the background of this part of the drop scene. Much play is made in the painting with the coloured pattern of the ladder, laid on in the flat colours of a barber's pole or signal post. This left-hand half of the curtain forms a natural or instinctive composition of its own, on classical lines, but according to the canons of the fairground. We see the belt round the mare's stomach that keeps her wings in place. It is not, then, the winged horse of mythology, but a circus mare, and the little girl is entirely credible who stands upon her back, although in pose and attitude this is the female cupid of an ex-voto picture. But the emphasis is all towards the other portion of the curtain, which the little dancer makes evident as she poses between the great pair of wings to play with the monkey upon the painted ladder.

The comedians sitting at supper, in costume, are seven in number. They have finished eating, and fruit and coffee are upon the table. It is a trestle table with a cloth thrown over it, and there is a rug or mat under their feet, so that they are all grouped together and have made a corner for themselves between the edge of the curtain and a bit of painted wall. An oblong drum, counterpart to the pushball, rests on the foreground of the mat, and an Alsatian mongrel lies curled up beside it. Sitting with his back to us, upon a bench, but turned in profile to watch the little girl upon the back of the performing mare, is a harlequin in dark red and black, the acrobat or strong man of the company, as we can see from his broad shoulders outlined upon the blank emptiness of the tablecloth. Opposite to him at the far side of the table, facing us, there sits a Spaniard strumming his guitar, the musician or Figaro of the strolling players. He wears the broad-brimmed hat and whiskers of the picador, an embroidered jacket, and cross-garters that touch upon the foot of the painted ladder and make another, and a lively, pattern with their black and white. Behind him, a negro in a white turban leans against the bit of wall. Next to him, at the table, sits a harlequin, but of another sort. He is little and undersized beside the Spaniard, while his chequered suit is in the flat colours of the sloping ladder, or of the barber's pole. He wears a white ruff, out of which his neck comes up like the neck of a puppet or a ventriloquist's dummy. He holds a wineglass in his hand, and his head looks jerkily in the direction of the little girl upon the horse's back. He wears the cocked hat of a harlequin, which is sideways to us, so that we see its double edges and its upturned brim. The young woman, next to him, leans her head upon his shoulder; that is to say, she rests her head upon both hands, clasped on his neck, as though tired after her turn, and his left hand touches her cheek and hair. She wears the white dress of Columbine, and her short sleeves have slipped down nearly to her elbows.

But a curious pair of figures, man and woman, fill the right-hand end of the drop scene. She is at the head of the table, and more than twice lifesize. The upper part of her figure is on a grey background, like a tilted canvas, so that we do not know if she is not a painting propped against the wings, a picture within a picture; but her left leg leans out of this, and her knee rests on the corner of a wooden packing-case. The man, sitting on this, lifts his right arm and has his hand upon her shoulder. She resembles the Wild West heroines of the early films, in a wideawake or cowboy hat, long blonde hair, and a necklace of sham pearls. Her features and large eyes are drawn with the exaggerated realism of an early cinema poster, and looking down her figure we see she wears a cowboy's trousers. Her companion is a comic sailor, probably an acrobat. He has a curling moustache, and a peculiar glazed hat, something like those worn by the Bersaglieri, but without the cocks' feathers, or by the customs officials who used to board the train at the Italian frontier when I was a child. He wears a sailor's shirt ; we can see the anchors on the corners of his collar. He has a knotted scarf at his waist, and holds his pipe in his left hand upon the tablecloth.

A particular note in the painting comes from the comedians' shoes. They have all black ends to their trousers, as of acrobats who have to leap and turn somersaults. They have white socks and flat, black-soled shoes. We can see the feet of both harlequins underneath the table ; and, as we have said, the black-and-white cross-garters and black shoes of the Spaniard. A little bit of the legs of the far harlequin, under the table, repeats the pattern of the ladder and the oblong drum. The comedians are more active with their feet than with their hands, when we compare this with other Mediterranean paintings in which the figures gesticulate, incessantly, with their wrists and fingers. Another sign of the provenance of the picture is the coffee-pot upon the table, forming a motif to itself against the chequers of the harlequin.

We have remarked already how wooden is the harlequin, and that Columbine rests her head upon his neck, and sleeps. Their attitudes are static. There is no movement. It is a supper-party of ghosts, no more nor less. The object has not been that they should be lifelike. Instead, they are formalised and rendered with the static stillness of the stereoscopic lens, a super-reality being imposed upon these figures whom a majority of the theatre audience would believe to be entirely fanciful and never to have had existence, though, as we know, they are ghosts from but a few years before, who, as to some of them, or their proto-types, could still probably be traced in life. The bright colours, the static brightness of the ornaments, which are the harlequins' shoes, the rungs of the ladder, the painted drum, the cross-garters of the Spaniard, these assist the stillness of this stereo-scopic vision. They are there, all in their places like a tableau, every time the drop scene is lowered. Only for a few moments, and then the drop scene is lifted and the curtain rises.

None of those seven persons is living flesh and blood. The nostalgia is of another sort. Since they are not taken from life they are allowed such distortion and emphasis as the painter pleases, and he can eliminate what does not interest him. Every-thing upon the drop scene, down to the cup and coffee-pot, is his creation. Although there is only fruit and coffee upon the table, the dinner of the comedians is not a *souper maigre*. This is far removed in mood from the starving beggars of the ' blue ' period.

The dog curled up in the foreground wears a dog-collar. We look at the pipe held in the sailor's hand. Someone must have a matchbox, but it is hidden in a pocket. Someone must wear a wristwatch and can tell the time. For how much longer will they be sitting at their supper ? Until the little girl moves on the mare's back and the monkey climbs down the ladder to the floor ? Is that the signal for them to move ? Then we shall hear the benches pushed back and the grating of the packing-case. At that moment the Alsatian dog will come to life. Some-one will pick up the drum and pushball ; someone will lead away the mare and foal. The little girl will go up and take her mother by the hand. The negro acrobat will unfold his arms.

The Spaniard will unsling his guitar and carry it away. The sailor will knock out the ashes from his pipe, and the film star take her knee from the packing-case and put her foot to ground. . . .

It would have seemed that Picasso, then in the plenitude of his talents, might have embarked, thenceforth, upon the huge canvases that were worthy of his genius. This did not happen. He could never be anything but remarkable in all he did ; but, his drawings apart, which in their miraculous powers are often separately and in their individual selves like the projects for as many careers of genius, he has wasted too much of his energy in experiment. Only once more in our lifetime has there been a great drop scene from the hand of this living master. It is necessary to recall this because the curtain in question formed the nearest living equivalent to the frescoes of the old masters, and because when twenty-one years old it seemed the harbinger of great expectations which have not been realised.

This other drop scene, which many of our readers will remember at the old Alhambra, was the curtain by Picasso for *Le Tricorne*. Upon a ground of grey, it showed the interior of a bull-ring, with a man in Andalusian dress, cloak and wide-brimmed hat, a woman sitting in a chair beside him, another group of three women in the opposite corner of the box, all in shawls and mantillas, and a small boy selling oranges. There was an extraordinary simplicity about the whole design. The *majo* leaned, with arm akimbo underneath his cloak, against the wooden partition of the next-door box. The arches and railing of the balcony ran round into the circle of the whole bull-ring. In the centre, the *chulos* with their mules were dragging out the dead bull by the horns. A picador, lance in hand, was waiting on his nag. But all these were hardly drawn at all. They were but indicated.

The bull-ring itself was a disappointment, for it avoided,

and did not meet, all difficulties. But let us look at the figures in the box, from left to right. We recognise Picasso in the shoes of the *majo*, black with white soles, for they are the shoes, exactly, of his harlequins. The *majo's* companion, in her black mantilla, is interesting only in her hand that holds a fan, and in the skirt of her dress which is drawn, miraculously, with five zigzag lines and   few dots. By some alchemy of genius it is the skirt of a Minoan priestess from Knossos, where there were bull-fights, too.

The group of three women is more typical of Picasso, the only great master of our time. Of the woman in the middle, we see nothing but her features, her black mantilla, and her fan. The two other women wear white mantillas. Their cowl-like headdresses and the sweep of the white mantilla nearly to their waists are combined, as it were, into one two-headed pattern, for they face each other, and the drawing again becomes almost miraculous in its simplicity, for the headdress of the left-hand woman is accomplished by a white shape and a single line in that ; she is given dark eyes and eyebrows, and her features are out-lined in white ; while the other white-mantilla'd woman, who holds a rose in her right hand, is drawn with the same white-peaked headdress and a single line in it, another line or two for her shoulders, and a line for her right arm, and that is all. They are a pair of Minoan priestesses, the left-hand woman more particularly, for her companion wears the Andalusian shawl draped round her waist, and its conventional pattern of white flowers on black, its fringes and loose ends, are the weak part of the whole drop scene. But the hem of her skirt has the true Gypsy flounces, as worn in Triana, or the Albaicín, where the dresses are in white, or bright colours, with a Gypsy train. The small boy, selling oranges, is a parody upon the page carrying a casque or helmet in El Greco's painting of St Maurice and the Theban Legion. He is brother to Murillo's beggar children, and to the bootblacks of the Spanish streets. The foreground of the painting is quite empty, just the wooden boards of the box or *palco*, with a bottle of sherry and two glasses on a tray. But we have left till last the most typical passage of the whole curtain. This is the chair on which the more Minoan of the two mantilla'd women is sitting, of which we only see a wooden leg, the crossbar, and part of the rush seat, with the woman's foot and ankle in a kind of diurnal moonlight, broken by the crossbar, and showing underneath her skirt. The rush seat is represented by a few broad hatchings, but these are like the convention for the folds of a curtain in Byzantine mosaic, and the little square composition of the seat and leg of the chair and the woman's foot and ankle form a moonlight picture in themselves, to which, in imagination, we might hear the serenading of the cats upon the tiles, and then we look up the white folds of her mantilla to the moonlight cowl of her headdress, raised upon a comb, and to the white moonlight outline of her features turned towards her friends. This painting, with the Andalusian costumes that follow, later, upon the stage, was intended in the first place to be in the style of Goya's tapestries, but it has become Minoan in the pair of priestesses, in the dots and zigzag lines of a skirt, and in the moonlight symbols of the foot and chair.

The curtain of *Parade* is a considerable painting, judged according to the old canons of the art. Nevermore in our lifetime has there been the opportunity. Or not upon this scale. It was the grand moment and it will return no more. According to rumour the curtain was sold for a large sum of money to an American museum, but we would prefer to believe that it had totally perished and disappeared. That would be a fate more appropriate to its transcendent qualities. It should be gone as utterly as the street music of its day.

Going back to that same year of 1917, I always remember

the hurdy-gurdy that played in Moscow Road when I went to see my sister. Why did I love the hurdy-gurdy and the barrel-organ ? I can only say that it was for the same reason that I called my first book of poems *The People's Palace*. Such or of such sort were the influences upon my mind and ear, bringing me back always to that hurdy-gurdy below the window of my sister's flat in Moscow Road. It can have been given to few persons to see someone so nearly related to them at such an extreme moment of her development. For she was at that time writing poems that are among the most personal and individual in the language. This is the nearest I have come in my life to being in the midst of works of art that were in the process of creation. If I have but once or twice in my lifetime seen great paintings in the making, I have at least known a time when poetry was being written. Thinking of these days, I could repeat the words spoken by Picasso to Gertrude Stein : " You forget we were young and we did a great deal in a year ". While we were speaking, my brother and sister and myself, or while she read her poems to us, the hurdy-gurdy would be playing in the street below. It would be banal on my part were I to give the tunes their names. It was street music of the ' blue ' and ' rose ' periods, for I can call it nothing else, and it may be that our mutual intuitions peopled it with many of the vagrant persons in those paintings.

(ii)

Recueillement

I propose now to gather together some impressions of what I would call the ' blue ' and ' rose ' periods of my youth. I am thinking of the time when I was nineteen years old and had begun writing poems. My first book of poems was published in June 1918, and I wrote the poems during the winter and summer of the previous year. I believed, then, in a popular art and in a future, when the war was ended. Humanity was not so mad that it would go to war again. When the world woke up from its nightmare it would surely turn to other things.

My days were spent at Chelsea Barracks, for the world was then suffering, as now, from its recurrent madness. I lived with my brother in a house in Mulberry Walk for what was, in fact, a few weeks only, till we moved to Swan Walk, Chelsea, but it seemed an eternity owing to the nervous and spiritual excitements of the time, sensations of which I still recall even so much as the taste and smell. Marinetti, the Futurist, was my living model at that moment, but I was reading as well all the older poetry I could lay hands upon, Marlowe, Dekker, Peele, Roberto Greene, in the 'Mermaid Series', and Andrew Marvell. Besides this, having long known Fra Angelico and Botticelli through my childhood memories of Florence, I was becoming interested in modern painting. A picture by Mark Gertler of a roundabout on Hampstead Heath,[1] shown at the Mansard Gallery in Tottenham Court Road, had been a seven days' wonder and my excitement probably imputed merits to it that were not in the painter's intention, but it seemed to me to incarnate the blaring of the steam-organ. I saw the picture again, only a year or two back, and was overcome for the moment by the violence of my memories. I heard the barrel-organ and the hurdy-gurdy, and the street music of that hot and fateful summer more than a quarter of a century ago.

There is no need for me to recapture the sensations of that time. I still hold in my hands the red and pink covers of *The Little Review*, in which the poems of T. S. Eliot are appearing. I am looking at the *Great Wave* of Hokusai ; or at the gaufrage,

---

[1] Painted in 1916.

the silver and mica and sprinkled gold dust of his surimono. I have found the Japanese books on Korin at the Oriental book-shop opposite the British Museum. *The Hundred and One Poets* grouped together in their curious black-lacquered hats ; his *Great Wave* screen ; the dazzling plumage of Jakuchiu's cocks and hens, no two alike ; the monkeys of Sosen on the flowering plum branches ; the snow and gold of Kano Eitoku ; these came to me at the same time as Fenellosa and the translations of Arthur Waley.

Renoir's painting, *Les Parapluies*, was on exhibition in the National Gallery and used to occupy my mind during the long hours upon the barrack square. This was the first great modern painting that I had ever seen. Its subject was the common people, the young women of the Paris suburbs. I had then, and for some time before, been reading Zola, distilling for myself the banal poetry of *L'Assommoir* and *Au Bonheur des Dames*, a condensation which comes from minute particles of fact exagger-ated under a myopic lens. I had been collecting, since my last year at Eton, the images from *Salammbô*, in a condition of intoxication from *Le Festin*, the opening chapter that describes the banquet in the gardens of Hamilcar, and from such passages as the sunrise over Carthage and that moment when the light strikes the polished carapaces of the turtles. I read and re-read that impression of a long summer afternoon in *Madame Bovary*, where nothing happens, and the only incident is the impact of a bumble bee upon the window-pane.

In Maupassant's *Une Vie*, written under Flaubert's influence, there were the accounts of country life in Normandy and the disillusionment of the honeymoon spent in Corsica. I even found poetry, of the bandstand and the arcade of shops, in *Mont-Oriol*, a novel about an inland watering-place. There were the invocations of Venice in D'Annunzio's *Il Fuoco* ; his images of the waves breaking upon the shore in *Il Piacere* ; and beautiful passages in *Forse che sì, forse che no*, a fervid romance with a setting in the lunar or volcanic landscape of Volterra, and a theme of incest and the early days of aviation.

I would not stress the importance of these influences if it were not that they possessed something of that strength of sensation which many writers and painters have felt when they beheld the blue waters of the Mediterranean for the first time. These other discoveries that I have mentioned shared in this urgency. I have named a few only among many. I could not yet appreciate Johann Sebastian Bach. I was exploring Russian and Spanish music ; the 'barbaric' instrumentation of the Russian masters, and the brilliance of such piano pieces as the *Seguidillas* of Albeniz with the opening phrases in the strict but scintillating rhythm of the dance, each section ending with a figure that is like a hand gathering up the tricks after a brilliant game of cards, while another piece, *Rumores de la Caleta*, exactly suggests the lights and sounds and the blue shadows upon the whitewashed alleys of towns in Southern Spain. The mechanical pianos playing Spanish tunes that I was to hear later, in Seville, coming from the doors of the wineshops, and the Pan-pipes of the knifegrinder sounding from the street corner, these were sensations akin to the barrel-organs of the London streets.

But the years of which I am speaking are the period in one's life in which to love Mozart, so much so that now I can hardly bear to listen to his music. In the early autumn of the year after the war had ended, when I was twenty-one, I went to Italy with my father. The preliminary days spent on Lake Maggiore, before we went to Venice, were passed in an obsession of sadness with the 'farewell' song from *Il Seraglio* never out of memory for a moment, night or day. It haunted the shores of the lake and the terraces of Isola Bella, and on wet days, of which there were many, became an unforgettable agony along the corridors of the hotel. It accompanied me to Venice and was ever in my mind, morning and evening, as I walked along the Zattere and in to the Gesuati to look up at the painted ceiling of Tiepolo on more than one October day, coming out again among the *trabaccoli*, the barges and sailing ships moored to the quay ; or went by foot or by gondola to the other outer edge of Venice, the Fondamenta Nuova, looking out over the lagoon towards Murano and the distant mountains. The 'farewell' song expresses by some magical means the pangs of parting. How, or why, this should be so, we cannot tell, nor was I thinking of any parting in particular, it was but a mood ; but when it became too sad in memory, and it will for ever haunt those places for me if I come to them again, I would turn to the serenade from the same opera, which belongs in spirit to the *Turkish March* of Mozart, and attached itself in my mind, in fantasy, to the Oriental figures in silken gowns and turbans to be admired in the paintings by Carpaccio at the little oratory of San Giorgio degli Schiavoni, that was built for the Dalmatian sailors.

To about the same period in Mozart's career, separated, indeed, by two or three years, no more, belongs his Piano Quartet in G minor of which the finale could be compared to a conversation between characters as airily fanciful as those inhabiting the pages of *The Rape of the Lock*, but a conversation, be it noted, released from the strict tyranny of the couplet. For months or years I dreamed of a poem or a work in prose which would possess those qualities, which would breathe that elegant, Augustan air, but the more one searched that flawless surface, in memory, the more natural but inimitable it became. His Concerto for Flute and Harp, written in the French style and composed, according to tradition, for a French Duke [1] and his daughter who played upon those instruments, is but another memory of how urbane the world could be. It is the epitome of Mozart's 'gallant' period. We have the feeling that it was composed for

---

[1] Duc de Guines. He had been French Ambassador in London.

that one performance only, and that never has such genius for improvisation been lavished upon an occasion. How beautifully it is written for those euphonious but awkward instruments ! The music of the *Nozze di Figaro* was a sensation of another order, comparable to that dream state in which we create for ourselves another land as rich in works of art as Italy or Spain ; or it more nearly resembles that alternative dream state in which the land is Italy, but everything is different and more beautiful than the reality. *Nozze di Figaro* possesses, indeed, the physical beauty proper to a musical comedy, but staged in another and a higher sphere.

Certain of Mozart's Sonatas that I heard played on the clavichord by Violet Gordon Woodhouse were so graceful and beautiful that I cannot think of them without emotion. They exhibit the light Rococo of his youth, and their heavenly interplay of symmetry and ornament had youthful texture and the poignancy of youth. Music more physically beautiful does not exist. It is beyond the possibility of imagination. But now our own difficulty arises, whether to describe them from memory, as first heard, or in the light of further experience. But it is not so difficult, because they attach themselves so completely that they become the enlargement of one's own personal sensations of being young, and other music by Mozart of more recent acquisition becomes the prolongation of its own eternal youth.

I am thinking of two Sonatas, in particular, a pair which are separated by ten years in time, but not in temperament,[1] proving that in the creation of Mozart this is a recurrent mood. The recurring date, we might say, is 1778, when Mozart was twenty-two. It appears again in and about the period of *Il Seraglio* and of the most lovely of the Violin Sonatas, and more rarely after 1786, the year of *Nozze di Figaro*. These pieces form, therefore, a group in his creation, being nearly related in mood and fantasy.

[1] Sonatas in A minor, K.310, and in C major, K.545.

The second of the two Sonatas that we mention was written, it seems, for a simple, easy music lesson. But what an occasion ! It is as beautiful as if it were the music lesson in the old opera, and one finds it all but impossible to believe that the convention of the stage is untrue and the teacher not in love with his pupil. The other Sonata has a first movement of Italian brilliance pertaining entirely to that trance or condition of the imagination to which we alluded, for it depicts an Italy which never existed or is not to be found, at least, among the creations of her own masters. The last movement of the Sonata, by this interpretation, is more Italian still with its modulations that lead in new and unexpected directions through the balsamic scene. Those who are doubtful if this music be Italian in feeling have only to compare it in their minds with Bach's Italian Concerto, in which language and imagery are identical and the same.

A further group of Piano Sonatas dating from the same year, 1778, includes the A minor, K.331, with its Rondo alla Turca, but the variations in the andante at the beginning are so Italian that we have the impression that Mozart, remembering Italy, has allowed his imagination to wander a step further in the Turkish Rondo. Mozart had visited Naples and stayed in Venice for the Carnival. In the latter city he will have seen Turkish merchants, the Turks of Tiepolo, on the quays and in the masquerade, while from Florence and Mantua and a dozen smaller towns he will have imbibed the ambrosial or balsamic airs of Italy. But these influences were heightened by the mannerisms of his Parisian or 'gallant' period. The andante of another Sonata, in C major, K.330, so near in date that it bears the opus number immediately before that we have been describing and may, therefore, be previous by a few days at most, is in this other or non-Italian style. This is the period of Mozart's sets of variations upon French airs, upon "Lison dormait", upon "La Belle Françoise", upon "Je suis Lindor" from Beaumarchais' *Barbier de Seville*, upon a march from Grétry's *Les Mariages Samnites*, upon "Ah! vous dirai-je, Maman", a ridiculous little tune, so perfect in its midget proportions, so typical of Mozart and, withal, still more typically French, that to those who love such things it has its place in the world of "Non più andrai", of the *Carnevale di Venezia*, that is to say, of the musical box. The sets of variations upon French airs were composed by Mozart for his own performances in Paris, and in this spirit is the andante to the Sonata K.330, of which we are thinking. But even more beautiful is the andante to another Sonata, in B flat major, K.570, written in 1789, the year of the French Revolution, and conveying a most extraordinary and ghostly impression of being alone with Mozart. Its artful and inconceivable simplicities open not less than a world, a whole civilisation of their own into which we may enter and wander, seemingly, at our will, little knowing how formal and defined are its boundaries. Mozart, the most delightful companion in the whole of music, here shows us felicities that may never have had existence, but, be this as it may, one thing is certain, that they have fled the world for ever.

The Violin Sonatas belong, also, to Mozart's youth, not as entirely as the Violin Concertos which were written when he was eighteen or nineteen years old, but the best of them were composed when he was twenty-five, during the months immediately preceding *Il Seraglio*, while the two or three exceptions, written later, are the recurrence of the same mood. One and all, this enclosed world of the Violin Sonatas is vernal and in blossom, which is to say, they have no equivalent except in Nature. At each hearing, we may wonder whether the particular Sonata of the moment be not the most lovely creation, physically, in all music. But so, too, at the moment of hearing is the heavenly sicilienne which forms the last movement of the Piano Trio in G major, K.564 ; and how interesting to compare it, in imagination, with the no less heavenly siciliennes of Handel ! Alas, that it would be invidious and redundant to discuss this music in more detail ! Its impact, which is so immediate and lovely, can be, intermittently, the pleasure of a lifetime, and how welcome is the absence of all pedantry and introspection ! But we cannot conclude without returning, once more, to *Il Seraglio*. It contains the haunting strains of the 'farewell' song ; the sparkling little brindisi or drinking song . . . and here is our picture or interpretation of its Turkish serenade.

(iii)

The Tulip Reign

It is Laleh Devri or the Tulip Reign.

Sheykh Mehmed Lalehzari is Master of the Flowers, and it has been enjoined on him in his credentials " that all gardeners recognise for their chief the bearer of this diploma. Let them not speak before their time, like the blue hyacinth which scatters its perfume before men ask for it."

Turkish historians have given to the reign of Achmed III (1703–1730) the title of the Tulip Reign, and the Tulip Festivals were made the occasion for endless fantasy, until " they actually began to interfere with State business and to prove a drain on the national resources by the reckless extravagance of the fêtes, which seemed to be regarded as even more important than the great national festivals themselves ".

The Turkish taste in tulips called for very long, pointed, and recurved petals, and brilliant colouring. Wild tulips were brought from Anatolia, and the florists came to Magnesia in the spring to dig the bulbs. The best of the cultivated sorts were brought from Holland and from Persia. Mehmed Lalehzari was commanded to make a register of the tulips in a great book, and to write down their changes into 'flamed' or 'feathered' as the petals broke their markings. In a pair of manuscripts (that were in the Library at Berlin) this Master of the Flowers to Achmed III gives a list of one thousand three hundred and twenty-three tulips, of which seventy-four are described in full.

The tulips are in the parterres in their different kinds, for more than one variety is never planted in the same plot. They cultivate, too, the rose, carnation, lilac, jasmine, hyacinth, and ranunculus. The hyacinth bulbs are gathered at the flowering season in the fields round Aleppo, while rose cuttings are grown at the summer palace near Adrianople. The ranunculus comes from Syria and the Greek Islands. But, above all, it is the tulip that is beloved by the Turkish fanciers, probably because of its resemblance to a turban.

There are melon patches, too, and strawberry and raspberry beds. All in the moonlight, for the Tulip Festival is held, whenever possible, at full moon.

Tulips sent by the Court Grandees are exhibited in the Sultan's pavilion, where they are displayed in the form of an amphitheatre. The flowers are arranged in glass vases upon rows of shelves, and between them are little lamps and glass balls filled with coloured waters. Songbirds are hung from the ceiling of the pavilion in their gilded cages. In the distance, here and there, are towers and pyramids built down the gardens. There will be music, dancing, and *ombres chinoises*, or Chinese shadow plays. Eunuch confectioners hand round sweetmeats. There are sherbets made of violets and sugar, and of the yellow nenuphar which grows in ports and rivers.[1]

But we hear a roll upon the kettledrums.

[1] Sherbet made of water-lilies, probably a survival from Byzantine into Turkish times, is still prepared by the nuns in one or two convents in Moldavia. Lily-petal sladko, the Bulgarian equivalent, is to be found in convents in the latter country.

A body of Zülüfli Baltajiler or Tressed Halberdiers, a hundred strong, are passing by between two rows of black eunuchs. Once a month they carry firewood into the Harem. Their uniform is a dark-blue gown, with a long pointed collar that they raise up as they come into the court so that they cannot see the women. Their false locks or chastity curls hung down from their scarlet caps, which are half an ell in height, and their ends are wrapped with gilded wires.

And the drum-taps die down into the distance, below the balcony of the Head Nurse.

When all is ready the Grand Signior causes the state of Kalvet or absolute privacy to be proclaimed. The gates of the Seraglio are closed. Bostandjis are on guard outside, and the black eunuchs within. " The women ", Flachat tells us, and his informant was the Kislar Agha or Chief Black Eunuch, " rush forth like a swarm of bees settling on the flowers."

But we have wandered from the hyacinth beds, and from the shelves of tulips.

And we come back in order to take up our station at an iron grating in the wall, through which we see the maidens playing at ball in the court. Thirty of the nymphs, or of the Grand Signior's concubines.

One nymph wears nothing but a little cap of cloth-of-gold, which but covers the crown of her head. Others wear coats cut like a soldier's mandilion, in all colours, like a troop of jockeys, and breeches of a white cloth, as white as snow and fine as lawn, for we can discern the skin of their thighs through their breeches. If it were not for their long hair we might take them for young men, but by that and by other plain tokens we know them to be women, and very pretty ones indeed.

Another wears fine Cordovan buskins ; and yet another has her legs naked, except for a gold ring upon the small of her leg, and on her feet pattens or chopines which are four or five inches high. The plain ones are made of walnut or boxwood ; but some are of rosewood or sandalwood, beaten with silver nails, and with embroidered straps. But the high pattens are a fashion brought from Venice, where they are worn by the courtesans with a skirt divided in front to show their breeches, cut like a man's, and gold-clocked stockings. And in that manner, walking as though upon stilts, for the pattens are as much as a foot and a half high, the Venetian women clatter slowly and noisily across the bridges over the canals.

Here, a girl in a pair of pattens as high as those, and inlaid with pearl and tortoise-shell, walks by. She wears a waistcoat, cut close to her figure, of rose-coloured silk brocaded with little silver flowers, and a little cap of cloth-of-silver, worn at an angle, with a golden tassel. And so she steps among the other nymphs.

In enchantment we watch one, and then another, undressing for the fountain.

But the one throws down her little harem cap ; the others take off their mandilions or satin jackets ; step out of their breeches ; or slip off their buskins. By their laughing manner they know that we are watching them.

She who throws her cap down shakes her auburn hair. One by one the wearers of the mandilion are undressing. We see a wrist come from a satin sleeve, and then the naked shoulders showing.

The turn of the yellow mandilion has come at last.

But look into the mirror ! It will not hold them all. She puts her arms behind her, and we behold the budding of the yellow crocus. The blue or yellow calyx is opening before our eyes. Her smooth shoulders are emerging. The smooth cup of the crocus is her naked body, and the auburn hair of the Circassian is its stamen. By a tilt of the mirror its whole circumference encloses nothing but the body of the crocus, from the shining lights upon her shoulders, lower down to the dusting of the golden pollen. And we look again at this nymph, who turns her back to us, and see her lift her arms up to arrange her hair.

We would use these youthful memories, contingent or otherwise, as our stepping-stones. It is a return to first principles, for every writer or artist, sooner or later, must search in his own beginnings and he will find, if he remains an artist, how little he has changed. Since then, the world has been struck by the second whirlwind which, now in its seventh day or year, has not yet died down. Nevertheless, to such persons, their 'blue' and ' rose ' periods are recurrent and may return again. That is our present meaning and the reason for this reminiscence. But in the meantime it is a ghostly introspection. Impossible, for instance, to recall what Italy meant to a person of our own taste and inclination without a sarcastic comment or a note in pencil in the margin. The very substance of architecture or painting, because of its special vulnerability, becomes a nervous nightmare akin to that in which you have forgotten to register or insure your luggage on a continental journey. At home, the landscape, in all probability, will have been spoilt by an electric cable or a power station, and the small Georgian house pulled down to make way for a multiple store. It is no good to resist these changes, for it will not be until worse befalls that improvement can begin.

The recurring mood must be one not of prophecy fulfilled, but of rage and fury at a world gone wrong. As to such an artist " he is, unimportant compared to all the others, an impostor or mountebank, someone who goes round from town to town and is no longer even young. Lost, for him, is the golden opportunity." And we continued that, " at once, the scene was transformed for ourselves, and for him, into the court of the Duke of Parma, or anywhere else that fame and fortune beckoned. It need have no name." The discerning reader will have known the man whom we passed in the rainy deserted street of our opening, leading his horse, and with his big black dog running beside him in the gutter. We saw him again, a moment later, in the Ratskeller where Hoffmann was drinking with the students and telling them of his loves, Olympia, Antonia, and Giulietta. We would remind ourselves that Ferruccio Busoni, the great pianist and virtuoso, when composing his opera *Die Brautwahl*, on a theme by Hoffmann, wished the magician Leonhardt to look like Liszt at the age of fifty. A portrait, therefore, in a mirror, for, by Liszt, Busoni intended such another magician and virtuoso as himself.

But Liszt is not quite typical of the kind of artist whom we mean, and Busoni still less so. For their agony was that, being wonderful executants, they were torn between performance and creation. It was, even, that they were not certain themselves of their own creative powers. The one half of their nature was in opposition to the other. " You ask me if I am happy. I confess I am not. To begin this strolling player's life again is humiliating at my age, and at the moral and artistic phase that I have reached, it is unendurable. And I see no end to it." We quote from Busoni's letters, written in 1919, after the war, when he had to take up his career again as virtuoso. He writes, two years later : ". . . I have been working like a horse (or a saint or an idiot), and when I have finished with Berlin, I have to begin an absurd series of concerts and journeys in England ".[1] He was then fifty-five years old, still " going round from town to town and no longer even young. Lost,

[1] Cf. *Ferruccio Busoni*, pp. 243, 256, a Biography, by Edward J. Dent : Oxford University Press, London, 1933.

for him, was the golden opportunity." And his memory must have reverted to days when he set forth for " the court of the Duke of Parma, or anywhere else that fame and fortune beckoned ".

It may be that neither of them, neither Liszt nor Busoni, is of the type to be chosen by us for our model. But we have had to borrow the histrionic trappings from such names as theirs, for greater artists, in their persons, dissimulate and try to be something other than what they are. Or they can even be quite ordinary. We need, therefore, an artist who is a man of action, since little of this nature is to be expected from one who is of sedentary habits and chained for ever to his desk. What we are witnessing in these pages is as though we looked into mirrors that reflect each other from every corner of the scene. They are permutations or metamorphoses of the imagination, put on paper, given action, and we must hope to prove they are not less tremendous than the truth. But they are themselves the reflection of greater and more fantastic persons. What we present, then, are a number of visions conjured up, in which we may recognise whom we will, or no persons in particular, for none may be intended.

And now, we would ask our audience whom they wish to see. But, before there is an answer, we behold and hear again the phantoms of our youthful days. Who, among those, is worth remembering ? I find in an old diary, under date 9 January 1919 : " Sickert showed us a very fine still life of some mackerel, and landscapes, interiors, etc., brought back with him from Dieppe. In a château near Sickert lives the sister of Berthe Morisot . . . Sickert compared Wyndham Lewis's drawing to the hippogriff which disdains entry for the Derby because of its race. He compared Lewis, also, to Balzac's Prince de Bohême and to Byron. . . ." Later, Wyndham Lewis published *The Apes of God*, 625 pages, a monstrous bomb or land mine, but laid without a fuse.

A genius of another order, to be loved and admired in his unsuccess, for it was not failure, rises before me in the person of Bernard van Dieren. I see him lying ill in bed, suffering from the tormenting malady to which he was martyred. I have found, in the last day or two, his setting of Heine's *Der Asra*, on the first page of which he has written : " Semper Idem 1917– 1927 ".[1] Sad, indeed, to think that those words were written nearly twenty years ago ! But they refer back, as we have seen, to the summer of 1917, when I was not yet twenty.

I first met van Dieren in Guilford Street, at the house of Jacob Epstein. The sculptor, his pocket full of little ivory sculptures from the Congo, had told us that besides being a musician and a Dutchman, van Dieren looked like a Frenchman of ancient family. In fact he had the appearance of, and was dressed like, an alchemist of the sixteenth century, with a touch in his clean-shaven features of the young Napoleon, being at that date about thirty-three years old. He wore a brown velvet smock the length of a jacket, for it did not descend below his knees, and had I known him only a few weeks earlier, I would have seen him conducting the small orchestra at his concert[2] wearing a light-blue velvet coat and a cap of the same light-blue material with a tassel. Van Dieren was, I believe, a great-great- grandson of Mme La Motte Valois, the adventuress who was implicated in the Diamond Necklace affair at the court of Marie- Antoinette, and through her he was descended from the Valois, for her ancestor had been the illegitimate son of Henri II (1547–

---

[1] " 29th August 1927 ! ! It has taken ten years before my slight tribute to you and your brother has within the narrow limits of my very modest fame, become a relatively public one. But since it has, I should be unhappy to think you were ignorant of the almost pathetic fact. Were it only because it may remind you of much affectionate appreciation that remained steadily alive through these intervening years. My inscription is as sincerely conceived as it would be today, and as much — if not more — an act of deep regard for your talents, now, as it was then. Whatever your opinion of the piece, you could not question the feelings that prompted its dedication."

[2] Wigmore Hall, 1917.

1559). As I say, he had some air about him of a youthful alchemist or necromancer, and his extraordinary mental attain-
ments were in keeping. A memory so prodigious that he could,
and did in my presence, recite by heart a whole article in a
newspaper he had been reading, while listening, apparently, to
our conversation. He was an expert carpenter and bookbinder,
making his own marbled endpapers, and, later, was able to earn
a living as an electrical engineer. The extent of his reading was
remarkable and his library of first editions nearly incredible for
a collector of his means. As well, he had a beautiful handwriting, and his musical scores were marvels of elegance and
grace.

The music of this extraordinary being must have been largely
conditioned by his perpetual ill-health. Not that he gave an
impression of physical weakness. He was, indeed, exceptionally
strong, but he was nearly continually in agonising pain. In
the result, his music, which is excessively complicated, has a
lassitude and a wavering or weary line. It must remain a mystery
how he possessed the fortitude to complete his symphony on
Chinese poems, one of the most complex and elaborate scores
in existence. His best works are probably his songs and his
string quartets, though these, too, are inordinately difficult and
reflect his contrapuntal mind. Van Dieren was an authority on
the ancient art of fugue and counterpoint, and it was here, perhaps,
that his Netherlandish origin was apparent. He seemed to me
a musician who should have been composing in another age of
instruments, of lutes and viols and virginals and chamber
organs. Yet, in another sense, he belonged to the century of
Baudelaire and de Quincey. But he loved Ronsard and Rabelais ;
while his own attributes of dress and appearance which attached
him to their century, as, also, the peculiar and extraordinary
circumstances of all that had to do with him, caused me to think
of him as an alchemical counterpart to Bernard Palissy, the

French potter of the sixteenth century. It was not only the difficulties and sufferings of Palissy, but, as well, their aesthetic tastes were akin. The naturalistic flowers and fruits, and the insects or reptiles of Palissy, were what van Dieren admired in his favourite Albrecht Dürer and in the Dutch masters. Also, the chemical experiments of Palissy, amounting almost to magical processes or to alchemy, made them alike. It may scarcely be believed that at the crises of his long and agonising illness the temperature of van Dieren rose to the fantastic figure of 112 degrees Fahrenheit. But a scene, not long before he died, in the prosaic setting of a rehearsal room at the B.B.C. gives the measure of this phenomenal and extraordinary man. The orchestra was rehearsing a piece by van Dieren under its conductor while the composer lay on a sofa, apparently too ill to move. At a passage of extreme difficulty van Dieren interrupted the orchestra, and asking for the first violin, took the instrument from his hand and showed him how he intended the passage should be played. The effort exhausted him, and when the conductor looked round a moment later to ask a question, both he and the members of the orchestra saw van Dieren lying on the sofa with a steam or vapour rising from his head and forehead. When he died, in April 1936, a musician possessing every attribute of genius except the health to carry his talents to their fruition had left the world, and this curious and dramatic last appearance on his part to hear his own music was in entire accordance with his strange mental and physical individuality.

If there is danger that so peculiar and unique a personality may be forgotten, it should, at least, be for the reason that he is obscured by many others. So little, though, so little was done between the wars. Poets rose and fell like meteors falling through the summer night. In my capacity of professional, but unemployed, firework watcher I have seen these Leonids or lesser shooting stars fall, not singly, but in twos and threes, and I forbear to give their names. They have, at any rate, the merit of not shadowing the horizon as in the case of certain British composers who have remained fixed stars for twenty years or more, but shine without refulgence and neither wax nor wane.

The writer or artist who contemplates this scene must be content with the personal image or with the lesser shades. What we recall over twenty years is the barrel-organ at the street corner and not the forgotten first night at the Proms. By ' lesser shades ' we intend those who, in their day, had little or no eminence ; poets who wrote little or nothing, and painters who did not paint ; authors without a publisher, and composers with no audience. Of such is the company in the tavern or Ratskeller, in the Café Royal, the Dôme, the Deux Magots, the Caffè Greco. We sit side by side with those who failed or have not tried. Rarely, rarely is there one who pays for all the others. But at least, one and all, they are to be preferred to the wronghearted who have been successful. The majority even live on credit and have had to borrow from the waiters. For, in a lifetime, we may expect to meet many characters, but not more than one or two great artists, and we shall find always the false mistaken for the true.

(iv)

" *Kennst du das Land?* "

Gone, all gone ; and we have, instead, the Cup Final at the Stadium. The highest award for valour conveys with it the right to take up position at the head of any queue ; and the voice of the prophet is heard along the platforms of smoky Paddington. " Standing room only ", among eternal evacuees, into the grey hills of Wales. You have an emergency ration card and money in your pocket. There is a film in Glorious Technicolor showing at the Odeon. The buses leave for anywhere at every quarter of the hour. The old suicide pond, disused for some years, is in the quarry behind the gasworks. How do you like your lodgings ? And the landlady ? Are there too many children upon the stairs ? I saw a child with a dirty face and a daisy chain around her neck. I saw a little girl picking groundsel, and another blowing a dandelion-clock on the bank of the canal. Some boys are fishing with a twisted pin and a line of string. We meet a little pushcart made of a soapbox on iron wheels. There are more children calling to each other further away, and a grey sky over the cornfield, and black soot upon the leaves.

Let us see what we may purchase at the penny-in-the-slot machines ! Your weight in pounds and ounces ; or a bottle of cheap scent, lavender or lily-of-the-valley. Pastilles, fragrant cachous ; caramels or butterscotch ; a folder of matches, or two cigarettes. But, as well, there are the peepshows. A kaleidoscope which turns with a handle and shows you coloured views ; or, like that I remember long ago on the platform of the railway station, a set scene with little figures in the finale of a ballet, turning, turning, to an old tune ; and far bigger, in a glass case, a clockwork model of Stephenson's first steam engine. For we are living amid wonders. The funicular goes up and down the cliff. For threepence you can have a tram-ride round the town. The blind man, " blind from birth ", is singing outside the fried-fish shop. He carries a walking-stick, painted white, and a tin collecting-can. This windy corner is set apart on Sundays for the Salvation Army band.

What did the Sergeant in the Home Guard tell me ? That he and his family always come here for the holidays. And why ? " I think it was the cemetery garden that attracted us. My wife's relation is one of the gardeners and lives in a house at the main entrance, where the trams and buses stop." Messrs. Coffen and Cakebread are cemetery florists in King Edward Road. They will supply funeral wreaths of all descriptions, and can undertake to keep a grave in order for a pound a year. There are graves edged with blue petunias. There is a weeping willow that droops upon an urn ; and Aberdeen granite, in the two kinds, red or grey, with appropriate lettering in black or gold. Where would you choose to lie ? In a lovely corner looking over the North Sea ? In the midst of hundreds robed in night-gowns or in winding-sheets, who will get up from their graves, together, on Judgement Day ?

Or there is the village cemetery on the steep side of the hill, beside a long stone wall. The wooden stile is just across the asphalt road. It leads to the short-cut through the cornfields down into the valley. Not much happens here. The loving couples wander off into the wood and lie down among the bluebells. But, supposing you are young no more, and are in love, where do you go ? If you are forty, which is August, the eighth month or the fourth decade ? For it is terrible to pass lovers who are half your age. It must be August, when the oats are white ; or, better still, let us be young again. But must we tell the names of those whom we have loved ? Look ! there are red poppies and blue cornflowers growing in the corn. There are tares in the wheatfield. The white convolvulus climbs in the stubble where the flax has been lifted and taken in. The next field is not cut yet. Pick a blade of corn and hold it in your hand, as lovers do ; or the dead stalk of a bluebell which pulls up so easily out of the mould.

How lovely on a summer morning to wake up with a new waltz ringing in one's ears ! To step out on to the balcony in a dressing-gown ! To look across the river to where the lights were glittering all night long ! To Messrs. Doulton's Lambeth pottery works ? To the Battersea Power Station, or the Red Lion Wharf ? To the bubble-dome of sweet Bedlam ? From the mimosa-laden winds of Pimlico where roses and honeysuckle wreathe the grimy porches, where a yellow fog dirties the iron spears of the area railings ?

How many miles is it from Pimlico to the Vale of Tempe, while there is civil war in Modern Athens, a strike of the telephone and tramway services, and a dockers' strike down at Piraeus ? How many miles from Pimlico to emasculated Rome ? To 'the road and rail centres' of Italy, to be taken one by one ? To 'art cities' where there have been no artists for two hundred years and the only craftsman is the fake restorer ? To troglodyte cities where rich and poor sleep all night in the shelters and peace will come like the morning to a drunken man ? How many miles from London back to Pimlico, for it is as quick to walk ? In all the world, wherever you go, it is as though you wandered in a circle. You come back to the broken hopes and shattered homes you started from. The houses are rebuilt, but do the old ghosts return to haunt them still ? The weapons for the next war have only just been put in use. Where is the sense in waiting when it is obvious what is coming ? But are you in such a hurry ? There are pauses even in a 'concentrated bombing', even in a 'saturation raid'. While the steel birds wheel and turn, while the weather changes and it comes on to rain.

Be brave ! Your homes are but houses built of cards. It is a game of chance and you do not even have to play your hand. Have as little to lose as possible and give away the rest. You will not miss it, and will be none the poorer. For it was not worth having. There may be a few little objects of sentimental value, but if you own anything better than that it should be in a museum. You will not miss it. You may even be happier without it.

There is a milk bottle on every doorstep. Oh ! where is the herd of goats that I saw led round from door to door ? But

JUIN 1885
"Le Journal des Enfants"

this is more sanitary. Steady there ! Do not cross in front of the traffic lights ! Behold what has happened ! The Temperance chapel has become a court for owls. Where the maternity home once stood the satyrs dance and cry to their fellows. As for the seaside lodging-house, the cormorant and bittern shall possess it. But only in metaphor, for there are no birds bigger than a pigeon or a sparrow and the only stray animals are cats and dogs that have lost their homes. I hear the wind singing in the telephone poles and the raindrops run like acrobats along the wire. Are the pavements of London never dry ? Does it weep tears of rain in London every day and all the night ? The buses are full and do not stop to take up passengers, and a taxi comes by with its flag muffled up in a piece of rag. The driver has ' had enough ' and is going home.

But, suddenly, it lightens in the tremendous West. We are living under a violent sunset and there have been stormy skies for days past in the morning. Portents, but nothing portentous. There is hardly any news. But the streets are golden. Can I ever forget that evening, towards the end of another war, when the distant street music sounded so wild and beautiful, and coming nearer, it was a woman playing " Roses of Picardy " on a cracked violin ? Who, that can remember them, will ever forget the ragtimes of the day, for they breathed the small hopes of those last few months of slaughter? To be killed, once, twice, or three times, is that the fate of the ' century of the small man ' ? But it lightens. The pavements and the roofs are shining. The pneumatic road-drill is hooded for the night. There is steam on the windows, and an aeroplane traces a great arch of vapour in the sky, high up, where of old the naked goddesses showed upon the clouds. Sculpture or architecture in the aether. But it fades and disintegrates, and soon it is no more than a fleece or mane of steam across the sky.

Bend down and dig the strawberry root, and wash your face and hands in strawberry water, for the world must be

revived by magic ! So long as the spell works it matters not
what it means, or if it has no meaning, but we are hungry and
thirsty for the transcendental mood. We would raise our hearts
and be lifted out of ourselves. We would forget the ticket
inspector and the taxation form.

Or we can have this picture from a fashion plate. Two
little girls, one in red and one in blue, are fishing from a boat in
a few inches of water at the edge of a lake. It could be in the
public gardens. A red and a blue dragonfly are hovering in the
reeds. The little girl in blue has light-blue ribbons in her hair ;
while her companion wears a red hat with a dark-blue ribbon
round it, a striped skirt of red and blue, and a red coat with a
dark-blue edging. A small boy and girl are sitting on a fence
within a few feet of them. He wears a sailor suit, but it is made
with breeches and not sailor trousers ; while the small girl in
straw colour and dark brown wears brown kid boots, a brown
coat and pleated skirt, and a 'pork-pie' hat of straw with a
brown ribbon and a cockade of flowers in it. Two other young
girls are yet more improbable. One is in pink and red from
head to foot ; she wears red shoes, and her dress and even her
pink stockings are covered over with red bobbins. She has a
pink straw hat with cherries in it. Her little friend in brown
wears a hat of blue and red and a white apron edged, like the
tricolore, with red and blue.

Or we come back to the children at the seaside, playing on
the sands. A little girl in tartan and her friend in a sailor suit
are sitting upon the shore. Another, in brown, wears brown kid
boots and blue stockings, that look like tights, an elaborate brown
coat and a brown 'pork-pie' hat trimmed with dark-blue flowers.
This fashion plate is dated Août 1885. An overgrown big boy,
dressed as a child in blue, has rolled up his trousers and is paddling
in the sea. There are crossed anchors on his shirt and on his

AOÛT 1886
" Le Journal des Enfants "

sleeves below the shoulders, and he wears a peaked hat like the pointed hat of Fra Diavolo and the Calabrian brigands, but it is a blue hat and it is bound with ribbons. At the far side of the group of children, a girl five or six years old with a shrimping net is dressed in rose pink. She has pink socks and a pink dress made like a nightgown in front and in the sleeves, but with a pink bustle, and a hat of pink straw shaped like a cornucopia turned upside down and trimmed with cherries. In front of her, and standing in the water, a little girl of three, with the fat face of Cupid and long golden curls, wears a white shirt or smock with red ribbons at her waist and red bows upon her shoulders, and a straw hat with a red lining. In her hand she holds a spade and pail. In the distance there is the blue sea. We see a row of bathing huts, and the white chalk cliffs, without a house upon them, die back into a cloudless sky.

The little goat-carriage draws up at the bandstand. But the conductor lays his baton down, the bandsmen put away the instruments into their cases and cover up the drums, and one of them collects the music from the music-stands. This is how every concert ends. To-night they will play the gavotte from *Mignon*, beside the darkening sea. " Dost know a land where blooms the orange and the lemon ? ", so runs the song ; but the rest of the programme will be popular.

(v)

Bacchus, Semele, and Apollo

How beautiful is the clear light of this spring morning !
My thoughts go back to the tram-ride to the Certosa, when I

was a child, starting from the flower market with its stalls of
roses and carnations and the bronze statue of the wild boar;
passing through the Piazza del Duomo, over the Arno, with
view of the Ponte Vecchio and the more graceful Ponte Santa
Trinità; and so, out of the Porta Romana, along the dusty
road to Galluzzo, where the Certosa first appears on its hill
among the cypresses. The white robes of the Carthusian monks,
their shaven heads and beards, their peculiar black square-
ended shoes, always left an extraordinary impression upon me,
as, having climbed that steep hill up to the monastery in the
blazing heat, we waited in the porch, and after a while a monk
came shuffling down the long, dark, cellar-like passages of the
interior, and we went together up the outer of the two open
stairways that led side by side, looking out over the vines and
olive trees towards Impruneta, where Callot once drew the
musicians and Gypsies of the fair; and so into the sunny open
court above, with pavement of red tiles; into the church opposite
with its marbles and frescoes and inlaid presses, a conventual
brother in his brown robe sweeping; down to the tombs of
the Acciaiuoli, and up into the great cloister with the cells of the
monks round it, the box hedges and the well-head in the middle.
Then to the bare refectory, with a plate and bowl laid in each
place; through minor cloisters, down the inner stairway, and
in anticipation along the dark, vaulted passages to the Spezeria,
a room fitted up as a magic pharmacy, where the monks sold
their chocolates and liqueurs, and cakes of soap, scented with
almond and marshmallow, wrapped in silver foil, and stamped

with the sacred monogram of the Carthusians above the lion and
leopard of the founder's arms.

That was, and could still be, in Tuscany, at the season when the blue or white wistaria is in flower upon the pergola ; and another memory, for it is contingent, takes me to Fiesole and its Etruscan wall. For I loved the Etruscans long before I knew anything of the ancient Greeks. I was fascinated by their mysterious origin and the curious countenances upon vase and tomb and painted sepulchre. But the most beautiful of their productions were the bronze mirrors. We know their purpose because we have noticed them in the hands of the nymphs as they wash themselves at fountains upon the painted vases. Some have been found in their mirror-cases, which are plates of bronze hinged together like the valves of an oyster shell. They have been discovered in Etruscan tombs.

But before we describe the most beautiful of the bronze mirrors, remember that it has lain in the darkness for twenty-five centuries and more ! The tomb is cut into the rock. In the distance are the Apennines and the snow-capped Sabine hills. We are in the plain. In the Maremma. No town or village within sight, for all lies in the desolation of a hundred years ago. Nothing but the shepherds' cabins, and we will enter into one of these.

They are tall, conical, thatched huts, propped in the centre upon two rough masts, and with a fire burning on an open hearth. The huge sheepdogs are in the doorway, white as new-dropt lambs, but fierce and shaggy, of the Maremma breed. Upon the fire there is a boiling cauldron, full of ewes' milk, or warm curd, which one of the shepherds drops with a ladle into the bowls of his companions for their morning meal, between times pouring it into wicker baskets in which it will be taken to the Roman market, the liquid part running off through the wicker, and the rest caking as it cools. On the same board stand the cheeses made from the cream.

The shepherds, twenty or twenty-five in number, are dressed

in goatskins, with the hair outwards so that their legs are like the legs of satyrs. They are celibates without the vows, and in such huts they dwell all the year round. Their festival is the sheep-shearing, at the season when the hard, dark berries have come upon the myrtle and the olive, and the ivy has grown into a dark-fruited vine.

The tomb is in the rock behind the shepherds' huts, and here the bronze mirror was found a hundred years ago. What we behold is the back of the mirror. For the mirror side is concave, ever so little, and serves to lift the water and pour it upon the body. The back has a border of a wreath of ivy leaves incised upon it, but the inner side is highly polished. A bronze mirror which can be held in the hand and which changes and alters, while the hand moves, inattentive, and the face looks into the mirror. To whom did it belong ?

I have known, and loved, this relic of the Classical past since I was twelve years old, when Dennis' *Cities and Cemeteries of Etruria* first fell into my hands. The engraved scene upon the mirror depicts Bacchus, Semele, and Apollo ; or in their Etruscan names, which are scratched beside them, Phuphluns, Semla, and Apulu. In other words, the young Bacchus and his parents. It is encircled, as we say, by the ivy leaves of Bacchus, and the circle of the composition is divided into two halves by an olive stem held in Apollo's hand ; or it is a rooted olive tree that the left hand of Apollo holds where the leaves begin. The olive is sacred to him. He stands beside it, and his head is on a level with the budding leaves.

He has a straight profile, long hair bound with a fillet, and wears a necklace. His right hand is on his hip ; and in hieratic pose one of his sandalled feet is behind the other and rests, indeed, upon the inner circle of the mirror so that it treads the ivy of the border. Behind him, a little satyr plays upon the double pipes. A little satyr who wears a necklace, too, and sits on a

ETRUSCAN BRONZE MIRROR
with Bacchus, Semele and Apollo

jutting rock, lifting his knees as though dancing to the music. His bushy tail breaks into the circle of the ivy leaves.

Bacchus and Semele, his mother, fill the right-hand half of the composition and their pose completes the circle. She is clothed and he is naked, but for a necklace. He stands with both arms thrown back to kiss her, so that the back of his head rests upon her bosom, while his hands clasp her by her neck and draw down her face towards him. Her hands take him by his ribs, above his waist. In her right hand, that is behind him, she holds the thyrsus, bound with ribbons, held close to the olive stem and to Apollo's hand. The rod of the thyrsus comes up through her fingers while they touch his side.

Their heads are one above the other. They make a perfect circle whichever way you turn them. As soon as the nose and forehead of the one are turned away from you, the nose and forehead of the other come into line. It is a circle within a circle, a design in a design, and alters most entrancingly when you take the mirror in your hand. He looks up into her eyes, and she looks down upon his lips. He is a boy, twelve or thirteen years old, and his height is to her shoulder. But his nudity is in contrast to his mother, who wears a patterned gown from neck to sandal, but of so simple a design that it is no more than a set of little dots or points symmetrically arranged. Her nose and forehead are in one straight line. She is a woman of about thirty years old, not a young girl, but Semele, the mother of Bacchus. She looks down into his lips and is about to kiss him. Apollo, her lover and his father, is looking on. The little satyr plays upon his flute. The immortal gods and goddesses are human. We see, on the naked bodies of Bacchus and of Apollo, the line on their chests which runs down into their navels. They were born of women.

When I first knew the mirror there was something equivocal to me in their embrace. The clothed figure of Semele with her masculine profile was a mystery, while I had no Classical Dictionary to consult. She was a goddess : but he was a child reaching up to kiss his mother.

Look again ! The flute of Pan is playing. There is in the expression of the goddess, the mother of Bacchus, that she consecrates him with her kiss. It would be with this kiss that the young Mars is sent by his mother Juno to the wars. Except for the Lydian softness of the line of Bacchus as he lifts his naked body in her arms. He is to instruct mankind in the use of the vine, the tilling of the earth, and the manner of making honey. These are the mysteries that she teaches him. It is for this she looks so closely into his lips. Not into his eyes, for those are the lights of intellect ; and here are instinct and sensual feeling.

And in accordance with the design of their heads, which is in a circle, we may imagine ourselves, one moment, looking down his neck and chest and naked body, upon the son of Apollo who is to conquer India and like his father is gifted with eternal youth, and then fancy ourselves with our arms about her neck drawing down her face towards us, and looking up not into her profile, her braided hair, and calm-lidded eye, but upon her full face with both almond-pupilled eyes and the rounded outline of her cheeks curving down into her youthful chin, and smelling her scented hair and scented breath, not perfumed with oils, but as of the goddess who sleeps upon a bed of flowers, and wakens each morning in the Golden Age. It is a wonderful thing to break, for a moment, their immortal pose, to separate them from each other's arms, mother and son, Semele and Bacchus, so that we see her move and see the carriage of her head upon that stem-like neck. To have the goddess walk before us with her immortal tread ! To watch the fluttering of her robe in the less-than-wind, for it is perpetual summer in the mirror ! To hear the clack-clack of her sandals !

Who makes the sandals for the goddesses? Who takes their measure on the bright sands? Her sandal is not low-heeled like the sandal of Apollo. The thong, at the back of the foot, is above her ankle. It touches where the beauty of her leg begins. Not like the sandal of Apollo, which is flat and not intended for ornament. But this draws our eyes. We are not accustomed to a goddess in a long, patterned gown. We are not used to this immortal being, who walks and turns and comes towards us. And now we have her double eyes, for they are in one line under her immortal brow, fixed upon us.

Her hair is dressed elaborately, with curls upon her forehead and by her ears, and she wears a broad half-band or fillet that is probably of gold. She has a necklace, too. What jeweller fashioned her necklace and her earrings? Her earrings are like a golden leaf at the joining of her neck and jaw; as she walks, they turn and dangle like the spinning poplar leaves. Her beauty consists in that straight line of her nose and forehead, and in the joining of her neck and cheek.

Yet she is of the lesser goddesses. There are no temples in her honour. Her father was Cadmus: her mother, Hermione, was born to Mars and Venus. She looks down upon Bacchus and inspires him. She whispers into his lips. She teaches her son Bacchus to have mortal longings. That must be the secret that she whispers to him.

Her tread is that of a goddess, or a peasant woman. Like that of the women who balance the amphora with one arm upon their heads, walking to the fountain. But they have not her fluttering gown and rippling sleeves. In the autumn she does not bow down beneath a load of faggots. We should not meet her at a corner of the stony path, where the gnarled olive throws an ancient shade. Neither would we find her helping to haul in the nets. Nor in a broad-brimmed hat among the foxgloves, having come in with a comb of honey from the hive. She is not the daughter of a husbandman, who has wedded and taken with her a portion of vineyard and of olive grove.

Instead, the flowers spring up in her footsteps. Where she passes the ivy climbs up into the tree. The berries come upon the olive and the myrtle. At the festivals of her son, the participants will wear crowns of violets in their hair and upon their hands gloves composed of flowers.

(vi)

A Rag and a Bone and a Hank of Hair

We are walking in the plain. In the springtime, for the corn is rising.

A young girl comes toward us ; but she looks back over her shoulder. She never sees us. She is a little goatherd, dressed no differently from other children. Walking barefoot, with some crumpled flowers in her hand. Not frightened, for she is not hurrying, but something has broken the monotony of the morning. Is it the hoopoe, with breast and back of cinnamon, striped wings of black and white, and lordly crest ? For a hoopoe lights in the corn, and flutters a little way, and preens himself again.

There is a line of mountains, far away, with snow upon them. And a classical simplicity, or the purity of early times. Not a human dwelling within view, but immense rocks as big as houses, thrown far and wide by the deluge and ready to roll down. No other living thing to be seen that has not wings.

A hawk that hovers and an eagle soaring with set pinions.

Listen ! there is no sound, unless it be the turning, turning of the world. And a chill wind from the snow-capped mountains.

But the rocks are flowering.

By a miracle we have found the dwarf narcissus. It grows in the detritus of the granite. First one, and then another, until we see that there are hundreds of the little flowers. This is the land of the fairy narcissi. They are the population of the mountains.

What shape of flower? A long funnel; not a trumpet, but a petticoat, for it is like an empty dress blown out by the wind upon a Lilliputian laundry line. Worn by no mortal, but where the snows are melting, and spring comes down and touches the bare plain.

The narcissi are in their hundreds, blowing in one way. All trembling on the wind. And a dwarf daffodil, three inches high, and more sweetly scented than any other. The cup or perianth of the narcissus has little spikes, that are like antennae, that are like the eyes and points of antelopes, they are so delicate, and that sense direction, or give the warning. They are all waiting on the wind. They are all facing toward the morning. They have come up between the stones. Out of the granite detritus. Last evening, or the day before, you would not have seen them. They are new-born this morning. This is their youth. And to-morrow? To-morrow may be their middle age.[1]

A fantastic landscape lies into the distance. It is the plain of Don Quixote and the Spanish Civil War. I wrote, too soon, that we have forgotten. There may be the arch of a Roman aqueduct casting its shadow to the left. But, to my mind, the plain should be reaped by giant skeletons. Then, and now, and in the years to come. It is enormous in extent to the far snow mountains.

A beautiful pied bird flies past, and gives it scale.

[1] The habitat of the miniature or 'fairy' narcissi is in Portugal and Northern Spain. They include *Bulbicodium conspicuus*, the 'Yellow-Hoop Petticoat'; the gazelle-like *Triandrus albus* or 'Angel's Tears'; and *Minimus Asturiensis*, three inches high, and most sweetly scented of the whole race. Unknown varieties may yet be found.

All of one colour, except where the corn is showing green. And reduced in outline to the simplest forms. In hue, as though it were of golden clay, which is to say, in high summer it will be of yellow dust, and the cornfields will be yellow, too. The hovels are of mud flecked with straws. Such they are now, and such they have ever been. It will never be otherwise. At midsummer the cistus will be in flower upon the sloping hills. There are the different sorts. The white rock rose has a brilliant blood-red blotch ; but there is a purple kind, as well, and one which is bright yellow with a chocolate spot. Growing in hundreds among the boulders, with their ilex-green, dull glittering leaves, and flowers that are dead by night, but renew by morning.

It is sufficient.

We come down by the leaves that glitter into the plain. There are some persons walking. Their dress consists of a long gown, like a toga, and they wear leggings which are in ragged descent from the Classical cothurni, as though five hundred years of Roman fashion had passed over them and gone by. Their heads are close-shaven, their eyes and both sides of their noses are seen ' in drawing ', so much so that it must be a racial mannerism, or the characteristic of an age. They seem tall, and move in a group the shape of a pyramid, with the tallest at the apex.

Next thing, we see a hand that paints upon a wall.

It is on the side of a house, within the fortifications of a town. We need see no body, but the decoration grows before our eyes. Huge whorls of leaves, that now, knowing more, we recognise to be the rendering on a flat surface, by a provincial hand, of the carved pilasters of Baalbek and of Leptis Magna. In those, the subject springs up from out a vase of flowers. Here they are drawn in freehand. Birds and fishes show between the garlands. We know the dove, the partridge, and the quail.

But now the hand draws a white horse, riderless, moving

away from us towards a tent or pavilion that is like a merry-go-round. Soon, many more buildings appear. The horizon shakes with towers : but it would be better to call them tiers of arches superimposed on one another, and open to the air. But, in fact, such buildings, in their original, would have been but painted wood or canvas. Here it is the whole of Classical architecture come down through incredible vicissitudes to the fairground, and copied by barbarians upon their walls. But in a land that has been Roman, and is now Christian.

The hand of the artist delights in its own handiwork, just as though the rocks have flowered where there were no flowers before. As spontaneous as that flowering, and as by a miracle that comes naturally, and not too often. That is the secret. Each time could be once in a lifetime. For they were not sated, as we are, by the graven image. We had better, indeed, let the machinery do as it will and must, and not prevent it. Let it be a thing apart, with its own wonders, which we will not imitate because that is impossible. And let the alternative be rare and infrequent, flowering where no foot has trodden, to be known on the instant by the pattern of its breath upon wall or canvas or upon the sheet of paper. For, of those times, we might say it is apparent that the hand that took up the brush or pen could not go wrong. There is a sure and certain unexpectedness to every touch and a sophistication, in spontaneity, that the later world has never achieved, nor attempted, until modern painting. But, behind that, there is an implicit magnificence, and the sense that what has been an escape fraught with agony and difficulty from the modern world into the fantasies of childhood, comes here as naturally as a flower, as easily as the wild narcissus that blooms among the rocks.

For the mind of their time, as we say, was not over familiar with the graven image. Its impact, therefore, had the unexpectedness of when you look down and the wild narcissus is growing at your feet. In the clear air of the mountains. Having come up, overnight, between the mosses and the stones of granite. It may even be growing through the melted snows. And you bend down to look at it, and the air you breathe above it is quite still with the smell of jonquils, a scent that is like the opening of a pair of lovely eyes, but only in that little place, and nowhere else, as though you have found the bed of the goddess where she fell asleep in happy wantonness and wakens to the innocence of the pure morning.

"Did you read in to-day's paper that the tomb of an early Spanish King has been opened in a convent near Burgos . . . and that they have found him lying there in his robes and golden crown ? "

I looked at once through all the papers, but the only mention I could find was in a paragraph of the local evening newspaper, *The Mercury and Herald*. This said that the tomb was in the convent of Las Huelgas a mile or two from Burgos.

I have been to Las Huelgas, twice, and remember it as a huge building of typical Cistercian architecture. I recall some splendid tapestries, but not those of red violet, nor of green, which Ford describes in his handbook, and that were the gift of Philippe le Bel. The abbess used to be a princess-palatine with powers of life and death over I forget how many villages of serfs, while the nuns were all ladies of noble birth. Once they were a hundred in number ; now a few of them, the shrunken remnant of the *señoras doñas*, still serve the convent. All is dilapidated. When I saw it, the storks had their nests upon the tower.

I am wondering which King it can have been. Alfonso VIII ? He founded the convent, and is buried there. It was probably Alfonso. But, for my taste, he is getting late in date. I would prefer an earlier King.

Who shall it be ? We like the names of Sancho, Ramiro,

Ordoño, better still, Bermudo, all early Kings of Visigothic blood, and can take our choice, for we have not been told. An early King, and that is all. Let us hear more names! Shall it be Recaredo, Gundemaro, Leovigildo? Sisebuto, Recesvinto, Wamba, or Don Rodrigo? All Visigoths. But, in fact, the name of the King matters not at all. Did we know it, it would tells us nothing. An early King has been found in his tomb. Is that not enough?

Why have we such a longing to be present at this opening of the tomb? Merely to read of it in the newspaper was thrilling, and brought a difference to the day. This is something new: and all the rest is old and stale. We need the promise that the world was young, once, and that the hand of man could not go wrong. We need to be restored in confidence. We would remember, and at the same time forget. We would go back to the beginning, and begin again. We would return to early times, when the same hand like a child's, in cruelty and innocence, slew the bird and pulled the wings from off the butterfly, but could not but be fresh and pure in its imaginings. In what it carved or painted. In sculptured capital and round arched doorway.

Have you not seen, at Monza, the iron crown of the Longo-bards? The silver hen with seven chickens for Lombardy and its seven provinces? The crown and fan and comb of Queen Theodolinda? The Egyptian Fatimite vessels of rock-crystal stolen from St Sophia, in the treasury of St Mark's? The coronation robes of the Holy Roman Emperors in the Schatz-kammer at Vienna? The mantle of red purple sewn with pearls, woven in Sicily by the Saracens, for the Norman Kings; the gloves and shoes and buskins of red silk? All in glass cases. Oh! put them away. And return the mummies of the Egyptian Pharaohs to their tombs. We would not that they were witness to our follies.

We will have this in our own way. There are museums enough already. We will not let it be that this is but another.

But do not anticipate a mere opening of the tomb. There is much more besides. We behold the dead. We see them . . . and they see us.

We will find an old mirror in the coffin. We will look into it, and see ourselves, and the face that leans over our shoulder. It will show us the past and the future, in this present. We will see the bones of the dead, clothed in their flesh, and the shadow of what is to fall.

We will find a rusty crown . . . AND A RAG AND A BONE AND A HANK OF HAIR.

In a stone box, with a stone lid that fits. And, inside that, a leaden coffin, and another, and another. It is triply sheathed in lead. Like leaden swaddling clothes. But it becomes more human. It has the shape of the shoulders and the head. It is like a body in a cradle, or a body in a bath. Only of huge stature. We would expect to find a two-handed sword between its legs, and its hands upon the hilt. It takes on the form of an old travelling trunk, which is hooded at one end, and this innermost of the coffins is covered with some stuff which has been silk or velvet, and is now in rags, but still soft to the finger-nails.

Who is it that lies inside ? The bones have been thrown down as though the coffin had been stood on end. But the level of the floor has sunk down, too. We have to allow for earth-quake and subsidence, and tremors of the surface.

We see no more of Las Huelgas, but leave it a decaying convent in the dust outside a crumbling town. In the distance there are the spires and crockets of Burgos cathedral standing out from the slope of the hill with its towers and lantern. But no concern of ourselves. It has but risen into the air while we have waited. It was not there when the tomb was sealed. Neither that nor Miraflores, where the hand of Gil de Siloe carved the retablo and the tombs.

For a month or two I forgot about it altogether. That is to say, consciously, I never thought of it. But, all the time, the theme was taking shape and plan. A subject or formula that can be read both ways, backward and forward, or upside down as in a mirror. We look up from the book, into the glass, and we see ourselves. Or the contemporary world : or the world as it could be.

There must be nothing between ourselves and the earlier time. For a little while, until the magic has begun to work. Till the mirror of bronze has lost its mildew : till the ivory comb is clean again : till the silken robe is patched : and the crown or diadem taken in the hand.

It is agreed that we would give anything to see this opening of the tomb. There was that little paragraph in a local evening paper . . . and that is all we have to go upon.

But all is ready. We can be present, in person and in imagination, at the opening of the tomb. We stoop down, and looking through a hole in the coffin, we see the King or warrior lying in state upon a bed of stone. He is clothed in full armour, and looks like a living man.

But, as we gaze, we see the body agitated with a sort of trembling, heaving motion, which is accompanied by a little and indescribable noise like a whispering, or like falling rain. This continues for what seems an eternity, but is of the duration of a moment or two only, while his figure trembles and he crumbles away into dust before our eyes.

We stay for some minutes, scarcely daring to move or breathe, hoping the illusion will return, but when we know that it is gone for ever, a bigger opening is made and we go down into the tomb. Upon the stone bed there lie a handful or two of dust, some fragments of his sword and armour, some pieces of yellow woollen garment and bits of bone. We find, also, a heap of black earth which had once been perfumes, and his crown of gold formed of golden lilies. All that is left of this King of the ancient world is A RAG AND A BONE AND A HANK OF HAIR.

ENTR'ACTE

Serenade

THE comb of Queen Theodolinda.

Or a girl or woman combing her hair before her mirror, now or two thousand years ago, or in the long, lost afternoons. There are the different measures ; that which is dilatory, undertaken in order to be alone and waste the time, and that which is as the bird that preens her wing, but when you look again, the bough trembles and the bird has gone.

We begin with the first sort.

I remember an oblong box upon a dressing-table ; a little box covered with an ' all over ' millefleur pattern and lined with yellow silk, and the cut-glass bottle within it, which had a stopper shaped like the big flopping women's hats of the early ' nineteen-hundreds ' and a gold label, in relief, with the bust of a woman, hatless, with her hair done in the fashion of the time, holding a bunch of flowers to her face, but looking upwards into that golden sky.

I remember the scent of the golden liquid, the name Houbigant — surely a stroke of genius on the part of Providence! — and a tortoise-shell comb. And many such hours, totalling to days or weeks : but long, long ago. So, now, for Theodolinda. Since everything we cannot see with our eyes, or touch with our hands, whether we miss it by a year or by twenty centuries, is dead, dead, dead, and we forget this too easily, until perhaps our own memories are of dead persons, or of the living who, like flowers, begin to droop and fade. And then it is late, and we cannot set down what we have seen and known.

The crown, and fan, and comb.

Ah ! Not the tuberoses and gardenias of my youth ; nor the magnolias of the Italian lakes, many of them like ghosts of themselves, with petals of brown parchment that still kept their shape ; with a living magnolia among them, a wonder within reach, and more, higher up, among the broad and brittle leaves ; and the citron smell of the magnolia, like a citron curd, in a breath or exhalation spilling from the lotus cup, as it floated warmly and dreamily upon the green-black moonlight of the magnolia tree. Also, nearer to Monza, I remember it raining, raining, in Milan between the thunderstorms. I never liked Milan. I loved the magnolia, but not the thunder and the lightning.

Her ivory comb is heavy : too heavy for her hand to hold. Her crown or tiara such as the swan princesses wear at the lake's shore where the mists raise ghostly forms among the bulrushes, and the snowflakes are falling. But we are thinking that if Theodolinda had a fan, a fan will be found where an early Spanish Queen is buried. Where there is a King there is a Queen, and she will have been buried with her fan.

But a woman combing her hair before her mirror is nothing else than a convention or set piece, like that moment of the ' letter song ' or ' music lesson ' in the old opera. We hear the stilted sentences in *recitativo secco*, and the accents and conclusions on the harpsichord.

We hear notes upon the clavichord ; upon the lute, or harp, or mandoline. The immortal song begins.

Theodolinda ! Where are your crown, and fan, and comb ? Olympia, Antonia, Giulietta, where are you now ? Shall I open the faded envelope and take out your lock of hair ? Listen, listen, it is the long summer afternoon. Those, there will always be. Did not someone tell you, when he was dead and buried, that his eyes would still look at you out of his coffin ? But there is no need to be serious ; for this is the Muse of Comedy.

We hear laughter, and music playing underneath the trees. And then the inner music, near at hand.

Indeed, some sort of a lute or guitar is playing in the room. Or upon the stage.

Is it you, Lindoro? We only meet on such hot evenings; or in the painted wings. You are singing under the balcony, dressed as a Cavalier, with your plumed hat and your riding switch held between your hands. That, again, is the old convention. We hear the rise and fall of the serenade. We hear the accompaniment, to the last dying note. And then silence.

And a little stir which could be the shutting of a fan. Or is it the lifting of the fingers from the clavichord?

The team of white mules, with jangling bells, waits noisily below. They are dancing and playing castanets in every quarter of the town. The hot hour strikes from the high tower. But, when you look again, Theodolinda has gone, like Lombard or Visigoth. There is nothing left but her crown and fan and comb, and a rose that has fallen upon the old and musty floor.

BOOK 3

THE KINGDOM OF THE BIRDS

THE KINGDOM OF THE BIRDS

(i)

Invocation to Venus

SHINE down, Venus, goddess of beauty, upon all that I have admired and loved ! Under whatever name, mistress of the graces and pleasures, mother of laughter, to whom the rose, the apple, and the myrtle are held sacred ! Your planet is in the train of the sun, and you are the morning or evening star according to your hour of rising out of the ocean, invisible at noon, but adding your light of beauty to dawn or sunset, when you burn alone in the hour of the dove or swan. It is by your gentle light that we judge of objects and of persons, not by sun and moon ; while your refulgence which is occasional but in obedience to the eternal laws makes you resemble the fires of inspiration, which are not perpetual, but come rarely and with no warning to their votaries.

The light of the sun and moon is not enough. The oar must lift the reflection of a star upon the waters. Such is the cold light of creation and of judgement, shining an hour before or after the rising or the setting sun. There, in its own firmament, and in the sparkling emptiness where we would look for it, the morning or the evening star promising the darkness or the day to come. The sun and moon are for men and women but your light shines for the arts and pleasures. Not the goddess of the philosophers, nor the mother of the poor, but a religion or faith apart with its own rewards and punishments. Oh ! lift the oar and touch the lute before we fall from heaven. Before we lose her favours, the eyes must come into the peacock's tail and the flour or meal upon the painted petals of the auricula. It is her influence that flakes or marbles the calm face of the camellia, that stripes or flames the tulip, and that spots or pards the tiger-lily. She dyes the rose, and makes glitter the leaves of ilex and of myrtle. She paints the cheeks of apples and gives a downy skin to peach and apricot, and more naked nectarine. Not the goddess of natural beauty, only, for she puts the freckles in the gloxinia, she stipples the wild foxglove and the calceolaria ; she dyes the coleus, which is nothing but a nettle, and makes it scarlet and maroon, rose-lake with green saw edge and creamy centre, or red splashed with yellow ; she tints the dracæna or dragon-tree to a deep and profound cinnamon with scarlet and crimson shading, and double-dyes the cypripedium and odonto-glossum. All these are not more glorious than the blossoming quince, or weeping rosebud cherry, than the white cherry with breath of almond, than the old pear tree upon the wall, but they are her exotics, one or more out of a million when we count the wings of birds and beetles, when we add the moths and butter-flies, and in one life there is not time to tell them all. There is only space for what our eyes have seen, or imagination fed upon in proxy, knowing that we can never touch them but must be content with what we imagine they must be, for our interior world is compound of real and unreal, but not of true and false, because things unseen, but felt, are of the same force in visual importance as though they had been physically experienced. They are identical in value and there has been no difficulty in describing them ; the golden altars of Mexico ; the rock-cut Kailasa in the Elloran quarry, dug down into the hill. I have found the snows of St Petersburg and palaces of the Sleeping Beauty as tangible as the stones of Venice. Naples and Mexico, the one known, the other unknown, have co-existed for me ; and it may be that no other writer has had this aptitude or been able to move, at will, from where the hand has touched to where the eyes have never seen. We invoke Venus, not as the goddess of natural beauty, only, but because she is most mortal and human of the goddesses and in the light of her planet, which is that of her eyes looking upon us, we have ever examined what we set out to find, by rule of beauty, born of poetry.

But we promised, did we not, to float with Giulietta by the decaying palaces and on the green lagoon? Giulietta, let us recall, is the courtesan who draws us after her to Venice, which comes to every young man, if only in his thoughts and dreams. If we have that way with women, well enough; but otherwise we can only ensnare them with our wits and nerves. Is that not the purpose of what little talents we have been given? But those are only of limited appeal in that direction; or avail nothing. The structures of our imagination, to this extent, are ruinous and empty buildings, entirely comparable to those decaying palaces, for we may be lacking in the power to people them with their appropriate inhabitants, or those persons are of dead generations and their parallel or equivalent has no identity in modern times. This is the unending plaint of all artists in any of the arts, alike Classical or Romantic, and at the same time the excuse or reason for their existence. No need, therefore, for explanation or apology.

At our opening scene in the tavern, where Hoffmann drinks with the students and tells them of his loves, we listen to his tales but it is not necessary to believe in them. Besides, it is not Hoffmann himself; it is his counterpart in the opera *Les Contes d'Hoffmann*, and his tales have been given another life in that minor, but immortal music. It is, after all, mere fantasy; as were our few days in late August or September spent in Venice with Giulietta. And yet . . . there could be one more, in number, than Olympia, Antonia, and Giulietta. This accords, curiously, with the opera, in which the chief singer, it will be remembered, appears in four different rôles, those of the mistresses of Hoffmann. In the first scene Hoffmann is in love with the automaton Olympia, a predicament which must have fallen to the lot of everyone who has loved a silent, fair-haired girl. It is in the second scene that Giulietta entertains her admirers in Venice, her favourite being Schlemihl, the man without a shadow. The action is concerned with the wiles of Giulietta to induce Hoffmann to exchange his own shadow for her love, after which she breaks her promise and betrays him to his enemies. The meaning of this involved plot may be all, or nothing.

But what we intend is not an exact picture of the decaying city, but a sojourn among the persons and buildings that are peculiar to our state of mind. Personally, then, it is not a particular episode, but the whole life and career of the artist, tending to one end. Not Venice, in detail, but the architectural and musical experience of half a lifetime ; things seen, real or imaginary, in company with Antonia, whom our first words indicated as an actress, a dancer, or a film star, and who, sometimes, wears a mask ; with the automaton Olympia, whose provocation lies in her silence, and who is of the kind that will burn our youth through in agony and suspense ; or with Giulietta. One and the same person ? Or does their total add up into a fourth ? This is the mystery. But the types are eternal and remain fixed for ever. They would have been the same in the sixteenth, seventeenth, eighteenth centuries as now. And this is true, the more convinced we may become that one particular person is the embodiment of her own time. The nearer the approximation to the moment, the more ultimate is this perpetual truth.

Under the light of Hesperus, which is the name for the planet Venus when she appears after the setting of the sun, it is the same with persons as with works of art. They have the taste and savour of their moment, but are of time eternal. Thus are they, while the light and influence of the planet Venus are shed upon them, by day or night, according to whether it shows in the morning before the sun, or follows it and appears some time after its setting, by which we intend that such persons or objects of whom we treat are viewed, not in the ordinary illumination of night or day, but under the beams and in the soft refulgence of that planet's power, " which gives beauty, grace, and elegance even to the most deformed ; which excites love, and kindles extinguished flames ". And just as there are day and night, there are the true and false radiance or heart of light in which, salamander-like, the persons and objects move and dwell, while the deprivation for several years now of the lights and colours of our choice may have favoured a false illumination, as of the theatre. When we witness, for instance, a party of persons sitting at supper they will be actors and actresses, and not a banquet of the gods and goddesses, for during this long imprisonment those fantasies have fled. It may be that the interior life has waxed or increased, while the outside world has waned. Even so, the feast will be silent and in dumb show, for the theatre has lost its language and ritual. Antonia, for this reason, is more of a dancer than an actress, though we are told she is a singer and we have seen the mandoline that hangs upon her wall. Olympia is silent. With Giulietta it is different, and there is a fourth embodiment, whom we have but mentioned, with whom Hoffmann was in love in Milan, and who may be another person altogether, or all three loves in one.

This is not to be a portrait of our immediate time past, present, or to come ; nor the history of any event whatever. Instead, being only artist or musician in appreciation, and having but that faculty to be spellbound or rooted to the ground, unable to move hand or foot while it lasts, by a magic that we cannot explain or understand, we would describe the descent of the god into ourselves and attempt a self-portrait and the picture

of our times in states of feeling. Those must be personal, for
the spirit wanders far and wide in search of persons. But this
is not the square of mirror put outside the window to reflect
the passers-by. It is to be our times ; but the world of the
individual, not the million. It is Notre Temps, our world of
imagination in which we live, for good or evil. We borrow the
superscription from one of the saddest but most beautiful of
Chopin's mazurkas, written we believe, prosaically, for an
ephemeral publication of that name, but it has adapted itself in
meaning to the more ultimate import of the title. The mazurka
would seem to be in comment or enlargement upon that theme
and soon launches into a narrative or progression that could be
nothing else than his meditation upon the mood of the years in
which we lived. Or it could be the mood of the moment, of
Notre Temps, the passing time, of a few hours, or a whole
morning, but listening we may think to ourselves that we per-
ceive in it his mind and person against the background of his
times. Intended, no doubt, in the form in which it is cast, a
mazurka, to reflect his patriotic feelings as a Pole, but it is, as
well, the picture of his inward emotions and his state of health.
Of course, should we prefer it, it is a mazurka, a piece of music
contributed to a periodical, and nothing else. But, be it what
it may, this is not to be tinted by those same shades of introspection. We borrow the superscription, but no more.

Nature, alone, is not our subject, since we are neither naturalist nor landscape painter, but works and deeds of human beings,
their achievement in all the arts, and the conscious or unconscious
moulding of nature to their tastes, as in the cultivated flowers.
The tulip has more of human history than the dandelion ; the
honeycomb dahlia hangs heavier than the thistledown. The
wild flowers are a mystery to themselves. Who would surprise
Herb Paris must know its quatrefoil of leaves, ragged corolla,
lighter, green sepals, and black polyp-eye or ovary, and wonder

THE KINGDOM OF THE BIRDS

at the mystery of its name which is more magical, even, than this green plant of Saturn in the anemone'd and starlit wood. But a man-made mystery, for the flower is not as beautiful as its mysterious name.

So raise the laughing espalier, the seven-branched candelabra or apple tree growing from one stem, let the thrush-soft, Tyrian-purple rose open its winy blossoms and shake to rose petals to strew the Muses' floor ; gather the jasmine for a pomander made of its white cloves or quills ; and let the Turk's-cap imitate the striped turbans of the Tulip Reign ! Here are irises so blue they stain the fingers ; Sweet Williams which, for all their name, are like peasant girls dancing in circles in print dresses to one bee-loud, droning tune ; and the carnations, flakes, bizarres, picotees of the old fanciers, flowers of more than human perfection, for they are nature trained and aided by the skill of man, and by that addition prink their painted petals which are stippled, flaked, and freaked, or edged, splashed, and dappled, but in so regular an order and distribution in their markings that the scent and shape and pattern are in like proportion and they are, or were, the triumph of the florist's art. To behold them blooming in their rows, behind them the taller purple byblœmens ; and under the apple trees or hawthorn hedge the gold-laced polyanthus, the china-blue primrose, scarlet pantaloon, jackanapes and galligaskins, the Dusty Millers, yellow or wallflower-red with mealy leaves and white paste eye, and matchless auriculas of the greenhouse frame, green or white or grey edged, or like the blood-red self, Adonis, but all touched or flecked with the white meal of the show auricula, and given that indescribable scent which comes with the lifting of the frame, when we see them, shelf after shelf, all alike in shape or truss, but different as the constellations or flowers of the frosty sky, this excels in wonder the spotting of the leopard and the striping of the tiger.

Shall we compare them to the metallic Humming Birds?
To the Sickle Bill, a green Thrush-like bird with long forked
tail; the Chimborazian Hill Star, a Humming Bird which lives
only in the snows of that Ecuadorian crater, Swallow-like, with
white front, blue head and green-gold gorget; to that group of
Humming Birds, which, fluttering, appear to be possessed of
four, and not two wings; the *Topaza Pela* or Crimson Topaz,
with breast of fiery crimson and long sickle tail; to another
group in which the females are like green-spotted Thrushes;
the Jacobins, blue-green and white, and owing to the shape of
their tails hovering like four-winged Swallows; to the Coquettes,
generally, with Jay-like crests and beaded, spangled wings, and
to Princess Helena's Coquette, in particular, which has three
whisker-like black feathers protruding from each side of its
Wren-shaped head? To the several sorts of Racket Tails; to
the Thorn Tail; or to the *Calypte* with ruby-red head and tailed
mantle; to the Wood Stars which are very small indeed, even for
a Humming Bird, with short wings; to the Shear Tails; to the
Loddigesia mirabilis, a marvellous Humming Bird with crossed
disks upon its tail feathers, as though in the act of signalling or
receiving messages; or to the Blue-tailed Sylph? To the group
of *Cometes* or Comets with green-gold metallic wings, and to
the Sappho Comet, especially, with its bright-red tail; to
Guérin's Helmet Crest; or to the *Chrysolampis* which is ruby
and topaz, with ruby crest and topaz gorget; to *Orthorhynchus
cristatus* with blue and green metallic crest, but there is one, also,
which is gilt and shaped like a Plover's crest; to the Sun Gems,
long-tailed, white-breasted, with red ornaments behind the ears,
like fans; to the Hooded Vizor-bearer with green and gold
metallic beard and a pendant, locket-like mark of crimson at the
extremity of the beard; or the *Heliothrix* which is a green and
blue group of Humming Birds of the shape of Swallows? The
Violet Ears are a sept to themselves, the prettiest being *Corus-*

cans, the chequered Violet Ear ; then there is *Chrysobronchus*, a golden half-Swallow, green and brown and gold, with long train and tail ; the Sword Bill, narwhal of the glittering dews and airs ; *Helianthea Eos*, which is golden star-fronted ; and *Heliangelus* or Sun Angel, gorgeted, with ruby-topaz throat ; the *Heliomaster* or Star Throat, of sharp-billed thrush type ; and *Eustephanus*, a beautiful green-spotted Thrush, with white-and-green fan tail, only found in Juan Fernandez, the island of Robinson Crusoe. The Tuft-Legs are a family to themselves, with white muffs, as it were, upon their legs ; and there are the Coloured Crowns, blue-necked, with crown of azure, and green and white spotted body like a lovely Linnet ; another group with miraculous green-spotted throats ; the tooth-billed Humming Birds of Ecuador, like the reptilian or saurian ancestor of all ; the tribe of Rainbows ; the blue-throated Helmet Crest ; and Bolivian Sylph.[1]

(ii)

The Corn Screens

If the Humming Birds are " a family unequalled for the gorgeous and ever-changing brilliancy of their hues, the variety of their form, the singularity of their habits, and the extent of their territorial distribution ", where can we find their equivalent in works of art ? It will not be found in the Occident. Searching

---

[1] *Monograph of the Trochilidæ, or Humming Birds*, 6 vols. and supplement, with 418 hand-coloured plates, by John Gould, 1849–1887. The darting or hovering flight of the Humming Bird is beautifully described in a passage from *The Naturalist in Nicaragua*, by a disciple of Darwin, Thomas Belt, first published in 1874. He is describing *Florisuga mellivora*, a beautiful blue-green and white Humming Bird, with a tail which, when expanded, forms a semicircle. He continues : " I have seen the female sitting quietly on

through the great work of Gould upon the Humming Birds and examining it, as perhaps has not been done before, in the light of an enquiry into their aesthetics, we discern that the whole race has fallen or divided itself into forty-four separate groups, each possessed of its own distinctive peculiarities and beauties, all but three or four of which families have been indicated or referred to in our description. For the only parallel, it is necessary to consider the highest sophistication of the Oriental aesthete, to a degree in which that has never existed in the Occident, as shown by their greatest creations in the way of decoration, where they surpass all that has been achieved in the West. These are necessarily the painters, not of China, but of Japan.

We have in mind the school of Kano Eitoku and his successors, Koyetsu and Sotatsu. This school of decorators, probably the greatest there has ever been, worked for the tyrant Hideyoshi, and in the succeeding generation for the Tokugawa Shoguns. The greater part of their schemes of painted decoration have perished, but many of their painted screens are still preserved. From the hand of Kano Eitoku there is a six-fold screen representing a reception of envoys at the court of the Emperor of China. This is more sumptuous than any Venetian ceiling painting. Enormous golden cloud-forms break upon the wooden palace architecture ; upon one screen the ambassadors are bearing their presents through a garden, with many flowering trees ; upon the other, the Emperor is seated on his throne among his attendants. Other screens have for subject the ladies

a branch, and two males displaying their charms in front of her. One would shoot up like a rocket, then suddenly expanding his snow-white tail like an inverted parachute, slowly descend in front of her, turning round gradually to show off both back and front. The effect was heightened by the wings being invisible from a distance of a few yards, both from their great velocity of movement and from not having the metallic lustre of the rest of the body. The expanded white tail covered more space than all the rest of the bird, and was evidently the grand feature in the performance. Whilst one was descending, the other would shoot up and come slowly down, expanded. The entertainment ended in a fight between the two performers ; but whether the more beautiful or the more pugnacious were the accepted suitor, I know not."

of the Chinese court. But this genius in decoration is at his
highest without human figures. There are screens by Kano
Eitoku consisting only of flowers upon gold or silver grounds ;
a two-fold screen of maples in their contrasting colours ; another
of hanging wistaria ; and a great six-fold screen of vines upon a
trellis on a background of dull silver.[1]

But Koyetsu (1557 or 1590–1637) is the greatest painter of
the school, and probably the greatest and most original decorator
in human history. It is the secret of Koyetsu's peculiar and
especial qualities that he came of a family of swordmakers and
was himself an expert judge of sword blades, for this cult of
the sword plays so large a part in the life and aesthetic of Japan
that we may think, without exaggeration, that we see the signs of
it in the quality of Koyetsu's line with its tapering curves, like
the edges of a tempered blade, in the miraculous damascening
and 'watering' of his textures, and in what, having regard to his
hereditary profession, we would call the fencing and in-fighting
of his technique, with its lightning thrusts and parries, the sharp,
flat edges of his flowers and leaves, and the speed with which
he closes in and finishes his subject. Koyetsu was, too, one of
the great masters of the art of lacquer, and a famous potter. As
lacquerer, he was expert in the most exacting and difficult of
processes in the whole of applied art, working with bold inlays
of lead and mother-of-pearl as well as upon the finished surfaces
of grained and sprinkled gold. In his ceramics this contrast of
materials is not present, but we hear of him working with the
cheapest of pigments and producing, in a few moments and at
the cost of a bowl of rice, works of art which were individual
and complete in themselves. In their adaptation of nature, but it
is a personal interpretation, a rough country style, near, like so

[1] The splendid paintings by Kano Eitoku of great eagles perched upon pine trees,
in the castle at Nagoya, are almost certain to have perished during the recent aerial
bombardments.

much in Japanese art, to caricature, these are the imaginative masterpieces of the whole art of pottery, as opposed to what has been achieved in porcelain by the Ming masters and the modellers of Chelsea and of Meissen.

The painted screens of Koyetsu may be appreciated and admired, even in illustration, and without nearer access to them, while their aesthetic value is enhanced by his handwriting, for he was noted as a calligraphist. One of the most glorious works of Koyetsu is a two-fold screen, upon a ground of silver leaf, with nothing but trailing vines, or it is a variety of ampelopsis or Virginia creeper in its autumn colourings, red and olive-green burning into yellow, with down-hanging tendrils, the whole cascading descent of the clusters, full grown, being contrasted with the luxuriant climbing of the creeper, and its weight appearing as if trembling on the wind after a shower of rain. The fan screens of Koyetsu are an extraordinary achievement ; each fan design forming a perfect composition in itself, capable of enlargement, not a miniature, and having for subject figure scenes, often in variation upon works of earlier Japanese masters, or fans which are flower subjects wonderful in themselves ; white or spotted lilies in their leaves, chrysanthemums with their petals in relief, or the red maples, the whole total of these fans, to the number of thirty or more, being combined upon one screen, on a ground of gold or silver, but the grouping or arrangement of the fans upon the screen is a feat in which the genius of the painter excels itself. The leaves of the fans contribute to the general pattern, but their whole spacing is an aesthetic pleasure in itself. They are painted lying at every angle, according to the rules of this Oriental art which is half calligraphy, half dressmaking, until we could believe that no other hand but that of Koyetsu had the taste and skill thus to arrange them. The new art of detailed photography, as applied to paintings, has its opportunity in the fan screens of Koyetsu, for from a single specimen thirty or more finished pictures could be obtained. Another pair of screens has grasses and chrysanthemums for subject ; but this instance has been designed to show off the calligraphic mastery of Koyetsu, and so the ground of the screen has many of the oblong forms upon which the Japanese wrote their poems disposed upon it, these, again, having flowers in gold or silver drawn upon them, over which Koyetsu has written out the poems in his handwriting. There is also a six-fold screen of a meandering river, in cream and silver, with a flowering magnolia for one centre of the composition, and for the other a palmate tree with leaves like open fans, and a maple in scarlet and dull silver. The foreground waves with river grasses, painted in cream, while a single wild pink or carnation draws the eye. It would be in vain to describe the rendering of the magnolia leaves, painted as no other hand, we believe, could ever paint them, drawn exactly in nature as they droop in clusters of two or three, no more, from their stems, together with the curious flat, spatulate character of the glossy leaves.

But the two great *Corn Screens* are the masterpieces of Koyetsu and probably the greatest decorative compositions, though much damaged, in the whole of pictorial art. Maize or Indian corn is their subject, a plant which had only recently been brought to Japan from America by the Spaniards, by way, perhaps, of the Philippines. With this, for motif, are combined the blue and pink and white flowers, some striped, of morning glory, and the scarlet cockscomb. Koyetsu discovered in Indian corn an entire world of tasselled and striving forms, a sort of humanity of leaf and head and edge, which he has subjected to a violent wind that blows them to and fro and beats them down. They are a pair of two-fold screens. The olive-green leaves of the maize are veined and lined with gold, and through them the burst calyx and thyrsus of the corncob show in a poetical ecstasy that loaded vine and yellow cornfield have never attained in the poetry or

painting of the Occident. There is a god, here, whom none has
ever worshipped ; a new thyrsus, a new cornucopia, a new lily
in the hand. Indian corn, by its structure, is peculiarly susceptible to wind. In ecstasy, it is as though careless of its pregnant weight. The swelling sheath is huge and portentous upon
the slender stem. The rod, dashed down and prostrate, leans
beside the fertile womb, which is male and female emblem in
the selfsame plant, a god that is heterosexual, god and goddess,
bearded and tufted, till the corncob bursts its calyx. A fruit to
gnaw upon, till nothing is left but the rind without its cells.
Fenellosa suggests that this pair of screens may be fragments of
large mural compositions. He compares the forms of the pregnant, tasselled plants to bursting bombs, and says of the crimson
cockscomb that it is like an erect drum-major's wand. He
speaks of the 'bomb corner' of one panel, and remarks that
the crown of one cockscomb has been almost split to pieces.
But admiration for this pair of paintings could be carried further,
for Fenellosa hears the explosion but does not see the god. We
could say that the burst calyx, where the cob has run to seed,
expresses in its tassels that they are lines of fire. That they
spread like sprays or flares from the parent, and are about to
start off the ripening or explosion of the pregnant calyx, near by,
that leans in heaviness towards them. The other heads, like
plumed pineapples, are not yet ready. They have to swell and
burst. In and out among them flows the music of the long
leaves, lined and veined with gold. But the thyrsus and the calyx
lift up, and thrust into the tangled air. The thyrsus lifts beside
the calyx, where the cockscomb is crimson red, lemon yellow,
or what is called by Fenellosa 'water-melon red'. This is the
male statue, the Priapus of the painting, but it was a token of
genius on the part of Koyetsu to associate with this the blue and
pink flowers of the morning glory, for these, in their multitude,
are the maidens of the god. They live for the day and have grown

old by evening.[1] Fenellosa compares them to fireballs that
'touch off the explosion'; and we should contrast them in
our own minds with the static wild flowers in the foregrounds
of our old masters; the anemones and daisies of Botticelli, the
weeds and harebells of Carpaccio that nod upon his wharves
and broken lands, the wild strawberry plant of Cima da Cone-
gliano.

But this is a rushing wind among the cobs of Indian corn.
The convolvulus, the morning glory that dances on the palisade,
has come up in the night to be the grape of the vineyard. We
can only believe that this pair of screens is a sketch or suggestion
for a mural composition that was never finished, and in all probability never begun, for it bears the marks upon it of the jet or
fire of improvisation. If painted, it can surely not have perished
without mention or recognition. For it is a work as transcendent
as the battle paintings of Uccello. A new religion of nature, or
at least it is found nowhere else. We have the knowledge, in
looking at this pair of screen paintings, that this is the male
principle at work on decoration; that it is not effeminate. That
here, as in the Birds of Paradise, as in the Humming Birds, as in
the whole Kingdom of the Birds, it is the male that wears the
painted plumes. This is a transference that has taken place at
various times in human history, more often, probably, than we
realise; whether it be with the popinjays of the period of Queen
Elizabeth or the Valois Kings, with the Cavaliers, or indeed,
through all Occidental history until the French Revolution and
Napoleonic wars, showing itself in all classes of the population,
down to the peasants in a hundred different localities, in the great
plains, in Alpine valleys, in the purple gorges descending to the

[1] Koyetsu is not the first Japanese painter to make use of the morning glory. A
beautiful screen of morning glories painted by Sanraku, son-in-law of Kano Eitoku,
is reproduced in *Selected Relics*, by Tajima, vol. ii. The great lacquer master, Ritsuo
(1663–1747), approximates in his rare paintings to Koyetsu and Sotatsu, and should be
studied in relation to them both.

forests, or in the fishing villages. Where, and whenever, that instinct is at work, the arts of decoration become different and masculine. They are not, as with ourselves, confined to the decorator, the dressmaker, the fashionable photographer.

It would seem, from what little is known of him, that Koyetsu may be the supreme instance of this principle at work. It is to be found, in diminution, in the works of his follower, Sotatsu. He is not a painter or decorator of the same order as Koyetsu, though immeasurably greater and more important than Korin, in whom vulgarity of temperament tends always into caricature. But the name of Ogata Korin remains famous,[1] while those of Koyetsu and Sotatsu are forgotten, nearly. The masterpieces of Sotatsu are, probably, a pair of eight-fold screens covered with fans, among them some wonderful war scenes, in the Imperial collection ; and the pair of screens of towel horses. This subject, as unpromising as the opening donkey bray of Stra-winsky's *Symphony for Wind Instruments*, and of the same order, develops into a most subtle arrangement of the cloths and stuffs that are disposed at varying angles, and in their patterns and colours, upon the towel horses. It is an animated abstract painting, as lively and satisfying as any still-life canvas by Picasso. The flower screens of Sotatsu have not the force and vitality of Koyetsu. They are decoration, merely, and not creation. There is nothing in Sotatsu that can compare with the screens of Indian corn. There is more, in those, of the poetry of imagina-tion than in any other painting of the fruits of harvest. It gives a new meaning to the word ' Indian ', as though Koyetsu had been conscious in it of the huge Pacific, for it depicts an Oceanian tropic. This is not the god of the Eastern sages, but a deity more vigorous and warlike. The chariot is not his vehicle, but the war canoe with many oars or paddles, and a carved and painted prow. In stature it is like a totem pole of many heads,

[1] The great-grandmother of Korin was an elder sister of Koyetsu.

one above another, of fish, flesh, and fowl. There is nothing in it of Hindu India, although Koyetsu was a Buddhist, and the worship of Buddha came originally from Hindustan. This is the corn god of the calyx, of the tasselled head and pregnant womb, made fertile by the tropic wind. In its fulness it expresses what is implicit in the Hellenic world by a bare emptiness. They stand, therefore, for the two extremes. What is apparent in the one by denial is affirmed in the plenitude and luxuriance of the other. They are the lunar and solar planets of their firmament. Nothing else needs to be said. All is contained in the mutual argument between them.

(iii)

Birds of Paradise

But we would continue, without pause, upon the Birds of Paradise. Among them are to be distinguished Van Duiven-bode's, black, with green metallic pectoral shield, and a black fan-like frill upon its hinder neck ; and *Seleucides nigricans*, the Twelve-wired Bird of Paradise, formed miraculously of black and brown and green, and the stomach of which is found full of a brown sweet liquid, probably the nectar of the flowers upon which it has been feeding. The wires, six to a wing, curve or spring backwards and upwards from the yellow plumes, and the rest of the bird is blue, green, and purple. The great Sickle-billed Bird of Paradise gives a huge billowing, black and green effect, with long tail and sickle plumes. One bird of this type has lateral flank shields which almost take the place of wings, approximating, therefore, to the ' four-winged ' Humming Birds. There is another, *P. apodea* or Great Bird of Paradise, yellow and green and brown, like a talking Mynah bird ' got up ' for a fairy story. The Marquis Raggi's has a magnificent red tail and yellow and green head. There are variations upon this, in the matter of more yellowish or red, till we come to *P. minor* or the Lesser Bird of Paradise, which is the same in colouring as the Greater, only a good deal more lovely owing to its cancan tail. Prince Rudolph's Bird of Paradise is a wonderful blue-green cancan dancer with blue streamers flowing from its tail. The King of Saxony's has long streamers with enamelled plaques, only these are head and not tail streamers and can be erected or depressed at will. Yet another, nondescript, or not so interesting in other respects, has two long white feathers from each side of its chest, four in all, which are held straight out when flying or fluttering from tree to tree. The Six-plumed Bird of Paradise is black, mainly to show its relationship or derivation from the family of Crows, but has a yellow-and-green metallic breast-shield, and the six plumes spring from above its eyes. There are three separate forms or developments of these. The *P. superbus* has an extraordinary shield at back of its head as well as a metallic breast-shield. There may be, in all, some ten aesthetic groups or divisions in the Birds of Paradise.[1]

(iv)

Trogons

The Humming Birds and the Birds of Paradise are the two most beautiful families in nature, being only rivalled by the Trogons. Among the Trogons most are red and green, but there are yellows,

[1] Cf. *A Monograph of the Paradiseidæ, or Birds of Paradise*, by Richard Bowdler Sharpe, 1897, with 80 coloured plates. This, the last of the great ornithological works of the nineteenth century, employed, where practicable, the fine plates from Gould's *Birds of New Guinea* ; in other instances they were redrawn by W. Hart, the artist who helped

SIX PLUMED BIRD OF PARADISE
(Parotia Sexpennis)

too ; the Beautiful Train-bearer is pre-eminent with its near relative, the Shining Train-bearer. There are eared Trogons, like Crossoptilon Pheasants, and a sudden break from scarlet and green into the yellow or orange-breasted Trogons. In general, the Trogons have barred tails of black and white, but in certain varieties the tail is blue, giving the Cuban Trogon, a form in which the tail plumes have a peculiar elaboration of cut as fanciful as the leaf edges of a tulip tree. Most wonderful of all is the Resplendent Trogon or Guatemalan Quetzal, the size of a Pigeon, with green feathery headdress, more like a feather bonnet, blood-red breast, green side plumes, overlapping, and long green tail feathers from which was formed the robe or mantle of Montezuma, so that it was the Royal or sacred bird of the Aztecs. The sitting Quetzal shows its carmine breast fringed or lapped with green and black undertail barred with white in two divisions, while, on the wing, it must be one of the most glorious sights in nature and little wonder that the Mexicans worshipped the Quetzal as a god.[1]

(v)

Pittas

Yet another family of birds of wider distribution, the *Pittidae* or Ant Thrushes, was the subject of a monograph by John Gould. An Indian Pitta, *Bengalensis*, has a buff waistcoat, white throat, black and white and dark-buff mask, green back and wings

Gould in the production of his plates for more than forty years. Since the publication of this work other varieties have been discovered. The Ribbon-tailed Bird of Paradise was only found in 1938.

[1] *The Trogonidæ, or Family of Trogons*, by John Gould, with 36 coloured plates, 1838. Second edition, with the plates entirely redrawn and the number increased to 47, published in 1875.

(wings black underneath with two large white butterfly spots), a red stern or rump, and a blue tail with a neat black edge and blue line. The Blue-tailed or Tigered Pitta, with lilac-blue sheen or bloom on its crossed bands of orange-yellow and deep blue across its belly, comes from Java. Van der Bosch's, a Sumatran Pitta, has a white throat, black and fiery orange mask, and its belly is deep indigo blue crossed with narrow crescent lines of fiery orange red. It is, then, a purple and red ' tigered ' Pitta. Gurney's Pitta, from Tenasserim, has a brown back and black breast with bright yellow flaming or feathering upon it, and a blue, lappeted crest. Elliot's Pitta, from Cochin China, wears a black velvety mask ; it has a ' tigered ' black-and-yellow belly, but only lightly striped, and the rest of the bird is a beautiful and pure ultramarine blue. The Great Pitta, from the island of Gilolo in the Moluccas, is black, velvety black, with breast of pure white, azure-blue shoulders, and bright-crimson belly. Another variety is similar, only with green wings and light-blue body. But, last, there is the Necklaced Pitta that comes from Borneo, red with blue eyebrows and a blue necklace upon its crimson breast. Briefly described ; for it has a lovely blue strip over, but behind the eye, like a trailing eyebrow, a rich rusty-red crest ; and then the blue necklace that hangs upon its deep scarlet stomach. This Pitta, however, is pre-eminently red, red, red. As to its peculiar and unique adornments, the necklace, according to Gould, writing in 1880, " reminds me more than anything else of the necklaces of shells (*Elenchus irisodontis*) which the Tasmanian women used to wear as I saw them years ago, before they became extinct from the face of the earth ".[1]

[1] *Monograph of the Pittidæ, or Ant Thrushes*, by John Gould, 1880. Only Part I was published, with 10 plates ; for Part II the text only was issued, without plates. The Necklaced Pitta is also illustrated in the work on the Pittidae by D. G. Elliot, with 51 coloured plates, published in New York in 1863.

(vi)

Toucans

But the grotesque *Ramphastidae* or Toucans are the most curious family in the kingdom of the birds. If we examine them, aesthetically, we find that they begin their permutations from a base of black or green. The Culminated Toucan is black as a Crow, with white throat and chest and narrow pectoral band of crimson, a band of brimstone yellow at the sprouting of its tail, and immense curved beak of black with an upper edge, down all its length, of pale straw yellow. The Red-billed Toucan would seem to be a natural development of this ; the beak has the same yellow edge, but the bill itself is crimson red with a black line between the upper and lower jaws or mandibles. Now comes a Toucan with black base of plumage, but its breast is bright lemon yellow, its eye is blue instead of red, and its upper mandible green with orange-yellow markings, its lower bill a bright blue shaded with green, while both mandibles are tipped or ended with a flaming red.

This type goes through many and various modifications till we come to a red-breasted Toucan with a green beak, with serrated edges, the first of its type, and pointing to another development that was obvious from the start. The next variation is the Cayenne Aracari, a Toucan with an olive-green back and tail, the colour of its predecessor's beak ; but this has a dull beak, itself, a yellow breast and stomach, and a broad abdominal belt or band of scarlet. From here begins the series of toothed Toucans, most of which, in compensation, have lost the naked bluish or lead-coloured patch of skin surrounding their brilliant red eyes, till we come to the Banded Aracari which has a mahogany-brown throat, semilunar band of black, broad belt of scarlet, jet-black band, straw-yellow stomach, and thighs and tail of olive green. The Many-banded Aracari (the Aracaris being a race or division in which the beak, in general, is less developed than in the Toucans), besides its toothed beak of black and yellow, has a black throat, a breast and stomach bounded at top and bottom with a thin line of scarlet, and consisting of a yellow ground dashed or splotched with scarlet, but with two broad belts or bands of black. This is, in fact, the 'tigered' Toucan or Aracari. In what contrast are the Swallow-like, grass-green, groove-billed Aracaris; or the lovely Grey-breasted Aracari with back of olive brown, and mottled beak of red and black and yellow, the dove or wood-pigeon among the race of Toucans !

But the most peculiar development is yet to come, the Curly-crested Aracari, with blood-red shoulders and back and tail of olive green, breast and stomach yellow, 'tigered' or flecked with crescent-shaped bars of red that thicken and grow redder lower down, lower mandible straw-coloured, and upper of olive green and blue and yellow and two shades of red. But the top of its head has a crest of curled metallic feathers, very black and glossy, formed from a swelling of the shaft of each feather, or an agglutination of the web, and becoming less curled, and flat and spatulate upon the cheeks. These latter, indeed, are flat quills, white, and tipped with black, and they, and the crisp and black metallic curls above, like metal shavings, give an extraordinary air of cunning and wisdom to this nut-cracking sage of the Amazon. There is no bird comparable in this respect, even among the owls and birds of prey, and I know of no equivalent unless it be the Vulturine Guinea Fowl figured in Gould's *Icones Avium*, a bird from Mozambique which, with its tattered, ragged vulture plumes of black and blue and white, like a vulture caught on emerging from a wind machine, is as wild and fantastic as a Callot etching, imbued with that artist's perpetual mental background of the miseries of war. It possesses, then, a kind of ragged, starving wisdom of the tramp or vagabond soldier pillaging as he goes, comparable in force of oddity or queerness, but not in kind, to the Curly-crested Aracari.[1]

(vii)

Hornbills

The *Bucerotidae* or Hornbills are not less curious and many are to be found among them to whom it is difficult not to attribute human personality or abstract qualities of cleverness and cunning. They belong to the company of bird actors. The Rhinoceros Hornbill is a fair example, coming from Borneo and Sumatra, in sober vest of black and white, but with its extraordinary casque or horn, curving backwards, and placed on top of and above the excessive beak. Another species, the Homrai, is more variegated black and white, and its casque is more peculiar still, being furnished with a double edge or brim. Wallace says of this bird that its voice is very harsh and grating, " and not to be surpassed probably by any sound that an animal is capable of making. Its flight is heavy, and performed by repeated flappings of its huge wings. It proceeds in a straight line and sails only when about to alight upon some tree. The strokes are made with great force, and the noise of its wings can be heard for more than a mile." There are Hornbills with brick-red beaks and casques, and another with a humped casque and bill, half red, half duckling-yellow, the casque in this species being perfectly solid, instead of hollow, its tail having black fan-like markings upon white,

---

[1] Cf. *Monograph of the Family of Ramphastidæ, or Toucans,* by John Gould, first edition, with 34 coloured plates, 1834. Second edition, with the plates redrawn and increased in number to 52, published in 1854.

and two long plumes that trail behind it when it flies. The Crowned Hornbill, black and white, has a loose, black feathery crown or headdress and immense beak ; but is not so strange as another, the Celebes Hornbill, in which the casque is red and high and keel-shaped, the beak yellow, the head and neck chestnut, but the skin is bare and bright blue round the eyes and upon the throat, a peculiarity that in yet another Hornbill is developed madly and to strange lengths, for it has a little bright-red casque, exactly like a baking tin, a white face and throat, and blue eyesetting, while the bare skin of the throat where the beak begins is bright pink with blue marks or dapplings, resembling the wattle of a Satyr Tragopan.

This is the start of another series of developments. A Hornbill, ranging from Sierra Leone to the Gaboon, and black and white as usual, has darker blue, bare skin for setting of its eyes and for its neck, below which there is a protuberant lump or sack, blood-red, and speckled, heraldically, with the same blue ; while the Rufous-necked Hornbill, from Assam, has no casque at all, but a splendid beak of bright canary yellow, its eyes and the appendage in front of its throat are blue and red, or purple, and its head and neck and chest are rufous or reddish brown. This pair of Hornbills is experimenting towards the Turkeys, a race that should be as magnificent as the Peacocks, but it fails and has only the Ocellated Turkey with light-blue wattle and flashes of the same colour in its plumage.[1] The Rufous-necked Hornbill has the peculiarity that it nests in a hollow in a tree, " digging it out of the solid wood and closing the aperture with an ingeniously contrived door ". Another observer comments upon the splendid attitudes of this bird when it dresses its plumes, " rising on its feet, exposing its strong legs, projecting the shoulders of its wings, extending and arching its

---

[1] A splendid plate of the Ocellated Turkey appears in D. G. Elliot's *Phasianidæ* : New York, 1873.

KING OF SAXONY'S BIRD OF PARADISE
(Pteridophera Alberti)

neck backwards, when it has the graces and even some of the terrors of the birds of prey ". The black slats or shutters of its wings are extended, the primary feathers, like the tail, deeply tipped with white, and its curious beak and cranium are in ceaseless motion as though intent upon some intellectual purpose, while we must imagine for ourselves the sound of its quills or arrows shuttling to and fro among the branches.

But we must come to the Crested Hornbills among whom invention works itself out in extreme and purest fantasy. Here is the Fantee White-crested Hornbill, a black bird with long ' glider ' tail, blue beak, and crest like the tail of a Laced Fantail Pigeon, giving to it an air of remote and elegant reflection as it sits upon the bough ; and its neighbour and near relation from the Cameroons, with more white markings, for its primaries and secondaries are tipped with white ; while wisdom of another sort is expressed in the Panayan Hornbill from the Moluccas with its black wings glossed with green, chestnut tail with a deep edging of the same colour, chestnut throat and stomach, shading lighter to a copious white mane or fleece that is its crest, and its red beak with six curious notches or indentations of orange yellow. The Black Hornbill, again, is a Fantee inhabitant with enormous black beak and casque, purplish-black plumage, and black Laced Fantail crest, the Hornbill of Niger and Senegal. Another African, the Black and White Casque Hornbill, throws back in feathery imitation to prehistoric time, for its huge casque and beak of the short and clumsy, not the pointed type, are backed with greenish-black cheeks, each feather peacock-eyed with grey, and it has a greenish-black crest that assumes the form and shape of the head of its mastodon or lizard ancestor.

This trait, though, is absolutely excelled and surpassed by Sclater's Hornbill, a bird of black breast and shoulders with green reflections, but with pure white thighs and tail coverts. Its beak and casque, shaped like a chopper, are deep black, but the prediluvian fantasy of this Hornbill occurs in its feather crest and mantle, beginning with the upright plumes stuck into its forehead, and continuing with the crest or mane that is composed of long, loose filaments, spotted with grey, in reproduction, as it were, of a maned or crested lizard.[1] Its wings and tail are pied, most particularly, the extreme ends of its pinions being dipped in black, and the long under-plumes, which are folded when the bird is perching, being black entirely, the two central or median feathers of its tail being black, too, except at their tips, and there being a broad band of black across the central portion of its tail, so that, in flight, it is a black-and-white pterodactyl, the " very specialised warm-blooded descendant " of ancient reptiles. Its immediate association is with prehistoric trees and flowers. It simulates the " graces and terrors of the birds of prey ". But the whole race of Hornbills are born actors. How wisely the Bushy-crested Hornbill perches on the bough ! And upon the wing ? " Their flight is almost noiseless, with none of the metallic clang so conspicuous in others of their race. . . . A few rapid strokes of the wing, a short sail with outspread wings, again a few rapid strokes, again a sail, and so on." The Hornbills, wherever found, dwell in fantasy, in a world apart. They are cast for rôles of wisdom, and as much human meaning may be imputed to them as to the marionettes or puppets of the shadow theatre. That, in fact, it portends nothing, and is mere unconscious play-acting, is the measure of their natural genius and in no way detracts from the message of their strange masks and plumes.[2]

[1] *A Monograph of the Capitonidæ, or Scansorial Barbets,* by C. H. T. Marshall and G. F. L. Marshall, 1871, with 73 coloured plates by Keulemans, illustrates the Dusky Barbet or *Gymnobucco Bonapartei,* a most curious bird from the Gaboon with red and yellow scale face and curly crest, much resembling this pterodactyl Hornbill.

[2] Cf. *Monograph of the Bucerotidæ, or Family of the Hornbills,* by D. G. Elliot, with 57 coloured plates by Keulemans, published in 1882.

(viii)

Mergansers

Of this, in another domain, that of snow and ice and water, the most remarkable specimen is the Harlequin Duck, not named, though, with entire accuracy, for what it resembles is a cheap coloured print of the clown Grimaldi. The habitat of this extraordinary creature is Iceland and Labrador, where it plays against a pantomime background of perpetual snows. Its home is in the old-fashioned winters of long ago. From the central ridge or cockscomb of black hair upon the head, edged with red, and its white painted cheeks merging into blue, to the motley of its neck and breast and thighs, this bird is the complete clown. The purpose of its masquerade cannot be other than that of colour and gaiety in the icy gales. The King Eider Duck has attempted the same effect, but carried it no further than a coloured mask of five colours, light blue and rose and white, and pink and green.[1] Steller's Eider has tried it, too, but the white mask conceals the whole face and the motley is not distinctive enough in its buff yellows and dark greens. The Puffins belong, also, to the world of pantomime, but their dress is plain. Their character, like that of many comedians, is in their tread and in their facial make-up. Mostly they have but a coloured mask or visor. Nobody who has once seen a Puffin waddling on the seashore will ever forget it, for this may be the first intimation of the comedy of Neptune's kingdom.

[1] John Gould in his monograph on the *Partridges of America*, 1850, illustrates Massena's Partridge, from Mexico, which is clown-masked in black and white, and remarks of it : " The male is rendered exceedingly conspicuous by the singular disposition of the markings of the face, which are very strongly contrasted, and forcibly remind one of the painted face of the clown in a pantomime ". This partridge has a black and white spotted breast. Compare also the Painted Sand-Grouse, of India, in Gould's *Birds of Asia.*

By comparison, how light and fantastic are the comedians of the fresh waters ! The Great Crested Grebe, like a dancer in a fox's mask. But it stays far out in the lake, or on the shadowed waters under tall trees, and is rarely seen. The Horned Grebe has more precisely, even, a fox's ears, a fox's forehead, and fox's eyes, but with green velvet cheeks blown out in disdain. The Mergansers are more far-fetched still. The Red-breasted Merganser wears a white collar and green feathery crest, ill brushed, the mask of a schoolmaster in a comedy ; with the American Merganser it is the female, not the male, that wears the crest, the reddish-brown fox-mask of a schoolmistress. The Buffle-head, another Merganser, wears a white cockade kept in place by a green mask that covers the face and comes round behind to form a collar. This could be called the clown of the sweet waters ; but the hooded Merganser is more fanciful. The male bird has the clown markings in black and white across its shoulders and a high fan-shaped white cockade, trimmed or edged with black, the headdress of an Auguste or eccentric of the circus ring, but out among the reeds and bulrushes, and which can only delight the dryads upon bluebell evenings when the doves are calling.

There is no end to these actors of the water flats. The grouse-marked Reeve, white-bellied, with the long legs of a wader, has the sharp beak of the Mergansers, and a pair of extraordinary ornaments at either side of its head, as large as the head itself, and like a pair of exaggerated ears, together with a most copious but incongruous feather ruff falling from the back of its ears to down below its chest, like a person in running clothes who has borrowed a feather boa, or like the bedraggled garment worn by one of the natural-born comedians of the back streets, proto-types of the dames of pantomime.

These freshwater birds, Grebes, Mergansers, resemble character sketches or costume drawings by the most delicate and evanescent of painters. It could be said that the masks of the Grebes and Mergansers are too fanciful to be carried out. They are so different in spirit from the *chinoiserie*, wherever found, in whatever clime, of the Storks and Cranes and Herons, of the Flamingos, Egrets, Pelicans ; from the Roseate Spoonbill which, male or female, is as far-fetched as the duck-billed women of the Congo, but lifted into high fantasy by its green jockey cap and lovely rosy plumage, rose petals on white for its wings, and rosy chest and stomach ; from the Flamingo, which is the bird of the *Fêtes Chinoises* tapestries by Boucher, even when it has no background at all but the salt marshes of the Camargue or the salt lakes of Tunisia ; from the Scarlet Ibis belonging to tapestries of the courtiers of Montezuma in their feather mantles, jade sceptre in hand, stepping down from their litters among flowers and animals of gold at foot of a stepped pyramid where the sacred birds walk with their attendants ; from the Snowy Egrets which I have seen, at Fez, roosting as though they were white camellias upon the branch, or among the blue or white irises in Europe or Africa, at either side of the narrow straits, ready to sail, it would seem, from tiled dome to minaret over the land-locked waters. Upon the glittering sands of the Camargue that crackled underfoot with little sea shells, I have gathered up handfuls of the Flamingo's rosy plumes ; and in the Danube Delta in the haze of distance, among the mirages, have seen what appeared to be white towns of shining houses, but they were meadow lands raised but a foot or two above the waters, and peopled from end to end with Pelicans. But the birds of the lagoons and marshes are as different from sea birds as a pleasure galleon from a man-o'-war. And their flotillas are gathered, more particularly, in Northern waters. Those are the breeding grounds, in Iceland, Greenland, and the Aleutians. Mostly they are the colour of warships. They are white-breasted, like the spume, and with grey wings. They follow the ship, day after day, and are part of the grey waste of sea and sky, participant in that, and not intended to be conspicuous or brightly painted.

(ix)

Tragopans

None of them compare to the Pheasants of the Himalayas, but those flourish among the Chinese primulas and rhododendrons. Most incomparable and glorious of all are the Satyr Tragopan and its near rival, Temminck's Tragopan, the latter differenced by the white drops upon its bright-red or carmine chest, which are like flecks of snow and not drops of frozen rain, as with the former, ringed with black, and growing bigger as they run lower down its front. The Tragopans may not be strictly and entirely Pheasants. They may be a link between the Pheasant and the Partridge. Two species of Quail figured by Audubon, and therefore American birds, seem to be working up towards the Tragopan. Both are crested, one with a short recurving crest and the other with a long crest of a pair of plumes, flowing back or trailing, but both birds have plumage that suggests the permutations possible in a Partridge or a Quail, with blue as the base, instead of the carmine of the Tragopan. The head of the Tragopan is more imposing than that of the Pheasants proper, which incline rather to the Peacock and would not be impressive were it not for their feather crests and mantles. But, with the Tragopan, the cheeks are blue or velvety black, with mask-like markings ; there are the satanic horns, and the white eyeing or ocellation upon the red plumage that we compared to frozen rain or flecks of snow. But, particularly, there are the coloured wattles of the cock Tragopans, only shown when the bird is courting or displaying, at which time, too, the pair of horns are blown out and become erect. No two of the coloured wattles, as in the case of the Ruff's strange ornaments just mentioned, are marked alike, though it has been proved that if every bird is different it at least never alters from its instinctive colouring and is the same in every detail for each new mating season. The Satyr Tragopan and Temminck's Tragopan differ, too, in the amount of blue upon their maskings, the former having a blue neck and the latter a blue neck and cheeks, though 'blue' does not describe the colour, while if its red chest is less wonderful it has a redder back than the Satyr Tragopan. But in what words are we to give a description of their coloured wattles? That of a typical Satyr Tragopan has a leaf or centre of blue or purple descending from its beak, the rest of the shield being pale green with bold scarlet markings; while Temminck's Tragopan, in one individual, has a bib or shield of a scarlet ground edged with light cerulean blue, green cheeks, blue eyelids, green satyr's horns, and the central ornament of its wattle is an extraordinary star pattern descending in ever larger zigzags like a 'crazy' stairway or 'monkey-walk' of cerulean blue, dotted with white spots or circles of different sizes, the whole suggesting some abstract image taken from watching the squid or octopus. This wattle or apron of the Tragopans swells and dilates and their satyr horns are held up erect, while they are displaying.[1] It is nearly impossible to describe the fiery magnificence of the Tragopan, flecked or ocellated with the white drops, ringed in black, that run down its carmine chest, except by saying that its home is among the rhododendrons where the glittering laurel leaf is aflame. The five races of Tragopans inhabit the mountains

[1] The wattle of the Tragopan should be compared with the curious throat ornaments of the Cassowaries; cf. "Monograph of the *Genus Casuarius*", by Hon. Walter Rothschild, *Transactions of the Zoological Society*, London, 1900, with 18 coloured plates. John Gould had made some preparations for a monograph of the Cassowaries, but the work was left unfinished at his death in 1881.

from Kashmir to China, and it is something added to the Himalayas to think of this Satyr Pheasant with its blood-red flecked with white, with its black velvet mask and horns, among the flowers and snows.[1]

(x)

Pheasants

The Eared Pheasants or Crossoptilons are the Mephistos of the breed. Of more slender build than the Tragopans, being true Pheasants, Brown-eared, Blue, and White, the last, which lives on the Tibetan side of the mountains, being white-bodied, too, moving, we might say, towards the Silver Pheasant which belongs to the race of the Kaleeges, most often to be met with of all the ornamental Pheasants, but not less beautiful for that. It has moreover, this romantic idiosyncrasy that, while it will breed easily and quickly in captivity, no white man has ever seen the nest and eggs of a wild Silver Pheasant. The fascination of its silver plumage, as much silver opposed to white as are the wings and breast of a Silver Pencilled Hamburg cock compared with a mere White Orpington or White Leghorn, comes from the marking or striation of black lines in it. But, as well, it is the blue crest and dark-blue body, the red legs and bright-red face

[1] Cf. *A Monograph of the Pheasants*, by William Beebe, with 90 coloured plates by A. Thorburn, H. Grönvold, and others : London, 1918–1922. This project, undertaken by Colonel Anthony R. Kuzer and the Board of Managers of the New York Zoological Society, enabled Beebe to make a trip of seventeen months' duration, covering twenty different countries, and visiting every one of the nineteen groups of pheasants. Later, the monograph which had been first issued in an edition-de-luxe appeared in a cheaper form in two volumes. It is the most sumptuous and beautifully illustrated of modern ornithological works. Connected with the wonderful family of the Tragopans are the Sanguine Francolins of the Himalayas, whose tangled plumes, green and white, appear to be bloodstained, or dipped or tinged with blood. This bird is figured in Gould's *Birds of Asia.*

of the Silver Pheasant. Swinhoe's Pheasant is another of the Kaleeges, and as I have kept this myself I cannot refrain from a description. This bird is only found on the island of Formosa. It has a mask or headpiece of bright scarlet, neat white crest, white mantle and long white tail feathers, dark crimson scapulars, metallic-green wings, and the rest of its plumage, its chest and back and train, are a dark, watered purple. A bird, therefore, that is pied white and purple, with panels of crimson and metallic green upon the wings, as it treads the aviary. In appearance neither Chinese nor Indian, but a bird apart, which we would place in our minds in Siam or Borneo, were it not for its close feathering, making it so distinct in race that it could occur only in an island. I have kept, too, another Formosan Pheasant, the long-tailed, blue Mikado found only on Mount Arizan in that island, and discovered for the first time about sixty years ago from its black, white-barred tail feathers worn in the headdress of a tribesman who had come down to carry the baggage of a bird collector into the central mountains. The Mikado is a purplish, blue-black Pheasant with white markings, living among bamboos and rhododendrons, a blue Pheasant which would seem fanciful and unreal upon a painted screen or Chinese wallpaper, the imaginary inhabitant, we would surmise, of the East Indies.

But the Fireback Pheasants are actual inhabitants of Siam and Borneo, two races of crestless Pheasants and three of crested. The Siamese and Malayan Firebacks are much alike, but the latter has white tail feathers instead of blue-green, and a blue and not a scarlet mask. The Siamese, moreover, has more gold and metallic purple on its back. Both male birds have Peacock crests. It is symbolic, too, that the Siamese, which has the most beautiful of all hen Pheasants, most fiery and wonderful in her under-gold, for it appears to flash from under the filaments of her plumage as though burnished but not brought to the glittering, shining finish, should come from a land where the Kings had several regiments of Amazons for their bodyguard. This bird and the blue-masked Malayan, for the hen, too, has a blue domino, are the Pheasants, *in excelsis*, of lacquer cabinets and of all works of art of indeterminate origin in which the painter or lacquerer, wanting in precise knowledge, has given to his tropical birds all the hues and colours of his imagination. They are, therefore, aesthetically, Indian according to the old meaning of the word, when it meant Chinese or Indian, indiscriminately, products brought home, in fancy or in fact, upon an East Indiaman.

The Peacock Pheasants, also, have to be compared to something imagined and not true. They are dove-shaped, like a dove in size, and may form a link between the Pheasants and the Pigeons. The Northern Peacock Pheasant, from Yunnan and Burma, is grey in colour with a myriad white dots or specks, and with two circles of eyes or ocelli which are green and purple and pale violet, with metallic lights, and which, when the bird is displaying, are made to vibrate so that they appear to revolve at a fantastic speed within their circles. Another Peacock Pheasant, the Palawan, comes only from the island of that name, between Borneo and the Philippines. The cock bird has a red eye-mask upon a white face, blue and green upon its body, and emerald-green eyes or ocelli in its tail. We are approaching the Argus Pheasants, one of which, the Malay, has minute ocellations in ' hundreds and thousands ' all over its dark-brown, rufous body and long tail, a Pheasant that is a synonym for a snowstorm in high mountains.

The Reeves' Pheasant is dissimilar ; it is ' tigered ', and has a longer tail. The tail, indeed, can be five feet in length, as long as that of a Yokohama Fowl, but it has a strange, incongruous white head, and body plumage that is as regular in scale as the carapace of a tortoise. The longer tail feathers of the Reeves' Pheasant were worn by actors in old China when they took the part of warriors. But the lovely Argus is the Pheasant of the

PRINCE RUDOLPH'S BIRD OF PARADISE
(Paradisornis Rudolphi)

'playground' or dancing floor. As well, it is the Ho-ho or golden phoenix of Chinese legend. It makes a clearing in the forest, three to six feet across, and keeps it clear of twigs and leaves. The actual display, when the female has been summoned to the dancing floor by loud cries, consists in the cock bird spreading his wings right in front of him, and shaking or shivering his plumes, forming, in the words of Beebe, " a great, vertical, concave screen or fan of feathers, the bird itself being completely hidden from view ", and he adds, " Naturally the bird is rather anxious now and then to see what effect the display of his beauties has upon the female, or if indeed she is still present ; and to accomplish this the head is poked through between two of the feathers, either of the right or left wing, a momentary glance taken and the head withdrawn. Thus, through the peephole in his living curtain, the feathered actor is able to keep watch upon his audience. In old males, shot towards the end of the season, it is possible to locate this peephole by the rather disturbed, frayed condition of the web in its immediate vicinity." And again, " In the display of the Argus Pheasant, we have a most elaborate setting, stage, and properties, with an actor who in turn is both company and orchestra, all unquestionably for the benefit of an audience which assembles one at a time and appears utterly and altogether bored ".

The identification of this bird from Borneo and the Malay peninsula with the Ho-ho or golden phoenix, one of the most common motifs in Chinese art, has been proved by a Japanese phasianist, the Marquess Hachisuka, who has traced its origin to Reinhardt's Argus. The Argus has a blue face and its head and neck are " vulture-like and almost bare ". Its general colour, in repose, is black and grey and brown. Its saturnine mask apart, it could not be characterised as other than dull and uninteresting—off the dancing floor. In legend, the bird is supposed to appear on the earth at or near the birth of a good ruler, and it has not been seen since the halcyon days of Confucius. It may be only when the blue-masked Pheasant spreads its wings that it is transformed into a phoenix, when we see its flying shoulders, its eyed slats or pinions, and spreading train. Then there is no mistaking it. " Its tail is graduated like the Pandean pipes, and its voice resembles the music of that instrument, having the five modulations. It is the Confucian emblem of peace and good rule, and worship of the past." But the phoenix is as rare a phenomenon as those impressions of gigantic hands upon the rocks, tales brought home by travellers from different lands, but in the instance of which I am thinking there are rocks standing like huge monuments above a winding river. The scene described was in the Bohea hills, where, of old, the most fragrant souchongs and pekoes were grown, and scented with gardenia and jasmine flowers for the European market. There were Taoist temples and tea farms upon the summits of all the hills, and in the hollows, lakes made lovely with the white and red lotus or nelumbium. The traveller and botanist, Robert Fortune, remarks on the curious and unnatural appearance of these strange rocks, partly in bright light and partly in the deep shade of evening, and tells us that in order to make this mountain seem suitable for the abode of immortal beings, chariots, barques, and other things of the same kind have been conveyed into the clefts of the steep rocks as a fantastical ornament. Above them are the impress of these gigantic hands, perhaps formed by the water oozing out and trickling down. They did not seem artificial ; but nevertheless a strange semblance had been given to these rocks by artificial means. Emperors and princes had caused this to be done, and at a distance the rocks had a most curious appearance. Below them, in the hunting park, upon the banks of an artificial sea, time nodded, nodded, and the Tartar Guard whiled away their endless leisure by casting their lines among the beds of water-lilies.

Somehow this episode is symbolic and makes a parable. For we have still with us the impress of these gigantic hands. Some, even, are so recent that their marks are still damp upon the plaster. And without the help of Kings and princes or rich men, who made the circumstances to be artificial by shaping the rocks and building temples and pavilions upon the crags, we would be left with no evidence.

Continuing under the shadow of those mysterious hills we are close to the Golden Pheasant and to its near relative, the Amherstian. In their light build and dancing step they are so alike as to be identical. But it cannot suffice to say that the Golden Pheasant is red-breasted. He is crimson or scarlet fronted. He is, primarily, a red and golden Pheasant ; he has straight-brushed golden hair, glittering like strands of brass, and flashing eyes. His cape is golden orange, and each of its segments is tipped or edged with blue. Below that, his mantle is metallic green with black edging, and his secondaries are dark purple. The saddle of his back is straight and golden as his hair. His long tail feathers are Pheasant-eyed. In display, leaping and dancing with quick steps, he distends his cape and, tautening his whole body, lowers and stretches his cape to its full diameter on whichever side his favourite hen may be. His beak is drawn back and nearly hidden in his cape, but he leaps as near as possible to the hen, keeps perfectly still, with his whole body taut and flattened by his attitude, and utters a sharp hissing noise, like the hissing of a snake. The Amherstian is so marvellously differenced from the Golden Pheasant that, always, seeing it, we may scarcely believe in its existence. The first specimen of this lovely bird was a gift from the King of Ava, from whom it came to Lady Amherst, the wife of our ambassador to China. The Amherstian is green and blue, and white and red. The feathers on its forehead are a smooth, metallic green, flowing back from which it has a little scarlet crest. It has dark-green shoulders and breast, with zones or concentric rings of velvet black. Below that, it has a dark-blue back and wings, with the same markings, but in broader bands. Its belly and lower chest, where those are red with the Golden Pheasant, are pure white. Most wonderful of all is the cape of the Amherstian, which is white with dark-green circular bands, and bars of the same colour crossing each feather. There is a little bright saffron-yellow upon its under-parts ; while the tail of this wonderful being, longer and heavier in filament than that of the Golden, is white, barred and mottled with broad bands and zigzag lines of blue-black or green. Four long scarlet plumes or quills spring out from each side at the beginning of its train or tail, and the start or socket of that is of the same scarlet. The Amherstian, all things considered, is more aristocratic than the Golden Pheasant. The feathers of its tail have a wonderful broadening and widening towards the middle, before they taper, and the black and white markings are set off by the four scarlet plumes to either side.[1] How miraculous are the green scales of its chest above the pure white of its belly ! How beautiful the green Peacock-head and little scarlet crest ! But the cape of the Amherstian transmutes the sexes and makes the cock bird into a princess and a serpent. The widening and intersecting of the scales or rings of its cape, dark green on white, or black in certain lights, give the serpentine air and glance to this King and Queen, in one, of the forest. How tawdry must have been the King of Ava in his golden dragon-barge upon the lotus-moat, in shadow of so many scented buildings, pagoda and pagoda of sandalwood, compared with the first Amherstian Pheasant !

The only vision more beautiful and ethereal would be a white Peacock. This bird must be seen treading like a dancer under

[1] In Gould's *Birds of Asia*, vol. vii, there is a magnificent colour plate of the Amherstian Pheasant by H. C. Richter, in which its plumage is contrasted with the leaves of two ferns, *Pteris quadriaurata argyrea* and *P. tricolor*, the foliage of the one being white down the base of the leaf which has green or golden lobes, and the other having a red line or filament to its stalk and touches of red upon its lobes.

the magnolia and oleander upon the decks or terraces of Isola Bella, the stone galleon floating in the lake, after the train from the murky North has left the tunnel and we are in Italy, but even then it is Italy, not India, Burma, Java, or Ceylon. For the Peacock is a temple dancer. All who have seen a score or more of Peacocks together in the forest, with the rising sun glittering upon their plumage, or such a spectacle as the twelve or fifteen hundred Peafowl within sight of the spot where an old traveller stood watching them for near upon an hour, will know that these birds possess attributes of beauty which can only be understood in human terms. They may be seen roosting upon the roofs of villages in some parts of India, and there are Hindu temples that feed and maintain flocks of Peacocks. Nowhere is the white Peacock found in nature, for they are bred in captivity from birds that show a predominance of white plumage. White, however, will breed white; and there are pied varieties in which the deep blue of the neck and breast is contrasted with pure white. There are two races, the Indian and the Green Peafowl, the latter being East Indian in origin, but it is the Indian Peacock, its black-winged mutant and white counterpart, that form the legend. How Indian is the harsh cry of the Peacock! When the Peacock struts and spreads its tail, that, too, is Indian. But most of all when, shivering its body, it rattles the quills of its tail, simulating the shaking of the Indian sistrum and the quivering of their drums that are beaten by the palm of the hand. How Indian, too, is the crest of the Peacock, like a crowned serpent! If we watch him intently, he becomes like a cobra transmuted into beauty. So much of Indian dancing is derived from the Peacock and the cobra. But the ghostly white Peacock is most beautiful of all. The spreading of its tail is one of the wonders of the world. The ghostly white Peacock is the shadow of the Milky Way, and as huge a mystery, meaning all or nothing.

If it be the reasoning of the Peacock that his crest and tail are an interpretation of the heats of India, as expressed by her inhabitants in their architecture that is calculated for coolness and snowy intricacy of dome and lattice, by the perforated opening and the lily tank, if he be willing to present himself upon the red sandstone wall or roosting upon a flowering tree, not as prisoner or domestic animal, but as honoured hostage or a prince at ransom, with his hen who is as hidden and veiled in beauty as the Oriental women, then there is excuse for his painted plumes and pride of step. But there are birds nearly as beautiful as the Peacock, and unknown to legend or superstition, who live remote from human beings or among mere savages.

(xi)

Fruit-eating Pigeons

For an instance, the Goura or Blue-crowned Pigeon of New Guinea, so beautiful a being that it could form the motif for a whole dynasty of painters. It is this bird, we feel, that has been omitted from the great schools of decoration, King and Queen, for the sexes are alike, of a tropical paradise, among flowers and fruits to which we could not give a name, knowing only the orchids and nepenthes or pitcher-plants, dyed or tinted red or purple upon their green, trees with aerial roots growing downwards, and such as Milton names :

> The fig tree, not that kind for fruit renown'd,
> But such as at this day, to Indians known,
> In Malabar or Decan spreads her arms
> Branching so broad and long, that in the ground
> The bended twigs take root, and daughters grow

About the mother tree, a pillar'd shade
High over-arch'd and echoing walks between :
There oft the Indian herdsman, shunning heat,
Shelters in cool, and tends his pasturing herds
At hoop-holes cut through thickest shade.

We might add, too, *Carpophaga concinna* or the Nutmeg Pigeon, bluish white in colour, with the back wings and tail of an intense metallic green, with golden, blue, and violet reflections, coral red feet, and eyes of golden yellow, so described by Wallace who first met with it in Banda, the nutmeg isle, where he heard at intervals a deep booming sound from the summits of some trees. He mentions another, also, with head and neck of an exquisite rosy pink colour and green plumage, feeding near to some wild strawberries upon a mountain. We are among the Fruit-eating Pigeons. These birds, unlike their prototypes of the dovecot and the aviary, have a predominance of green. That, indeed, is a colour only found upon the lustrous necks of the domestic pigeons. It is a metallic reflection, and no more. There is no green in the Fantail or the Almond Tumbler.

But the Fruit-eating Pigeons are in tones of green and lilac, of rose and purple. They possess the natural, not the formal beauties of the fancy, and all of them, considered as motif, have existence in an imagination of their own, in which willingly we would pass a few hours of this too short day. They are lilac or purple-bellied, rose-crowned, red-crowned, rusty-banded, white-throated, yellow-tinted, with crests or crowns or topknots. The iridescent pigeon throat, as we know it in the loft or feeding on the beech mast, is diffused on their entire plumage in hues of the immortal sunrise, of the birth of day. The Goura or Blue-crowned Pigeon awakens to the rosy strokes of light and holds erect the quills and silky barbules of her crest. Her blue habit, in the midst of day, is as conspicuous as the planet Venus, and like that, tells the pomp and pleasures of the queen of night. But the other Fruit-eating Pigeons are more lustrous or dawn-like in their colourings. There is a double-crested Pigeon, of two different colourings ; and a Crested Turtle, like a Peewit, clove brown, with violet tail and green metallic lustre, each feather tipped with white. The Magnificent Fruit Pigeon, *Carpophaga magnifica*, has a golden-green body, wing coverts spotted with King's yellow, and a streak from the neck downwards of finest auricula purple, the base of the feathers being a deep sapphire green. Another has a cap of amaranth or rose-lilac bordered with King's yellow, an orange belly, and the rest of its plumage is a bright parrot green. Then there are the Bronze-Wings or Ground Pigeons, imitating the Plover in form and habit, laying their eggs upon the sand, feeding upon berries, and dwelling in the Australian scrub, but within those limits the Bronze-Wings are most fanciful in colour, as the Harlequin Bronze-Wing ; or another with a breast of rosy lilac and metallic spots upon its golden green, cupreous, and deep-purple wings. Pied Plovers are the Bronze-Wings, with crests, too, like the Peewits ; but their plumage has become a livery carried out in brilliant colours in which they run to all corners of the arid sands. No one, at first sight, would know the Bronze-Wings to be Pigeons. They are so pied and dappled in their markings. Nothing could be more different from the great Blue-crowned Pigeon of New Guinea, morning after morning, making its hoarse murmuring or cooing in the trees, and a deep booming which is a mystery and that we cannot understand.

(xii)

Cordons Bleus

The Redbreast Robin upon the wintry bough, who may keep near us like an embodied spirit or familiar soul while we are sawing wood, and hop from bough to bough upon an afternoon with no other illumination than the frost upon the sleeping yew, has been transformed to pink or rose or yellow-breasted, to pied or breast of flame, or to the Norfolk Island Robin, paragon of his ragged race, indeed to all the colours that we might imagine for him as he flits off and comes hopping back again upon a winter day. It would seem impossible that this humble bird could so change his colours. Yet here he is, the same in build, but with vest of saffron yellow, pink campion, or *Redouté* rose petal. The Wrens, too, are incomparable in their brilliant and gay suits. Their black or russet transmutes to amethystine violets, purples ; they are barred or striated, banded in colours like the Parrots ; and one of them, the Emu Wren, has its tail feathers elongated into filaments that resemble the spines of a feather fan. The Finches are become as gorgeous as the Parrakeets. Crimson, fire-tailed, chestnut-breasted, scarlet-tailed, with yellow rump, red-eared, red-eyebrowed ; or most beautiful of all, the Gouldian Finch, a little bird whose variations of plumage are as puzzling as any problem of identification in aesthetics. John Gould, who named this little Australian Finch for his much-loved wife after her early death, has mistakenly, but most appropriately, figured the female instead of the male bird in his coloured plate. For there are red and black and yellow-headed phases or plumages of the same species, according to their stage of moulting. One naturalist suggests that " this is a case of a trimorphic species, and that the difference of colouring in the head is of no more importance than it is in members of one human family ". In whatever state, this little bird is of extreme beauty, surpassing in its Parrot hues the Painted Finch and Diamond Sparrows which, in comparison, are but scarlet-tailed with spots of white upon their black chests and sides. The Gouldian Finch has its mask, of whichever colour, backed with cobalt blue shading into Peacock green, a neck and back and wings of golden green, lower back cobalt blue again, black tail, and breast of golden or saffron yellow, with a belt or stomacher of violet ultramarine or pansy blue.[1]

We are among the Dwarf or Fancy Finches, known commonly as Love Birds, little beings of whom it is remarked by one authority that " at the dealers' shops hundreds may be seen in one cage, sitting as close together as they can, trying to keep each other warm, and lovingly arranging each other's feathers ". But there is not time enough for the Grosbeaks, Waxbills, Weavers, Whydahs ; for the Red-headed Cardinal, the Pope-bird or Dominican Cardinal, so called, the Yellow-billed or Cloaked Cardinal, the Black-crested or Green Cardinal, and Cardinal Grosbeak or Virginian Nightingale, all of one family ; for the Scarlet or Violet Tanager ; for the Green Amaduvade, most beautiful of the Waxbills or Astrilds, and the Violet-eared Waxbill with cheeks and eyebrows of bright lilac, chestnut body, and long tail feathers of metallic blue, a little being brought to Europe as long ago as 1754, when the first of them to arrive was in the possession of Madame de Pompadour, and in fact it is the boudoir song-bird of a gouache drawing by Boucher or Lavreince; the St Helena Waxbill or Golden Pheasant ; the Indian and African Silver-bills or little Silver Pheasants ; and the little *Cordon Bleu* or ' Butterfly-Finch ', so called from the way it hovers above its nesting-place, the Crimson-eared Waxbill,

---

[1] The Robins, Wrens, and Finches here described are Australian, and figured in Gould's *Birds of Australia*.

coming from the White Nile and the highlands of Abyssinia. This little creature is pathetic and mouse-coloured as to its back and forehead, with face and breast of sky blue and tail of stronger, cobalt blue. The cock bird has patches of crimson upon its sky-blue cheeks. The hen bird has no red patches and her cheeks and breast are a paler but beautiful sky blue. The *Cordons Bleus* are provided, sometimes, with a nest of plaited rushes wherein, turn by turn, they take their share and show their blue breasts in the opening. " He is ", we read, " very well-mannered in the society of other small birds, and exceedingly loving towards his mate. Cock and hen bird will perch as near each other as possible and frequently improve and preen each other's plumage." To those missing the warmth of affection in their lives, in long solitude and absence, separated, or about to be separated, and in dread of that, from the school child weeping before it returns, to persons of older affections, not dulled, nor less acute for that, the image of the mutual love of these little beings for each other is enough to cause a tear to fall upon the page, a tear quickly absorbed and dried up in the sheet of blotting-paper in the very moment when we know that in another day or two we will be looking, in sorrow, for the rounded rain mark, round as a childish face and tasting, like all tears, of childhood, it may be a beloved childhood that we have to imagine because we have not seen, having been destined only to meet later and join our lives together, but the mark has gone, and in the long, solitary summer days we shall look for it in vain. Such are the thoughts arising from seeing a pair of *Cordon Bleu* Finches in captivity, but we would sooner think of them in liberty in their tens of thousands, they and their brothers and sisters of the painted airs, innumerable in multitude and in variety too numerous to name.

We would frequent, in imagination, the wood of lemon trees in the shelter and shade of which whole clouds of Fire Finches, little Amaranths, or Little Red Astrilds, are accustomed

" at midsummer to assemble for their night's repose, meeting towards sunset with lively and shrill piping and passing a good time in noise before they go to rest ". Here, earlier in the year, we could have seen their flask-shaped nests made of agave or aloe fibre and wild asparagus sprays. But, also, in another continent we would find the Leek-green Amandine with its face or mask of cobalt blue shading through bronze-green and golden bronze into bright rosy scarlet, green back, and crimson tail feathers washed with vermilion, living in the bamboo glades of Borneo and Sumatra ; or the Parrot Finch of New Caledonia with sap-green wings and body, carmine mask and carmine tail. What could be more beautiful than the Red-billed Weaver, a bird so frequently met with in some parts of Africa that " travellers do not appear to have taken the trouble to study its life history ", but this tells us nothing of the black mask covering its forehead and front of face and chin, brown back and wings, and roseate body formed indubitably of rose petals, like cloth-of-roses — were that ever woven — and as perfect in gradation as the rills and flutings of a lovely shell.

(xiii)

Halcyons

But here is another painted being that lives upon the airs, the Warty-faced Honey-eater, a black-and-yellow bird of striated feathering pictured in the act of feeding upon the eucalyptus tree, an inhabitant, therefore, of the Southern continent where the stars and winds are other than those to which we are accustomed, where, as we have written, the Wrens and Robins are transformed by the influences of earth, air, and water into wings and breasts as brilliant as the semi-precious stones. Except for one species, the Bee-eaters are absent from Australia ; here are devourers of honey, but not of the honey-makers, while the Kingfisher, most lovely of English birds and in his bright plumage like the harbinger of worlds to come as he flashes like a fiery meteor across the brook, transmutes into the colours that were only hinted as he flitted over the cornflowers and the poppies, past an edge of the white harvest, to glide into the reeds.[1] Leach's Kingfisher — how inadequate the name ! — has a black-and-white head and blue wings in two shades of blue, but there were never such blue tints on the petals of a flower. They are blue flames lapping into each other, fires of another element lit by new emotions, passionate and fiery, and withal sweet and piercing, nothing comparable to the soft affections of the pigeons.

Still lovelier are the smaller, sharp-billed Halcyons, species of Kingfishers to whom a curious gravity is given because of their disproportionate heads and beaks. It is not the expression entirely of wisdom or mere cunning. The blue fire of their plumage is too intensely beautiful for that. Neither does it convey, like some of the bird masks, a calm beatitude. Rather, in some peculiar manner, these little birds must appear to us to be the ghosts of genius. They have features of an extraordinary sharpness or acuity, the premature or seven-month children of the tinted egg. Their food, we remark, is not the honey or nectar of the flowers. They are devourers of flesh and bone. Ghosts, therefore, of that order of genius that has tasted blood and may die young. Not necessarily, for their long heads suggest they may have the wisdom to survive into old age. But at least they have been poets of fire and intoxication, not mere poets of the oaten pipes, or of the lonely conch along the

[1] Cf. *Monograph of the Alcedinidæ, or Family of Kingfishers*, by Richard Bowdler Sharpe, 1868–1871, with 120 coloured plates by Keulemans.

coral shore. Genii, in fact, of fiery inspiration ; but, in fact, their name is in metaphor for the soft, warm gales, and for the halcyon hour. For the happy hour that may never return again, and that comes before the storm. For the hour of the rainbow after the warning, but before the blacker storm that is to follow. Genii, therefore, of the interlude, of the golden lull. Days or hours of the halcyon ; maybe while the buttercups shine in the meadows and the chestnut shade grows heavier into burning June. When a particular flower is in blossom ; the day of the white syringa, or the noon and evening of the blue iris in its breath of violet root. More still, when there may be neither time nor emotion left to count the flowers. Before parting, when the aching, empty days and nights cast their dark before them and already the rooms are silent and the voices stilled. When, to-morrow, dead objects will be the only association with the living. The emptied rooms will be tomb-like. Ah ! we would shut the windows even on this summer day lest something should escape and leave still less behind it. But enough. The halcyon hour, the whole of youth or half a lifetime, is drawing to a close. It will end to-morrow ; or can be delayed no longer than a fleeting day or two. Perhaps, even, this is not the reign of the halcyon but the rule of Hymen. So weep not, for his torch is burning, and the striped roses are coming into flower. The rule of Hymen is not ended. We will turn to the true halcyon and its mate. They are the ghosts of illicit passions and of the exceptional or transcendental hour. Of the blue dawn and incandescent evening that never darkened, but smouldered all night through. To the pair of halcyons clinging together upon the sempiternal bough ; to the halcyons of the poet Shelley in his Caucasian Vale ; to our own halcyons nesting in the mermaid's net upon the little stage, or among the gardenias in her dressing-room ; or not far away, upstairs in the half-furnished flat, while Antonia worked at her sewing-machine, all a summer afternoon, the yellow laburnum was flowering in the gardens, we heard the passing train upon the Underground beneath the terraces of Ladbroke Grove, and saw the shadow of her mandoline with its ribbons upon the white-washed wall. Among the halcyons it is the male bird who is lavish with his affections; the female is not indifferent but accepts it as her due. Ghosts, therefore, of whom the one lover takes the other lover with him. No more is needed than the half-acquiescence; and one who could be the ghost for others is a ghost eternal. Thus, the pairing of the halcyons who, like embodied spirits, are inhabiting unhistoried lands. They may be among the most beautiful of smaller birds. Nothing surpasses the burnished fire of their blue wings and shoulders. They are the epitome of burning summer weather. I have seen the black-and-white Kingfishers of the White Nile, but never the blue halcyons. They should be as brilliant as the meteors, and of as much, or little, meaning.[1]

(xiv)

Woodpeckers

Kingfishers, Humming Birds, Birds of Paradise; but there is a whole aesthetic system in the Woodpeckers. It is the spectacle of infinite variation upon a common theme.[2] Not that it is

---

[1] A green Kingfisher that inhabits the banks of the Amazon is illustrated by R. B. Sharpe, not less fiery and beautiful than the blue Kingfishers. And there is Lindsay's (green) Kingfisher from Luzon in the Philippines.

[2] Cf. *Monographie des Picidées; ou Histoire Naturelle des Picidées, Picumninés, Yuncinés, ou Torcols* : four volumes with 123 coloured plates by M. Delahaye representing between 600 and 700 figures of Woodpeckers, by Alfred Malherbe, Metz, 1861–1862; a very rare ornithological work of which only 100 copies were printed and coloured at the author's expense.

ordinary, within its limits, but it is universal to most lands and not of rare occurrence. Yet it shows that there need never be an end to the imagination and that diversity can come organically without recourse to changes in the structural form. In the garden upon which I look down, while I am writing, the Green Woodpecker is an ordinary inhabitant and I see him with his green back and wings, red crest, and spotted breast, most mornings, upon the unmown lawn. One summer for two mornings only, under the copper beech and by the old stone wall, in an enclosed garden, therefore, near to the house, we had the Hoopoe like a guest from the old Orient, with striped back and tail of black and white, breast and back of cinnamon, and lordly crest, and he was as much an exotic as the turbaned Orientals in Carpaccio's paintings. The Green Woodpecker is only accepted because familiar, for he is as brightly painted as the Parrots. The rarer Great Black Woodpecker, who never visits us in our corner of Northamptonshire, is not less magnificent in his livery of black and red and white. He is, indeed, the Woodpecker to match the stems and bark, as he 'drums' upon the dead wood, just as his companion is green to tone in with, but show distinct from, the green lawns and summer boughs.

But, from these beginnings, or within these limits, the Woodpecker breaks into fantasy in other lands. There is the Red-headed Woodpecker, with cherry-red face and cheeks, blue-black body, and large white patches upon the wings and tail. There is another kind with a head and neck of rose and lavender, a red band behind its ears, spotted breast and body like a Thrush, dark-brown collar, and bright-yellow linings to its wings and tail. When its tail is spread, the plumes are like a quiver of yellow arrows with their points dyed black. The Ivory-billed Woodpecker has, or had, for it is all but extinct, a Cormorant-like head and body, a black crest with red in it, a black-and-white livery with the white markings only showing

while it clings upon the bough. Another, the Pileated Woodpecker, has a red crest as flaming as a Red-hot Poker or Kniphofia,
black-and-white markings to its vulpine face, and white wing
linings which show only when this 'noisy quarrelsome'
Woodpecker is flying.[1]

The smaller Woodpeckers are innumerable and to be distinguished only by a diversity in the mock-tortoise-shell patterning
of back and wings, and by their foreheads of cherry red or
orange yellow. These are white-breasted ; but there are kinds,
too, which have spotted breasts, like Thrushes, tails like a conventional quiverful of arrows, cinnamon, with dark-brown tips,
and some, a rufous head and neck and yellow belly ; others, a
cerise throat and neck, for there are so many different tints of
cherry, vermilion cheeks upon a dove-grey neck and mouse-
brown forehead ; cerise cheeks only, and a cerise belly, with
spotted breast, brown wings and tail, and dark-brown throat and
forehead ; or, perhaps, loveliest of all, a red cap and white throat,
or soft blue forehead and soft red band behind it, cinnamon
breast, and back and wings mottled and clouded like the blond
tortoise-shell, but minute and wonderful in regularity of marking
and cross-barring.

These smaller Woodpeckers compare to Humming Birds
in their long thin bills and in their manner of crouching upon
the bough. They are, in fact, Sapsuckers, distinct, therefore, in
habit from the true Woodpeckers, but belonging to the same
family. They drill holes or sap-wells into the living tree, and
do not feed upon the grubs and maggots of the tree bark. They
are different from the Woodpeckers that live on ants and insects

---

[1] The Woodpeckers, so far described, are mostly from Audubon's *Birds of America*,
but no fewer than twenty-two birds of this species are figured in Gould's *Birds of Asia*,
the finest of all being the Yellow-naped Woodpecker of Darjeeling, and the Yellow-
faced Woodpecker of the island of Negros in the Philippines. But also there are the
Heart-spotted Woodpeckers of Java and China, varieties in which the spottings are
conspicuously heart-shaped and not like the markings of tortoise-shell or clouded amber.

and bore their nests into the trunks of trees ; eaters of nectar, and not insectivorous.[1] The larger, crested Woodpeckers which are quite other in their attitudes and in the way they cling to the branch or climb upon the stem, are more approximate in type to the Jay, even to our common Jay, but this bird, too, transmutes to something incomparable and transcendental, as in the Blue Jay of North America, an apparition that is only unnoticed because it is so common from Newfoundland down to Florida, and that released in our woods and spinneys among the violets and white anemones, close to the kingcups, would tint the cuckoo kingdom. It has a blue Jay crest, roseate cheeks, a black line like the black fastening of a mask, a rainbow neck or collar of all hues, breast of rosy cinnamon, and its back and wings and tail are of the intense blue with black barrings upon its pinions and white points to the primaries and to the long feathers of its tail. It is, after all, the Blue Jay, and those two words should describe it. Audubon figures another, the Magpie Jay, mistakenly, for it inhabits Mexico and not North America. This wonderful being has a crest of separate and disconnected feathers, like the headdress of a cacique or an Aztec King, disproportionate wings, for they are not much longer than its flowing crest, and an immense and spreading train and tail, the train tipped with white, and the long tail plumes deep blue down all their length. Not so much the blue Magpie Jay as the blue Quetzal bird, for it suggests or anticipates that marvellous creature though the Quetzal is not crested. Both these blue Jays are interesting because of their pattern contrast to the Woodpeckers, and as showing the incomparable diversity deriving from a pair of parallel themes. We have our own Jay, and our own native Woodpeckers, green or black ; but what imagination could work out or prophesy such transmutations ? Limitless time and

[1] Malherbe illustrates in his *Les Picidées* a beautiful and conspicuous cactus pecker from Mexico or Guatemala.

LESSER BIRD OF PARADISE
(Paradisea Minor)

perpetual energy, spread over so long a period that its strivings are imperceptible, this must be the only answer. But directed to whose benefit ? For we are no longer willing to believe, as were our forebears, that its purpose is human pleasure and divine instruction.

Most curious of all, the hen birds in all the races of birds appear to be indifferent. They are not interested, but careless or oblivious of these beauties. If designed for them, they are not appreciated. The direction seems to be more for the male bird's satisfaction. They are for his own contemplation and enjoyment. He generates the forces and directs their spending. These are pleasures of looking in the mirror, not of standing in the window to be seen. Even so, it is one of the deepest mysteries of nature. The impulse towards perfection can only come from perpetual competition among the males. It is as though the females had not been consulted. Are they still evolving new species ; How many centuries, or millenniums ago, for an example, did the Amherstian separate from the Golden Pheasant and fix its type ? Did this take place, unrecorded, but within historic time ? Are not the raisers of new irises and daffodils creators in their own little sphere ? Gold or silver-laced polyanthus ; the stippled auricula in its frame, with the peculiar scent only to be known on an April day when the lights are lifted ; flakes, bizarres, bybloemens all in row ; are we to love the formal more than the natural ? They are but bright uniforms or liveries compared with what is magnificent and eternal. They revert and are but temporary. They are not fixed in Time. They return to the ordinary ; to the stock on which they were grafted ; or to the humble parent as do many of the children sprung from the most illustrious marriages. But the show bench must not compare with the winds and clouds of Nature, for she is omnipotent and, when in the mood, will compete and carry off all the prizes.

(xv)

Kingdom of the Birds

Even now, there are so many beautiful families of birds that remain unrelated in our narrative. And for isolated examples, the Hurrial Bee-eater and the Paradise Flycatcher, both Indian, the latter with blue-black crest and long white tail shaped like that of a Bird of Paradise ; the Hairy-browed Cuckoo, of Luzon, with tufts of red hair-like feathers that resemble the headdress of a Red Indian chief ; the Black Gorgeted Phyllornis, in a race which is green, predominantly, but wearing the white cap which is insignia of its tribe ; a wondrous brown-and-yellow Thrush, the only beauty of its family, from Timor ; and spotted and Lunated Wagtails or Forktails of the Himalayas, pied, in some instances, not black and white but black and yellow, and making poetry of our humble Water Wagtail that darts along the drain or takes his little run and preens himself before the puddle. *Hirundo filifera* or the Wire-tailed Swallow, clinging to the rock, with maroon cap, snow-white belly, and the blue wings of its nation ;[1] and the wonderful Blue Pies of Hindustan, six varieties figured in Gould's *Birds of Asia,* and giving new romance and meaning to our particoloured, mediaeval Magpies of the lanes and hedges as they glide, according to the season, over the dog-roses or the black-fruited elders, birds, in fact, that demand for themselves

[1] *Monograph of the Hirundinidæ, or Family of Swallows,* by Richard Bowdler Sharpe and C. W. Wyatt, with 103 coloured plates, 1885–1894. *Hirundo filifera* is the most beautiful of its race, and it is figured, also, in Gould's *Birds of Asia* ; but the above work should be studied by airmen and by designers and draughtsmen of new aeroplanes for the innumerable and wonderful wing forms of the swallows. Scarcely less interesting from their point of view must be the *Monograph of the Petrels (Order Tubinares),* by F. du Cane Godman, 100 hand-coloured plates by Keulemans, 1907–1910 ; but here it is a question of Atlantic, Pacific, and great ocean crossings, not forgetting the Polar routes over the Arctic and Antarctic ice.

a whole school of china modellers and painters. Flycatchers, Honey-eaters, mostly red, the latter, in Gould's *Birds of Australia*; and the green Cat Birds in his *Birds of New Guinea*, with their different black, white, and yellow breast markings. The *Coraciidæ* or Rollers, including the Racket-tailed Roller from Africa that compares with the Humming Birds that have racket tails. The Rollers are blue, mostly, but there are a few greens, and the beautiful Azure Roller from the Moluccas. The Bee-eaters are lovely birds, too, lighter in shape than the Rollers and the Scansorial Barbets;[1] but, penultimately, we have the Sun Birds. These dispute for beauty with the Birds of Paradise, the Humming Birds, the Trogons, and the Pittas.

(xvi)

Sun Birds

The Sun Birds, which range over India, China, the East Indies, and have one race in South America, can be compared only to the Humming Birds. They even much resemble those in their iridescent and golden plumage with its metallic reflections, in their long thin sickle bills, and in the peculiar darting and hovering that is characteristic of their flight. The Malachite Sun Bird is a coppery green ' self ' as though cut out from the heart of the Siberian copper mine ; while a Sun Bird from Ceylon has a throat of amethyst reflecting lilac and purple, a yellow belly, brown-purple wings, and a little bright-green cap. The Natal

---

[1] Cf. *Monograph of the Coraciidæ, or Family of the Rollers*, by H. E. Dresser, with 27 coloured plates by Keulemans, 1893. Compare also the same author's *Monograph of the Meropidæ, or Family of the Bee-Eaters*, with coloured plates by Keulemans, 1884–1886. For the Timor Thrush, above mentioned, see *Monograph of the Turdidæ, or Family of Thrushes*, by Henry Seebohm, with 149 hand-coloured plates by Keulemans, 1902.

Sun Bird is scarlet-chested, with green wings and back, and comes from the district of that name in Brazil, near the Atlantic coast, and not from Zululand. It is to be contrasted with Dabry's Scarlet-chested Sun Bird from Burma and China, with red-purple cap and golden rays or reflections, red chest and back, yellow belly, and blue tail. The Superb Sun Bird from Madagascar is a wonderful pure emerald green with black wings ; and there is a bird from the Gaboon, along the Gold Coast, with crimson chest, green head, black wings, and throat of violet. Shelley's Yellow-backed Sun Bird from the isle of Palawan, between Borneo and the Philippines, has a greenish-blue metallic crown, a crimson cape upon its shoulders, and a blue tail. From the isle of Negros in the Philippines comes a Sun Bird that is black-bellied, with a yellow back, a small blue cap, a tail of violet blue with metallic reflections, and the rest of its plumage is a bright blood-red. Another Sun Bird from the Philippines has an olive belly, a deep red mantle, metallic lilac throat, and scarlet chest. A Sun Bird from the Australian continent is yellow-breasted with dark brown-green wings, there is a patch of wonderful metallic violet below its throat, and the rest of its plumage is a deep violet ' self '.[1]

It must be evident that with the Sun Birds we are among a nation of birds in whom nature has given herself untrammelled play. The colour ' breaks ' are so entirely pure and bright. There is not so much invention of new ornament, of pectoral shields, crests, gorgets, head or tail streamers, feathers like chest ribbons, wired or disked tails, as in the Birds of Paradise or Humming Birds. The analogy is more between the Sun Birds and the Pittas or Ant Thrushes. It is pure colour play. And, for these purposes, the forms are kept simple. It is a matter of palette, and the colours, as in the Pittas, are produced in bold

[1] Cf. *Monograph of the Nectariniidæ, or Family of Sun Birds*, by Captain G. E. Shelley (nephew of the poet), with 121 hand-coloured plates by Keulemans, 1876–1880.

contrast on an unbroken ground. But the Pittas have not the metallic reflections, the *reflets d'or* of the Sun Birds. These five races of birds, the Sun Birds, Trogons, Pittas, Humming Birds, and Birds of Paradise, are, all in all, the most beautiful of the works of nature, but for conclusion we would know her, neither lyrical, nor elegiac, but in the spirit of *L'Allegro*, wearing the masks of Comedy, for which purpose we come down among the Parrots.

(xvii)

Bird Actors

The Parrots are bird actors, and I have been drawn towards them since my earliest recollections. It must be the memory of the Parrot feathers collected out of the cages for my grand-mother (my mother's mother) that inspired one of my first poems :

Psittacus, Eois imitatrix ales ab Indis (Ovid)

> The Parrot's voice snaps out —
> No good to contradict —
> What he says he'll say again
> Dry facts, dry biscuits —
>
> His voice, and vivid colours
> Of his breast and wings,
> Are immemorially old ;
> Old dowagers dressed in crimpèd satin
> Boxed in their rooms
> Like specimens beneath a glass,
> Inviolate — and never changing,
> Their memory of emotions dead ;
> The ardour of their summers
> Sprayed like camphor

On their silken parasols
Intissued in a cupboard.
Reflective, but with never a new thought,
The Parrot sways upon his ivory perch —
Then gravely turns a somersault
Through rings nailed in the roof —
Much as the sun performs his antics
As he climbs the aerial bridge
We only see
Through crystal prisms in a falling rain.

A poem, dated 1 March 1918, so that forgetting the long years that led up to it since my childish recollections, first and last, I have been meditating for some considerable time upon the Parrots, and come no nearer to an answer to this mystery of the bird actors. And what is this secret? For, in truth, there is no mystery at all. It is merely that certain members of this bird family have the faculty of mimicking the human voice. But why the Parrots? Why not the Sea Gulls, for that is no more improbable — they follow ships for days and weeks on end? Why not other races of birds that are in special proximity to man? For instance, the cocks and hens of the poultry run? It can only be that the Parrots are predestined to this power of imitation by their peculiar shape of head; by their beaks and noses and observant eyes. By their invisible, small ears. But then, they are only prone to mimic human noises. It is a genius that, apparently, lies dormant in them until they are made captive and come into contact with human beings. They will imitate, it is true, a dog barking, or the purring of a cat. But always it is some domestic noise, in proximity, and owing its existence to the human race. Never, or hardly ever, sounds in nature; and if so, only in human terms and as affecting human beings. A talent, therefore, that is only inspired or called forth in company with men and women, children particularly, and the very old. Alone, in their native haunts, they imitate nothing and no one, not even themselves. They need human association, though they are useless for other purposes, and human company is often fatal to them. The Engineer Officer, or 'Chief' as he is called upon a destroyer — as always, a great character — has told me in a telling phrase, how, when he was a young seaman, the "whole Atlantic was a graveyard for Parrots". Every sailor brought one home with him from Africa or South America. They had done so since the days of Drake and Queen Elizabeth, and nine times out of ten the Parrot died. In his bright plumes he was dropped into the sea. For centuries the first words learned by those Parrots that survived the journey will have been the sailor's oaths and swear words. The African grey Parrot and green Parrot from the Amazon were the most common of these travellers and more readily acclimatised than the rarer sorts. In classical times the first Parrots were brought to Greece and Rome from India, or more precisely from Taprobane, now the isle of Ceylon, as a result of the expedition into India of Alexander the Great. To the ancients, therefore, to Pliny, to Aristotle, and to Ovid, the Parrot was an Indian bird, being in all probability the Alexandrine Ring Parrakeet and Rose Ring Parrakeet from the East Indies, birds still possessed of a "facility of pronunciation inferior to none others of the race". These three birds, then, one from each continent, Asia, Africa, America, are the typical Parrots and show the wide distribution of the nation. But to an even greater extent, especially with the more beautiful and smaller kinds, their home is in Australia. It is curious, indeed, that these mockers of the human voice should be spread over four out of the five continents. The bird actors are ubiquitous, and the naturalist can only illustrate and not explain their presence from Carolina [1] to Patagonia, and from

[1] The Carolina Parrakeet (*Conurus carolinensis*) figured by Audubon in his *Birds of America*, is now so rare that it has not been taken since 1904. Formerly, it ranged from the Gulf States to the shores of Lake Michigan upon which Chicago stands, and was found within earshot of the polyglot Babylon of New York.

the Gold Coast to the Barrier Reef.

Companions, then, but not lovers particularly of the human race. Involuntary companions, for so far as we know they do not of their own free will attach themselves to human beings, but prefer their native wilderness or forest. In captivity, except for the small Love Birds that are so faithful and affectionate among themselves, Parrots are " old and amusing acquaintances " but not agreeable friends. If they are fond of one member of the household they may be treacherous and anything but pleasant to the rest. Their nautical background apart, for in our imagination they are compound of tropical forests and the Seven Seas, we have to regard them as a troupe of comedians, a company of the *Commedia dell' Arte*, and like those, to be loved but feared. A comedian, be it remembered, has to be funny at the expense of another, and a member, probably, of his audience. This trait of cruelty is implicit in the Parrot's mask and beak and in his claws. But the beauty, as with the Italian comedians, apart from the performance is in the actor's clothes. Some, not the least fanciful, are dressed, like many of the comedians, in white ; others, as we should expect, are particoloured. All have masks and beaks. Many, if not most, have strident voices. " By its harsh, discordant cries this many-coloured bird seems to proclaim aloud that it fears no foe. Its formidable beak protects it from every danger, for no hawk or predatory mammal dares attack a bird so strongly armed. Here the necessity for concealment does not exist, and sexual selection has had no check in developing the brightest and most conspicuous colours. If such a bird was not able to defend itself from all foes, its loud cries would attract them, its bright colours direct them, to its own destruction." Thus Thomas Belt describing the blue, red, and yellow Macaws of Nicaragua. It would appear from this that the Parrots revel in their own loud cries and brilliant colours. That they are self-confident and assertive characters. That they have the qualities and defects of the born actor. That, in the way of wisdom, theirs is vastly different from the sapient Owl who stares, and winks an eye, upon the branch. By no stratagem could the Owl become an actor. He is more the silent, nocturnal chess-player who comes out to take his pawns. But the Parrot's wisdom is of another sort. We wait, uneasily, for him to cease speaking nonsense and talk sense. We have the feeling that his movements and actions are human : when he inclines his head to one side ; when he scratches his forehead with a claw ; when his cage is opened and he gets down and walks across the floor. But, above all, when he does nothing but stare in front of him, and we wait for him to speak. The Parrot is a bird oracle ; but his utterances are mere imitations. He is mocking us ; and then, medium-like, may produce the voice of someone dead and gone. Or some little noise or household episode.

Never was bird so domesticated as the Parrot. The farm-yard cock but crows and treads the dunghill. He expects nothing but to give battle and trail the wing before his hen. He has learned nothing ; not even to fear the cooking-pot. His only prophecy is to lift his voice an hour before the rising sun.[1] But the Parrot is so tamed that he has taught himself to speak. It is a gift that no one dog has ever learned, however trained and intelligent in other ways. The dog understands the meaning

[1] It may have seemed strange to others, besides myself, that this propensity of the domestic fowl has not been further studied and developed. I have lately read, however, that such has been the case in Japan. A little book on Japanese Poultry Breeds, by V. Kinugawa of the Agricultural Faculty, Tokyo University, speaks of the Naganako-Dori or Japanese Long Crowers, " Very few in number and preserved for many centuries in Japan for the purpose of announcing the dawn ". There are three breeds : Totenko, brown in colour, with a shrill plaintive tone, the length of the crow being generally 7 to 8 seconds and the longest crow sometimes taking as long as 20 seconds ; Tomaru, black in colour, the highest and clearest, the length of the crow extending from 5 to 6 seconds, and the longest being from 12 to 13 seconds; and Koeyoshi, brown in colour, a deep solemn bass, 5 to 10 seconds. These Long Crowers have never yet, it seems, been brought to Europe. As an idea it must be of great antiquity, dating back to a most primitive world of poetry and legend, and we may think that the living figures of those early dawns can have been not less curious than the ghosts that they dispelled.

of a few words, at most ; but in answer he can do no more than bark. He can perform his trick, to the bidding ; but he is only a dumb animal. He cannot speak. The Parrot talks ; but only copies. He is unreal, therefore, like an actor. He must lead a life of his own behind his mask. He must have his private opinion of human beings. But not one word that is original escapes from him. Is it that he cannot ? Or is it that it is outside his part ? Has he been given in mockery ; that he makes himself at home, but only imitates ? That his rôle is mimicry ; and that he has, for those purposes, his mask-like beak ? The Parrot has not even his own song to sing. His tongue is raucous and discordant. But he will whistle a little air. It need not even be taught to him. If he hears it often, he will pick it up. Any song, or any sound, so long as it is domestic and concerned with a human dwelling. Or of human interest and association. Papageno's song with its little refrain, the thought of which upon this rainy summer day must remind me of the flute call of the knife-grinder in Seville, morning after morning, in and out among the whitewashed alleys while I wrote in my bedroom behind the Plaza San Fernando ; not far away from me the tower of the Giralda climbed every morning into the blue sky ; I could not but think of the court of orange trees below it, and near at hand could hear incessantly the castanets from the dancing school across the road. Even so, Papageno is a man, or an actor, pretending to be a bird and not trying very hard, while we would never accuse a Parrot of pretending to be a man.

Parrots are heartless mimics. Somehow a perfect imitation is more natural and less mysterious when coming from a talking Mynah bird, because the Mynah is an ordinary bird, not unlike a Thrush or Blackbird or a Nightingale. He is not uncanny like the Raven. For the Raven is always like the servitor of some old and dread religion. Perhaps with his hopping walk he drew the lots for death and immolation. Now the religion is gone and only the Raven is left of it. His black beak and black livery are not those of other birds. They are a ritual costume. But the Mynah is a quite ordinary but çlever person ; as it might be, a clever locksmith or a clockmaker. The cleverest bird to be met with in a long life. Cleverer far than any Parrot. A real person, too, and not an actor. For Parrots, one and all, are masked and beaked. They are not the little homunculus, like the Bull-finch, which has " imitative powers of a high order and may be taught to pipe a little tune more readily than any other native bird ". The Bullfinch could never be an oracle. It is a little living musical box, a little toy or puppet, with two legs, a bright-red breast, a little beak, and bright and lively eye. It finishes, and can but repeat its song. But, with the Parrot, we never know what it will say or do at any moment. It has that formid-able beak and mask, and that empty but sagacious eye. It under-stands no more than the actor, who speaks his lines, but could not write the play. The bright colours are to attract attention to itself. The same naturalist, Thomas Belt, who had also seen the White Cockatoo in its habitat, Australia, writes that " it is equally conspicuous amongst the dark-green foliage by its pure white colour, and equally its loud screams proclaim from afar its resting place, whilst its powerful beak protects it from all enemies excepting man ". He is comparing it with the Macaws. He had seen both natural comedians in their native setting. They are the most immediately striking and gorgeous of the Parrot troupe ; the Macaw coming from Central and South America, and the Cockatoo from Australia and New Guinea. We would regard them, not as savages but highly sophisticated natures, granted, too, a longer span of life than human beings. These are the acrobats or comic dancers, for it is the green or grey Parrots that are so talkative and loquacious. The others are like those acrobats who utter loud and meaningless cries· upon the trapeze, or while attempting feats of danger. If they speak at all it is but a few words in a foreign tongue. But we would treat of the whole race of Parrots in terms of comedy, as though we were watching a troupe of comedians, for that is the only way in which to relate them into aesthetics. We would dip our pen into the same ink as though in order to describe paintings or drawings by Watteau, or such a spectacle as the Carnival of Venice. Such, however beautiful, are but man-made hybrids. They are artificial varieties and not the natural species. Nature's comedians have more of genius and are more brightly coloured than any upon the Italian stage. They form the huge company of the bird actors.

(xviii)

Macaws

The Parrots, according to the rules of science, belong to the order *Incessores* and pertain to that primary division of the *Scansores*, so placed because their habit is climbing and prehensile. This tribe or division, in turn, forms one of the five circular groups or families, the others being the Woodpeckers, the Toucans, the Cuckoos, and the Creepers. In the Parrots, generally, an old naturalist remarks that we find a plumage which, for richness and variety of colour, yields to few others in the Kingdom of the Birds, though he warns that, like the tulip among flowers, it may by some be thought gaudy; and later, writing of the Cockatoos, he animadverts on their plumage, which, though of a more uniform and plain attire, being white or white tinged with rosy red or pale yellow, is in his words " firm, close, and adpressed, in some species even assuming a scaled or tiled appearance ". The whole family of Parrots or

Psittacidæ is divided into five groups : the " splendidly attired " Macaws, all of which are confined to America ; the short-tailed or true Parrots, old friends of the bird-cage ; the Cockatoos ; the scarlet-clothed Lories ; and the Broad-tails and Parrakeets with whom are included, generously, the black Parrots of Madagascar. Thus many, and varied, are the masquers.

The Macaws, following that earlier suggestion, are the Parrot tulips of the race. They have the fringed and variegated petals ; and are masquers dressed as tulips. It would be tempting to delay at *le grand Ara militaire*, the *Psittacus militaris*, or Great Green Macaw which, of old, appeared in its hordes as the communal terraces of maize or Indian corn began to ripen, and was frequently given to the Peruvian Incas by their subjects as an acceptable gift. There we may imagine it, alighting in its flocks in the clear air under the huge Andes. So much for the military Macaw or tulip, though few soldiers and fewer tulips ever wore green predominantly ; but we pass on to the Red and Blue, and Blue and Yellow Macaws which are more familiar. Their habitat is Central America, Guiana, and the Amazons, where they live in the swamps and forests. The sight of their tropical and flaunting plumage, in days of happy ignorance when the Indies lay everywhere to East or West, must account for the name *Psittacus Macao* and the legend that they had any connection whatever, excepting only what it is a delight to marry in the imagination, with the old Portuguese colony of Macao on the coast of China, with the painted junks and sampans lying under the golden galleons, and with the grotto of the one-eyed poet Camoëns. But how to describe them ? With the Blue and Yellow Macaw the bill is " entirely black and very large and strong ". It has a naked white space round the eyes. The neck, breast, and belly are rich saffron yellow ; the upper plumage a beautiful rich blue, and the tail and greater quills approaching violet. With the Red and Blue Macaw the bill is white ; most of the plumage a bright vermilion red, middle wing coverts yellow, greater quills a deep azure blue, largest tail feathers vermilion, and undertail coverts from azure to deep ultramarine. Although there is a balance in the colour of these two Macaws, one blue and yellow and the other red and blue, they are not matched as evenly as the Amherstian and Golden Pheasants. It may even be that another of the race of Macaws, the Hyacinthine, is the most gorgeous of the family, but these two are so defined, with such clear markings. They are, we repeat, the Parrot tulips of the species. But they are spoilt by their raucous and discordant cries. Those, however, we must understand as proper to their rôle or turn. For the Macaw is 'Horace' of the Parrot troupe. It is his part to utter loud cries from the trapeze, or swinging on the perch. Then we look up at the scarlet, blue, or yellow petals, and at the white mask and black or pale beak of this most flaunting of the Parrots.

(xix)

Cockatoos

Following in the footsteps of the aforementioned naturalist, who had seen both families in their native haunts, we proceed straight-way to the Cockatoos, finding it irresistible to quote from another source this passage : " They seem to possess a superior under-standing to that of the common Parrot, and are more docile, kind and sincere in their attachments. This amiable disposition was particularly manifested in the subject of my Plate, for its fondness, affectionate attention, and attachment to the person who had the care of it was beyond expression." The portrait is that of the Great Red-crested Cockatoo of Sumatra and the

Moluccas, a lovely and fascinating creature, ' tiled white ', if
we may adopt that phrase, tinged on the back with shades of
cream, and on the head and breast with a soft delicate rose, a
breath or blush of rose petal, no more than that, and then the
folding scarlet crest, inclining to orange, which this paragon can
elevate or depress at will. Not the least charm of this bird is the
red iris, the ladybird-red iris of its eye, in which intelligence and
affection are animate as though spoken aloud.[1] The Lesser
Sulphur-crested Cockatoo from Molucca and the Philippines is
the Cockatoo in ordinary, delightful, yes, and even comically
beautiful, for the Cockatoo is one of nature's comedians ; but
it is necessary to voyage south and east from the scented islands,
to cross Wallace's ' divide ' which he placed between Java and
Timor, and come to the southern hemisphere and to another
continent, to the empty and age-old Antipodes.

Here we find *Cacatua Leadbeateri*, the Tricolour-crested or
Leadbeater's Cockatoo, a Parrot that offers itself in such a
ravishment of roseate colours that it is difficult indeed to believe
in its existence. Gould says of it that " its rose-coloured wings
and glowing crest might have embellished the air of a more
voluptuous region ". The coloured drawing of Leadbeater's
Cockatoo in his *Birds of Australia* is the most beautiful, we are
disposed to think, of all the two thousand nine hundred and
ninety-nine hand-coloured plates with which his works are
illustrated. It is, as Gould suggests, an anomaly that this wonderful and ecstatic being should be lost and wasted on the desert
scrub. For its hues and tones of white and rose petal are nothing
less than an ecstasy or ravishment. It is after this pattern that
the most poetical imagination might suggest a Cockatoo in
paradise, having seen already what nature had accomplished
in the matter of rose pink and sulphur for the plumage of her
Parrots. Leadbeater's Cockatoo, moreover, has a very special

[1] *The Osterley Menagerie*, by W. Hayes, London, 1794.

crest, a tricoloured crest of scarlet, white, and yellow, which lifts up and spreads out like a fan, like a fan-crown or tiara, the plumes being scarlet at their base, then yellow ; scarlet, after that, for the tips of the short feathers ; and then the larger points or spikes are white. A white-pointed crown, therefore, or diadem, with yellow and scarlet for the short plumes, of this fan or crest of feathers. The whole of its body is white, tinged with rose pink, and the underwings are crimson red. But the rose tinting on the chest and body is that, exactly, of a rose petal or of the fluting of a lovely shell. As with most, or all, of its family, the feathers of this Cockatoo have the peculiarity that a fine white dust adheres to them which may be rubbed off, and which stays upon the coat-sleeve like flour, or like the meal of the auricula or Dusty Miller. This is common, as we say, to the race of Cockatoos. The female of another sort, the Gang-Gang, which is dark grey or nearly black in plumage, but with a scarlet chest and cheeks, has a sulphurous hue as if powdered with sulphur upon its wings. There are three or four of the black and red, or black and yellow varieties. And there are the small and delightful Cockateels, Crested Ground Parrakeets as they should be called, not much bigger than Love Birds, in sober plumage of dark grey and white ; with white edging to their wings, that is to say, canary-yellow mask, canary-yellow crest, and a round mark or dab of red upon their cheeks. This little being is a perfect instance of the Parrot mask. We might regard it as the type of the actor in miniature, the little manikin or marionette, but as though to avoid confusion and attract attention to itself the type is restricted to this one form only, and not produced like the true Parrakeets in endless variety and profusion. The little Cockateel remains, therefore, fixed in memory, particularly when we consider it, not as a Cockatoo *in parvo*, but one of the innumerable Parrakeets taking to itself a crest and masquerading as a Cockatoo.

MARQUIS RAGGI'S BIRD OF PARADISE
(Paradisea Raggiana)

White, and rosy pink, and a little of sulphur yellow are the colours of the Cockatoo. But there is the Roseate or *Psittacus Eos*, which has a white crest, grey wings and back, a black tail, and a rosy breast. It is this bird which was so plentiful in New South Wales, a hundred years ago, when Gould was at work upon his *Birds of Australia*, that in the streets of the towns they were as tame as cocks and hens, coming to the door to be fed, and he describes whole flocks of them turning together in the air and showing the rose-colour of the under-surface of their wings. Their home was in the gum trees, that is to say, in the eucalyptus glades. Here, too, lived Leadbeater's Cockatoo. This most tender and spiritual in hue of all the Parrot masquers, for it possesses the pure beauty, the ravishment of an air, and we can compare it in our own mind to nothing else than the immortal, the rose-petal youthfulness of *Voi che sapete*, this crowned or crested rosy seraph of unclouded skies dwelt, then, in the eucalyptus grove. Well might Gould remark that its beauties " might have embellished the air of a more voluptuous region ". Approving for the other, its companion, *Psittacus Eos* as a fitting name, we can only suggest that the ' Leadbeater ' be dropped and this most delicate and beautiful of the Cockatoos be known as *Cacatua Cherubino*.

For convenience, before the rainbow colours, this is perhaps the moment for the promised black Parrots of Madagascar. Particularly because it is thought that they may form a link between the Cockatoos and Parrots. These birds, besides their sable plumage, are characterised by differently shaped beaks belying their actual disposition, which is tame and ineffectual, in fact obsolete. Their bills are curved down and cruel in expression, the cranium is longer and less curved or rounded. They are long-headed. They have the appearance less of Parrots than of emasculated Eagles. It is tempting to imagine that these are the early forms of Parrots. They belong to the peculiar isolated fauna and flora of Madagascar, that huge island cut off from Africa by a deep channel, and connected prehistorically with India or Malaya. With them are to be grouped the now extinct *Lophopsittacus*, a large Parrot of Mauritius, companion to the Dodo ; another extinct Parrot of Rodriguez, the near-by island ; and far across the ocean, the still plentiful Nestors of New Zealand, and the still more interesting *Nestor productus* of Philip Island, found nowhere else in the world, which inhabited the little islet which was the only land in sight from Norfolk Island, the convict-hell of last century, and is no more than a high mound of red clay with a solitary pine tree, here and there, rising out of the sea like the lunar or dead satellite of its dread parent isle. Not Parrots, these, conspicuous for their gay colours, but as though belonging to a more serious age before the dawn of laughter, when human beings said nothing worthy of imitation.[1] And indeed, Philip Island had never human inhabitant, while the Maoris did not reach New Zealand in their war canoes until entirely recent times. The Nestors and extinct Parrots, generally, are not true comedians any more than, superficially, they are true Parrots. We must conclude that they were formed, and died, before their time. These indeterminate or intermediate forms include others like the *Dasyptilus*, black and red without the proper Parrot mask, and the Stellated Geringore, disappointing member of the wonderful Parrots of Australia, for in appearance it seems not to have made up its mind what it would be. Neither bird is to be numbered with the comedians, not being dancer, acrobat, nor mimic. Mere figurants then upon the Parrot stage and not wearing, even, the true Parrot mask.[2]

[1] Mention should be made of the nine species of Pygmy Parrots to be found in New Guinea, and of the curious racket-tailed Parrot, *Priorrhinus setarius*, of Celebes, comparing with the Rollers, Kingfishers, and Humming Birds that have racket tails.

[2] For the extinct Parrots of Mauritius, Rodriguez, Philip Island, etc., cf. *Extinct Birds*, by Lord Rothschild, with 45 coloured plates by Keulemans and others, 1907.

(xx)

Parrakeets

But it is from a line drawn beyond Celebes, and embracing New Guinea and all Australia, that we enter the rainbow airs of Papageno. There are two primary companies or divisions, the Parrots and Parrakeets,[1] the Lories and the Lorikeets.[2]

The first begins, aesthetically, upon a basis of bright green ; but the Lories, mostly, like King Solomon's lilies, are clothed in scarlet. They are found impartially in New Guinea and in Australia, in which geographical order we follow them to describe their permutations, but the Parrakeets exist in a less diversity in New Guinea and arrive at their climax in Australia. The Beautiful King-Parrot of Papua is a large red-and-green masquer, with vermilion breast, green mask, yellow wing edged with scarlet, and grass-green body that moults from green into red. The adult male King-Parrot may be a green bird turned scarlet to the rhythm of its mysterious changes. Another, the Josephine Parrakeet, has a red ground, that is, a red face and chest, green wings, and a red, green, and yellow meteor tail, by which we intend that its tail shafts and spreads forth like the sky comet in a primitive painting.

Those are Papuan Parrakeets ; while the Australian series

[1] Our account of the Parrots, Cockatoos, and Lories of Australia and New Guinea is drawn from the coloured plates in vol. v of Gould's *Birds of Australia*, where some fifty or sixty Parrots are illustrated, and from the forty-seven Parrots and Lories shown in vol. v of his *Birds of New Guinea*.

[2] The authority on the Lories is *The Monograph of the Lories, or Brush-Tongued Parrots*, by St. K. Mivart, with 54 coloured plates by Keulemans, 1896. Our attempt has been to describe the aesthetic groups or divisions out of this wonderful and extraordinary profusion. Beautiful drawings of Parrots by Edward Lear appear in his *Psittacidæ*, 1834, with large coloured lithographs ; and in vol. vi of Sir William Jardine's *Naturalist's Library* (Edinburgh, 1836), with small hand-coloured engravings. We must also mention *Parrots in Captivity*, by W. T. Greene, with 81 coloured plates, 1884–1887 ; and *Parrakeets*, by D. Seth-Smith, with 20 coloured plates, revised edition, 1926.

may begin with the Green Leek or Barraband's Parrakeet. Forehead, cheeks, and throat of gamboge yellow, a collar below that of a bright brick red, a shade or sheen of blue upon the hind head and the outer of the quill feathers, and the rest of its plumage is a clear leek green. The hen is green, entirely, without other marking. The Yellow-collared Parrakeet or ' Twenty-Eight ', so-called from its peculiar cry, has a head of velvety black, a yellow torque or neck ring, green wings and breast, and a beautiful blue tail. We are among the blue-tailed Parrakeets, where they break into fantasy and away from their grass green. In the company of the Parrakeets, but never with the scarlet Lories, the wonderful blending and opposition of the rainbow tones is in the pure and clear pigments of Fra Angelico. His angels wear the leek-green dresses, and others are robed in the blue meteor tails, derived in his paintings from powdered lapis lazuli. Such are the colours of his vision of paradise and his celestial city. We meet with them in his pure skies, in his green hills, green like the wings of a Love Bird, and particularly in the detail of his buildings where he mixes his rainbow tones for a marble pavement or a column of marble, and makes it like a rosy lapis lazuli or a mottling of yellow rose leaf. So many of these Parrakeets, the blue-tailed especially, pertain to Fra Angelico. By right of innocence they are his Birds of Paradise, and passing them in succession from one to the other until we reach the scarlet Lories, we are reminded at each new plumage of his pure colours and sweet harmonies.

But here is a black-tailed Parrakeet. The cock bird is coloured jonquil yellow ; he has black points to his primaries and black edges to his wings. His hen is a smooth almond green. One of the more facile permutations from black to yellow, but this Parrakeet is no longer like the bird out of an Italian primitive by reason of its black tail. It is a yellow or green ' self ' according to its sex. The mask is not clearly defined yet. The bird compares to a dancer in a morality play. It has not joined with the comedians. But the change is imminent into the bird actors. We are not to conclude, meanwhile, that these masquers occur only in Australia. In Calcutta and in Ceylon the Ring-necked Parrakeet is found wild in every garden. The green mask is secured to its green body by a black line or ring ; while the Plum or Blossom-headed Parrakeet is found on the Madras coast and in the woods and gardens of Ceylon. Attached to its green body it has a perfectly shaped mask the colour of peach-bloom or a ripe plum. There are the little Conures from Brazil and Paraguay, the Parrakeets of South America ; but it is only their wings and the fire plumes in their tails that remind us of the shooting stars and leonids of the eucalyptus glades. The Conures have mottled breasts ; they lack the colour of the Parrakeets that live upon the wattle shrubs.

Bauer's Parrakeet has a black mask covering its entire head, blue cheeks, green throat, green wings, yellow collar, yellow stomach, and blue tail. The beauty of this indescribable being is its blue Parrot cheeks, its green-and-yellow livery, and the ultramarine or sapphire of its tail. It has blue cheeks to its black mask, and the fantasy extends to its blue comet tail. But Barnard's Parrakeet has a green head with a black band on that as though to keep the mask in place, a vermilion forehead, chin of lapis blue, a yellow lunar band or crescent like a collar round its grass-green chest, and its broad blue tail is bluer still. The permutations of this bird are the lapis blue and vermilion head markings, its yellow ring or torque, and its tail dipped in deepest midday like a meteor seen in daylight, and not the meteor itself, but the blue rush of air, the blue displacement, and the form or ghost after that upon the clear hyaline, the diamond morning.

The Adelaide Parrakeet was as common a hundred years ago in that capital city, then a town of wooden shacks, as the sparrows in the streets of London. It is a bird of lazuline blue with scarlet head and chest ; it has a green-yellow belly in the true Parrot colours, and lighter, lazuline blue wings and tail. A blue masquer, wearing lapis lazuli and a bright red or scarlet mask. What a world could this have been where such birds were the common sparrows of the streets ! But Pennant's Parrakeet is yet more wonderful of plumage. In the words of one commentator, " its colours, if anything, are too loud to please all tastes ". It is so gorgeous, indeed, that it is popularly mistaken for one of the scarlet Lories, though entirely different in head character, which is to say, in the peculiar pluming or striation of its feather mask. A scarlet-and-blue Parrakeet, in scarlet livery, with patches of blue purple upon its lower cheeks, a wholly scarlet head and forehead, black scales upon its back and wings, the wing feathers, that is to say, being outlined or edged with red, and an outspread tail of a beautiful pale blue. The immature bird, to prove its permutations, is of an obscure or dull green with spots of the red showing through it, and we are told that it used to be found in great flocks among the ripe fields of Indian corn, and that its favourite nesting place was in the peppermint tree.

But we come to one of the strangest and most beautiful images of the Antipodes. For we read that the Yellow-billed Parrakeet was a favourite for pies. The blue wings and tail feathers of this lovely being are as pure and luminous as those of Pennant's and the Adelaide Parrakeets. Parrot pie, and we can believe it, was most delicate in the eating. But what a sacrilege ! And that it should have been eaten by the settlers or squatters of a hundred years ago ! Hot Parrot pie ; or a half-eaten Parrot pie upon the sideboard ! There are two or three other Parrakeets not much less beautiful, with blue tails and yellow breasts. But Parrot pie, by right, could only be served up at a supper of the greatest comedians and comic actors. Once in years, once in a lifetime, when they sup surrounded by relics of their illustrious dead, by the clown's dress of Tom Matthews in his Cachucha burlesque or Cashew Nut Dance, by the clown's mask of Little Dicky Flexmore, the "last of the Romans", who married the dancer Mme Auriol, by the bats of Ellar and all the English harlequins and the slippers of Howell the famous pantaloon.

The Rose-Hill Parrakeet is a masquer of another order. It has white cheeks and a crimson head and breast, a yellow belly, blue primaries among its wing pinions, black, green, and yellow scales upon its back, and a spreading tail of blue and green. To ourselves, this is the Parrot of the Venetian Carnival. It wears the white mask or *volto*, which does not hide the mouth, and the crimson *baüta* or head covering to keep the mask in place. There is another Parrakeet much like it, but with a 'tigered' head, the sort of difference that is the only indication of person when the whole world is wearing masks, but with no yellow in its plumes, and a tail of scarlet, black, and blue. The Earl of Derby's has yellow cheeks, red head and belly, green and blue wings with black scale marks, and a cerulean tail. The Beautiful Parrakeet has a black cap, red forehead, black shoulders, green belly, and there is much red upon it in the way of scales and markings. The Scaly-breasted Parrakeet is a little grass-green Parrot with olive wings that are lined inside with crimson, and with yellow scales or 'tigerings' across its chest. But the Splendid Grass Parrakeet has a green cap, blue cheeks, a crimson chest, and yellow belly. And there is a Cockatoo Parrakeet which has a citron-yellow crest, red ears, and much of white upon its green-and-yellow wings.

Masks, so far, of green, the primary colour of the Parrots, but also blue cheeks, crimson faces, saffron or citron yellow, and on occasion a pure white mask. We have noted their permutation into broad blue tails; the black marks or scales upon their wings and backs, as regular as the mottlings of tortoise-shell; and the arbitrary transition of the entire plumage as in the

Pennantian Broad-Tail, from green into crimson and pale blue or purple. This world of forms is inexhaustible. It includes the Undulated Grass Parrakeets and the familiar 'blue birds' of so many cages, with that name so trite that we forbear to mention it. In so many of the Parrakeets, large and small, our comparison of the Parrot head to a mask is fortified by a line or collar of another colour, by painted cheeks, and by a nose and beak that are nothing other than those of the masked or beaked comedian. It must be a magical comedy to behold a Parrot flying by. This air of comedy is remarked by all who have written on the Parrots, and is implicit in the awkward or comical gait in which all Parrots walk upon the ground. But on the wing these comedians are in their element. It may be only the African Grey Parrot who is happier in the cage. The multitude of other forms should be seen in their flocks, chattering and screaming, when they alight, wings drawn back, feet down, on the ripe maize, or to suck the nectar of the flowers. Better still, could we but have seen them in the streets of the first settlements, or in a mining town during an alarm of gold.

(xxi)

Lories and Lorikeets

The scarlet Lories or Brush-tongued Parrots, and attendant Lorikeets, come last. They differ from other Parrots in the shape of the bill and tongue,[1] but more visibly, in the style of their

[1] This distinction is made no easier by the professional language of the ornithologist. The tongue of the Lory, we quote from one authority, " is furnished with a pencil of setaceous papillae or bristles, similar and analogous to the filamentous tongues of the tenuirostral *Melliphagidae*", an account which for lucidity only lacks the concluding phrase of Mr. George Robey's well-known song, " In other words . . ."

bird masks. Those are less smooth and more profusely feathered. In texture they are whiskered, and not ringed or scaled, being on that account still more like headpieces, like a fake head and mask sewn upon a dress. They possess an extraordinary spiritual resemblance to the more fantastic figures in a carnival or scene of popular rejoicing. Not ordinary, but festive Parrots, even after the gaudy Macaws, crested Cockatoos, and rainbow Parrakeets. This is because of the scarlet ground of the Lories ; and it must always be regretted by those disposed to love such things that the Lories and the Birds of Paradise, both found principally in New Guinea, should have been discovered at so late a date that they could make no entry into painting. The scarlet Lories would have been the Parrots of the Venetian painters from Carpaccio to Veronese, but all those artists knew were the grey or green Parrots brought home by sailors.

There are a few of the unimaginable Lories or scarlet Parrots from Australia. It is an epithet that they deserve, for the imagination could hardly conceive that the ground of the grey or green Parrot could be turned to scarlet. The King Lory is a glorious full scarlet bird with sap-green wings, and the hen is green entirely. But the Red-winged Lory, in still more glorious contradiction, is all green, a light verditer green, with black back and wings of scarlet. This pair of Lories are the direct opposite of each other, as though the plumage of the one bird was turned inside out and he was wearing the lining of the other. And we arrive at the Lorikeets. They are short-tailed Lories and stand in the same relation as Parrakeets to Parrots.

Swainson's Lorikeet or the Blue Mountain Lory, with red irides to its eyes, a lilac-purple mask, green collar, red beak, scarlet stomacher, belly of turquoise blue, and back and wings and tail of green with a light stripe down the centre of each feather. The Swift Lorikeet from Tasmania is migratory. It flies north in the winter in large flocks, the shape of its wings and rapid flight causing it to be called the Swallow of its race. But it is a little green Parrot with dark wings, a little imitation mask of red and black, scarlet throat, and so many touches of scarlet and yellow upon its chest and belly that description is not possible. There is a Red-collared Lorikeet, and a Scaly-breasted; green birds, both Australian, and the latter feeding only upon eucalyptus honey. A Varied Lorikeet, also, with a red head, and yellow striped upon its green body.

In all there would appear to be twelve red-winged Lories, but this is including New Guinea which is the Kingdom of the Lories. A dozen varieties that have scarlet wings; but there are so many contradictions. A Black-winged which has purple eye-patches, and its scarlet pinions are tipped with black; a Yellow-streaked Lory; the Blue-streaked; the Red and Blue, which is a Lory completely mottled scarlet and lapis lazuli; a Black-capped with red throat, blue tail, and clear green wings; and a Cherry Red, not the least beautiful, having exchanged scarlet for that more unusual hue. Among the Lorikeets, the Blue-bellied which comes from Papua has all the components except the scarlet wings; yellow shoulders, crimson chest, blue stomacher, green wings and tail, and a 'whiskery' blue mask of powdery blue. The Varied Lorikeet has green wings and tail and belly, a crimson chest, a scarlet cap, a yellow mask, and the mask is streaked with a broad band of powder blue. The Orange-winged, more like a Parrot, has a yellow and green tail, green body, green-blue wings with orange lining, and powdery mask of pale blue and white.

Among the Parrot masks, already noted, none could be more typical than those of the Varied and Blue-bellied Lorikeets. They have something of the wild ferocity of fancy of the Roman or Venetian Carnival. The first, with its broadening band of powder blue running through the feathery yellow mask, below the red iris of the eye and little scarlet skull-cap, is sinister and un-

TWELVE WIRED BIRD OF PARADISE
(Seleucides Nigricans)

meaning yet full of menace, and compares exactly, as a symbol, to the daubs of paint upon the face of a clown or pantaloon. The other is the blue feather headpiece covering the entire head ; the complete Parrot masquer, no more nor less. The filaments of the mask are combed and fluttering, as though stuck on. They are sewn or gummed on to the cloth or skin below. It is hard and cruel as a disguise, and gives no clue as to identity or character. This blue-visored Lorikeet should appear among the beaked masquers in Guardi's paintings of the Venetian Carnival.

The Pectoral Lorikeet, a Papuan, is of another order. Red-headed, but inclining to bright cherry, a blue crown, of purplish black more precisely, yellow streaks on breast, blue wings with green outers, and a blue meteor tail. There is a Red-backed ; a Green-backed ; and better named, because more easily re-membered, the Arfak, a honey-eating Lorikeet, and Gould adds : " Fancy a little bird, scarcely bigger than a Bearded Reedling, with a tail like that of a minivet, and exhibiting a silvery tear-mark running down a cheek of smutty blue ". The Wilhelmina Lorikeet has blue streaks upon the back of its head behind its scarlet mask, yellow streaks on its green breast, and scarlet wings. The Beautiful Lorikeet, though nearly inde-scribable because of the subtle differences in male and female, in mature and immature, appears first in canary yellow, or it could be called the snuff-coloured uniform of Skinner's Horse, with dun wings, and the lower part of its body a pale ultramarine. When mature, this paragon parades itself in a little scarlet mask, a dark cap, yellow cheeks shading to turquoise towards its shoulders and to Parrot-green upon its chest, lilac shoulders, a little touch of crimson, grey-lilac wings, cerulean stomach, lower belly ' tigered ' rose on white, and tail of dun and blue and green. The hen of this little martinet is a bright mustard yellow, and when we look at her more closely, green-scaled upon her yellow mask, flecks of green and crimson down her yellow chest, dun wings, and tail and underbelly of aquamarine and turquoise blue. What are we to say of the Green Lory; the blood-red Blue-streaked Lory, one of the most gorgeous of the race; of the Red-fronted Lory which, in contradiction, is mainly a full green; or of van Musschenbroek's which is among the most ornate and painted of the Lory tribe?

We conclude with the Papuan and Stella Lorikeets, which are red masquers with green wings, the one much like the other, the former having a brilliant scarlet ground relieved with yellow, green, and azure blue. Upon the nape of its scarlet neck are two azure bars, one below the other, and there are azure patches on its thighs and rump; green wings, and longer tail feathers grass-green tipped with yellow on their shafts, the green plumes of its meteor tail shading from green to yellow as they spread out into a fan. There are patches of saffron yellow on its breast and thighs. The Papuan Lory, in fact, is crimson and azure on its upper body, and wings and tail are yellow green. Another, the Purple-capped, is a rich scarlet 'self' with a saffron-yellow collar on its upper breast, violet-purple crown, wings that are green on the upper surface with margins and flexure of a violet blue, feathers upon the thighs azure shading into green, and back of orange yellow. Last of all, a pair of Lories from the Pacific islands; the Tahiti Lory which is deep blue like the blue of ocean, with a white bib or apron like the foaming surf, like the long oceanic rollers, a Lory for which we prefer the old Otaheite as a name; and following the painter Gauguin from those islands to his last home, the Marquesas, another and last Lory that is ultramarine blue, with blue head, blue-and-white cheeks, green back and wings, and a blue breast that is flecked or mottled, foam-like, with little marks or spangles of pure white.

Many of the Head-streaked Lories, and those the most characteristic, have blue streaks upon their scarlet masks. But it is not 'blue'. It is done by a brush dipped into lapis lazuli, a gritty powdery 'blue' ground down from the precious marble. Such are the Lories, when their permutations are forgotten. Scarlet Parrots, and for preference a scarlet 'self', with the mask of the bird actor and blue streaks or striations in the feathers of its mask. We prefer the red and purple Lories to the more ordinary green Parrakeets.

The blue-streaked Lories, one and all, belong to the genus *Trichoglossus*. Of these there are no fewer than fourteen main colour types in the great illustrated work upon the Lories. In general, they wear blue-streaked feather masks, green wings and back and tail, and a chest and belly that is red and blue. But there are others, not of the *Trichoglossus* family, that are no less beautiful. It is invidious, for its name alone, not to mention the Pleasing Lorikeet or *Hypocharmosina placens*; and the Fair Lory, *Charmosynopsis pulchella*, with entirely scarlet chest and head, yellow streaks upon its belly, green back, and red and yellow and green tail. No mean stroke of invention on the part of the naturalist who evolved the names of *Charmosynopsis* and *Hypocharmosina* for two such fanciful inhabitants of the Kingdom of the Birds. But the lists are full. There is no space to mention the names or colours of the other masquers. They are manœuvring in their thousands and their tens of thousands. The eternal day is fading, and we have to rehearse to-night's entertainment and its prelude or interlude in the lit airs of the theatre.

ENTR'ACTE

Harlequin and Columbine

(Arranged from *The Life and Reminiscences of E. L. Blanchard, 1820–1889*, London, Hutchinson & Co., 1891 ; with assistance from *Complete Book of Ballets*, by C. W. Beaumont, London, Putnam, 1937 ; and the same author's *History of Harlequin*, London, 1926)

FOR our last scene there is to be a party — a Fête and Ball in the palace of Giulietta upon the Grand Canal — and now, and always, we would spend the evening in the theatre before attending that all-night entertainment. It will, this is our object, put us in the proper mood for what is to follow, while we part from the old world, perhaps for ever, and watch it go down, at sunrise, among the guttering candles.

We start, therefore, for the theatre.

But the transformation can begin earlier in the day. "October 2nd (1850)", we read in the old diary that has been our inspiration to this interlude, "Flexmore (clown) calls for annual song and spends afternoon". Could there be a more welcome but fantastic visitor? What would we not give to have seen the comedian in the parlour? For the clown, we know from old prints, had a particular way of sitting upon a chair. How was he dressed, we wonder? Had he the marks of the clown's greasepaint still upon his face? Were the clowns of the old pantomime as easy to recognise, by certain marks and traditions, as are the matadors in Spain, where they wear their hair in pigtails, and have scars upon their faces? Another entry in the same diary, for 4 September of the next year, reads : "Flexmore comes in chaise with Mme Auriol about pantomime". Such visitors, alas! never get out at our door. But in the diary,

only ten years later, under date 21 August 1860, we read :
" Write memoirs of three clowns — Paul Herring, Flexmore,
and Nelson — and sad memories of the past ". Here the diary
entry is a little muddling, for Blanchard writes : " Record
death of the poor old clown, Paul Herring " for 16 September
1873. The little that we know of Paul Herring is that he served
his apprenticeship in Richardson's Show and was seventy-eight
years old when he died. Of Nelson, we are told only that he
adopted " the talking clown as his vocation ". But Richard
Flexmore — Little Dicky Flexmore — a son of a comic dancer
of the same name ! Little Dicky Flexmore — " the last of the
Romans ! "

We are among the English pantomimists of the golden age.
But Dicky Flexmore was not a clown only. He was a dancing
clown, and the son of a comic dancer. He burlesqued the great
dancers of the Romantic Ballet. Presently we will come to
harlequin and pantaloon. But Flexmore was the greatest grotesque and comic dancer of his time, probably of all time ; and
perhaps it is typical of the English race that they should excel,
not in ballet, but in the burlesque of ballet. " Mr. Flexmore,
a clown whose fun and frolics never ceased, and whose evolutions,
leaps, falls, dances, and aerial flights, kept all alive to the end ",
who, also, according to *The Times*, " executed what he termed
an obbligato on a penny whistle . . . in a novel but irresistible
style of drollery ". He was " especially noted for his close and
natural imitation of leading dancers of the day, such as Perrot,
Carlotta Grisi, and Cerrito ". It was Flexmore, says one authority, who created the conventional garb of the clown as he is
known to-day. He abandoned the old costume of Grimaldi, "and
being a dancer and wishing to keep his legs free, encased them in
tights and short frilled trunks embroidered with red and blue
braid ". In 1848 he revived *Esmeralda*,[1] a ballet which is still, a

[1] *Esmeralda* was first produced at Her Majesty's Theatre, London, 9 March 1844.

hundred years later, in the repertory in Russia and performed from time to time. He played the rôle of Gringoire, the part created by Jules Perrot, the greatest male dancer of the age, and Mme Auriol took the name part. In the next year Flexmore produced *Les Patineurs*, to the music of Meyerbeer, dancing *A Slippery Pas*, one of his comic masterpieces, and in the same year he married Mme Auriol, who was a daughter of the French clown, Jean-Baptiste Auriol. They played together on the Continent ; but Dicky Flexmore turned consumptive and died in 1860, when only thirty-five years old.

A great and unique comic dancer, but not the greatest of the old English pantomimists. That was George Wieland, the imp or sprite, whom Blanchard considered to be the greatest exponent of the lost art of pantomime whom he had witnessed in the course of a long experience, speaking from his personal memories of Grimaldi, Ellar, Bologna, and all the famous pantomimists of his time. One of Wieland's favourite rôles was the part of Asmodeus in *The Devil on Two Sticks* (*Le Diable Boiteux*), an old ballet by Jean Coralli, whose dances are still admired, or their shadow, when we see a performance of *Giselle*. Fanny Elssler created the part of the dancer Florinda in *Le Diable Boiteux*, and danced her famous cachuca in that ballet. In the words of Théophile Gautier, " she comes forward in her pink satin basquine, trimmed with wide flounces of black lace ; her skirt weighted at the hem, fits tightly over the hips ; her slender waist boldly arches and causes the diamond ornament on her bodice to glitter ; her leg, smooth as marble, gleams through the frail mesh of her silk stocking ; and her little foot at rest seems but to await the signal of the music ". There are scenes in this old ballet in an alchemist's laboratory, in the foyer and green room, upon the stage and the dressing-rooms of the Theatre Royal at Madrid, in front of a Moorish palace " among the noble trees and scented flowers of Spain ", and outside the capital on the banks of the Manzanares, where amid the crowd " the *tambour de basque* is heard, the castanets begin their sonorous murmur, the guitar tinkles, and the natives of each province display their local music and dances ".[1] Of the performance of this ballet, when given in London, *The Times* remarks : " Wieland, who, of course, plays Asmodeus, is perfectly exhaustless in invention. The gestures into which he throws himself, with the assistance of his crutches, his extravagant outbreaks of passion, are *chefs d'œuvres* of grotesque art. Wieland must think in arabesque." Later, Wieland played in other ballets ; in *La Fille du Danube* ; in *La Sylphide* (nothing whatever to do with *Les Sylphides*, but the ballet created by Filippo Taglioni for his more famous daughter, and first and greatest of the Romantic Ballets) ; in a burlesque of *Le Diable Amoureux* ; and in *Alma, ou la Fille du Feu*, wherein there was " diablerie by Wieland ". But Wieland, too, died young, in 1847, when no more than thirty-seven years of age.

Flexmore at thirty-five, and Wieland at only thirty-seven ! But not all of them died young. Tom Matthews, another clown and burlesque dancer, lived to eighty-four. His great part was his parody of Fanny Elssler and of Mlle Duvernay in their cachuca in *The Devil on Two Sticks*. This was even performed in the actual ballet with Duvernay as Florinda and Tom Matthews as a comic doctor ; then Matthews, as clown in the pantomime that followed, burlesqued Duvernay in her cachuca. This was precisely his famous Cashew Nut Dance or Cachuca burlesque. The survival of Tom Matthews into old age is the more remarkable when we consider that the early deaths of George Wieland and Dicky Flexmore were occasioned by the " dangerous department of the art in which they excelled ". As to Wieland, Blanchard tells us that " after being shot up traps and sent flying

[1] Cf. *Complete Book of Ballets*, pp. 145, 147, by C. W. Beaumont : London, Putnam, 1937.

off on wires at perilous heights for nearly a quarter of a century, the reflection that so many of his limbs were left unbroken used to astonish him in his frequent moments of serious meditation ". He had been upon the stage since he was a little child.

Another of the dancing clowns was W. H. Payne, who also lived to be old and was the father of a famous family of clowns and dancers. Payne had " studied " in his youth under Grimaldi and Bologna, and the *Dictionary of National Biography* tells us that " he prominently figured in grand ballet with Pauline Leroux, Cerrito, Carlotta Grisi, the Elsslers, and other dancers of note ". And there are the Byrnes, beginning with James Byrne, who was dancer, choreographer, and ballet master. He it was who affected a revolution — and how pleasant this is compared with other sorts of revolutions ! — in the dress of harlequin, discarding the loose-fitting Watteau costume traditional since the days of Rich and Weaver for skin-tight fleshings, and amplifying the " five attitudes of harlequin ", so that it was said of him that " his attitudes and jumps were all new and his dress was infinitely improved ; the latter consisting of a white silk shape, fitting without a wrinkle, into which variegated silk patches were woven, the whole being profusely covered with spangles ". The diamonds of many colours were the invention of French clowns, but the white silk ground and the spangles were introduced by James Byrne. Thus Charles Dickens in his *Memoirs of Grimaldi*. Oscar Byrne, most debonair of dancing clowns, was his son, " looking as young and silly as he used to do, and dancing, if anything, better than ever ". Of the " five attitudes " of harlequin it should be further remarked that they were supposed to represent admiration, defiance, determination, flirtation, and serious thought ; while of his colours, red stood for temper, blue for love, yellow for jealousy, and brown or mauve for constancy. When harlequin wore his mask down " he was supposed to be invisible, and when his wand was filched from his grasp he was supposed to fall into the power of the clown ".

Of Henry Woodward, an earlier eighteenth-century harlequin, contemporary of Garrick, whose body lies buried in the vaults of St George's, Hanover Square, dumb witness to so many fashionable funerals and weddings, it was said that he would strike a series of poses, according to the rhythm of the music. Here, then, is a scene in which we have Woodward, the harlequin, pretending to eat a bunch of currants. " Soft music was played ; he came on, sat at a table (on which there was placed *nothing*), and made the pretence of taking up the stalk of a bunch of currants. Then, holding high his hand, with the points of finger and thumb compressed, he seemed to shake the stalk, and to strip off the currants with his mouth. In like manner he would appear to hold up a cherry by the stalk, and, after eating it, to spurt the stone from his lips. Eating a gooseberry, paring an apple, sucking an orange or peach — all were simulated in the same marvellous fashion. In short, the audience perfectly knew what fruit he seemed to be eating by the highly ingenious deception of his acting." This is the material, surely, of stage poetry ; and such another poet of action must have been Rich, the harlequin, " whose every action was executed to different agreeable music, so properly adapted that it properly expresses what is going forward ". In one particular dance Rich is said to have executed three hundred steps in a rapid advance of three yards only. He had a famous trick, too, of scratching his ear like a dog. But, for ourselves, we would prefer Rich in his *Scene with a Statue*, or in *Catching a Butterfly*. Of another scene, where harlequin is hatched from an egg by the rays of the sun, " from the first chipping of the egg, his receiving motion, his feeling the ground, his standing upright, to his quick *harlequin* trip round the empty shell, every limb had its tongue, and every motion a voice, which spoke with most miraculous organ to the understanding and sensations of the audience ". But, returning from the eighteenth century to later times, Blanchard tells a somewhat similar story of Wieland, whom he met on one occasion at a supper party, and who, " upon being asked to give a specimen of his art, said it was difficult for him to do so without the aid of a definite story, and costume and scenery. He, however, threw a sofa cushion on to the hearthrug, which was supposed to represent a dead child, whilst he, as its father, portrayed such grief and sorrow, by his action alone, that he moved his audience to tears."

And we come to Tom Ellar, the harlequin, of whom Blanchard has a marvellous tale to tell. " Time ", he begins, " ruthlessly shatters the magic mirror of life in which we peered so delightedly in the days of our boyhood ; but, after all, there is some pleasure in looking at the fragments. . . . As he grew up, the present writer enjoyed the enviable privilege of coming into absolute possession of the very bats used by the Covent Garden harlequin, whose silver wand was at that time invariably renewed twice a week ; and his firm belief in the retention of their magical property long survived all the shocks of scepticism resulting from the persistent obstinacy of any article of household furniture to become something else after administering to each the proper word and a blow. That Mr. Ellar was an ordinary mortal I refused to credit during the whole period of my elementary studies at a preparatory school in Lincoln's Inn Fields, notwithstanding the almost incredible statement of one of my small fellow-pupils that he knew where that mysterious person lodged, and had once seen him walking down Great Queen Street with an umbrella under his arm." Ellar, who had been chief dancer at the Crow Street Theatre, Dublin, made his first appearance at Covent Garden in 1813, in the pantomime *The Swans, or The Bath of Beauty* ; and two years later it was advertised on an old Covent Garden playbill that " Mr. Ellar will positively, for this night only, fly from the back of the gallery to the extremity of the stage, a descent of upwards of two hundred feet, in a most surprising manner, never before attempted by any other person ". " This daring feat ", Blanchard adds, " was most likely undertaken to assist the sale of a few tickets among the harlequin's acquaintance. . . . In association with Grimaldi, James Barnes, and afterwards with that admirable acting clown, Tom Matthews, Ellar played harlequin at the same theatre for several successive years. . . . Of course he was always the young prince or the rustic lover in the opening of the pantomime, and generally contrived to show a little glitter about the ankles, as if to indicate he was quite ready to claim his magic bat on the shortest notice. His walk was so peculiar — leaving the heel about an inch above the stage whenever he walked across — that he could always be easily recognised in any disguise he assumed. . . . As soon as he had changed he would finish his series of attitudes by spinning his head round with remarkable velocity, as if the masked face was only a whirling teetotum revolving on the centre of his frilled neck. This curious and rather unpleasant accomplishment he had learned from old Bologna, who originally adopted it to show the effect produced upon the brain by the bowl of arrack-punch he had ordered in a scene representing Vauxhall Gardens, and from which he only recovered by the columbine taking the bat and making him spin his head in the opposite direction. Other harlequins repeated the trick, without any other reason than that its skilful performance generally gained a round of applause.

" It was not till the Boxing Night of 1836, when the pantomime of *Harlequin and Georgey Barnwell* was produced at Covent Garden, that I enjoyed the long coveted privilege of being near the object of my childhood's veneration. Holding a very humble appointment on the theatrical staff at that time, I was nightly behind the scenes as Ellar threw off his ' slip-dress ' of Alfred Trueman, and was changed by the Fairy Industry into the glittering harlequin. As I stood at the wing and heard the plaudits of a crowded house greeting the transformation, I felt a sadness and a sorrow in curious contrast with the mirth and joy of the holiday-makers on the other side of the curtain. Ellar was then fifty-six, and when he came to the prompter's box, where I was standing, looked a decrepit old man. He raised his mask to cool his face, as he came off the stage after his first trip with columbine, and tears mingled with the beads of perspiration trickling down his cheeks. I noticed with surprise that his features were strangely discoloured, and that his skin had a bluish tint, which even stage cosmetics could not subdue. Afterwards I learned that the cast-off mistress of a chemist had a year previously administered to him, in one of her jealous moods, a mercurial poison which had thus changed his complexion, while enfeebling his frame. As he moistened his parched lips from the bottle of barley-water, which the 'call-boy' Charles Bender, held in readiness, he dropped the bat, immediately wanted to change a trick already brought on to the stage. It was the first time I had ever restored the magic wand of harlequin to its lawful possessor, and with moistened eyes I was about to say how glad I was of the golden opportunity, when a summons from the clown, C. J. Smith, hurried him on to effect the transformation. . . . During the run of the pantomime it was painful to note the physical exhaustion which followed even the slightest exertion of his powers ; and one evening in the following February he smote his wand upon a scene intended to represent the enlargement of every newspaper consequent upon the removal of the stamp duty, and fainted in my arms before the stage-carpenters could reveal the size of the tremendous broadsheets supposed to be the result of the potential bat. What a host of boyish memories were then recalled ! . . . Ellar's later days were so wretchedly passed in struggling with extreme poverty that I am reluctant to dwell on the sad close of his life.

For some time he gained a precarious existence by playing the guitar after nightfall in fashionable squares, or dancing at the miserable music halls which then existed at the East End." To this may be added what was written by Thackeray of the sad end of Tom Ellar : " Our Harlequin Ellar, prince of many enchanted islands, was he not at Bow Street the other day, in his dirty, faded, battered motley seized as a lawbreaker for acting at a penny theatre, after having well nigh starved in the streets, where nobody would listen to his guitar ? No one gave him a shilling to bless him, not one of us who owe him so much." Ellar died in 1842, aged sixty-two, at his lodgings in Lambeth, " leaving a wife and child totally unprovided for ", as a newspaper paragraph at that time recorded.

His old associate, James Barnes, the pantaloon, died a few years before, shattered in constitution, though he had scarcely passed his fiftieth year. " His infirmities ", Blanchard remarks, " were the result of colds caught in the exercise of his professional duties, as he and Grimaldi often changed their dresses in a hackney-coach while proceeding from Sadler's Wells to Covent Garden, playing at both theatres the same evening." It was Barnes who first introduced the English pantomime to Paris. He was driven from the stage by his infirmities and provided for by his friend Tom Ellar, and later by Wieland who got up a benefit for him ; but it was too late, Barnes died soon afterwards, saying on his deathbed : " There stands Tom Ellar, a man who never deserted me. We have known each other since the year 1814. Many and many is the sovereign he has lent me when I did not know which way to turn. Since I have been out of the profession he has been more than a father to me. I have never till now had it in my power to pay him back a farthing. He shall be the heir to all I have in the world — money, pictures, everything. God for ever bless you, my dear Tom ! " But distant relatives put in a claim ; and, unable to go to law, Ellar received but a scanty bequest from the will. In conclusion, slightly altering one of Blanchard's sentences, while envying him his memories and experiences, we may agree with him that " one, at least, among the passengers along the streets sees more spectres arise out of the pavement as he passes the modern buildings than will stir the imagination of belated pedestrians a hundred years from now ".

And now, using Blanchard once more for guide, let us choose the minor characters to play in a Benefit performance of our own. Let us have Le Barr, a fop and sprite ; in *Mother Red Cap, or Harlequin and Johnny Gilpin*. In the same bill we observe, also, Lupino, pantaloon ; the name of the harlequin being Hildebrand. Or we can have Donato, the one-legged dancer, who " made a great hit on his first appearance ". And who else ? " Hit of the evening." Real Bohemian Polka danced by Mlle Louise, of Her Majesty's Theatre, and Mlle Adèle from the San Carlo, Naples. But, in the case of Donato, the one-legged dancer, we would desire to see him in the zapateado, a Spanish cobbler's dance which requires much rhythmic stamping.

Clown Jefferini, or Jeffreys, who kept a tobacconist's shop, the " Little Snuff Box ", in Garnault Street, Clerkenwell ; Chapino, Deulin, harlequins : Herr Cole, Grammani, pantaloons, for this is a " double harlequinade ". But we add others, for it is to be an augmented or Benefit performance. More clowns, Buck, Ridgway, Collier ; Bradbury, Johnston, Naylor, Paul Kellino, pantaloons ; and harlequins, Harvey, Fenton, Herr Furth, or should you prefer them Italian (though good English), Veroni and Milano. Columbines, in pairs ; Caroline Parkes and Mlle Nathalie ; Ellen Honey and Mlle Boleno ; Lizzie Grosvenor and Marie Charles ; or Mlle Henriade and Phoebe Lauri, sister to a clown and to a pantaloon. It is time to pause.

Jefferini, as clown, we may imagine for ourselves without assistance ; but what excellent names are Chapino and Deulin for a pair of harlequins ! They even portray, in their sound, two different styles of action. Buck, Ridgway, Collier, are clowns who could keep barbers' shops or public-houses ; Bradbury, Johnston, Naylor, are Elizabethan pantaloons, but Paul Kellino (Kelly, in all probability), neither English nor Italian, in his name, suggests that he belongs to the race who are born and die in the theatre. We omit the harlequins, in order to come quicker to the columbines.

Caroline Parkes was wife to Fenton the harlequin. We may conceive of her as in the Hoxton print of Mrs. Sarah Lane, with a mandoline slung round her neck. This, at least, we know from other playbills, that she was prima ballerina. Mlle Nathalie, we are to imagine, was a French columbine, remote descendant, though her family were never off the stage, it may be, from Watteau's columbines. Ellen Honey, what a charming and lovely name for a columbine ; Mlle Boleno, a name that sounds to our ears like a ghost from the theatre, it could be nothing else, but like a phantom, too, from Hampton Court ! Mlle Boleno, who for her beauty was one of the most famous of the columbines of a century ago, was wife to the clown Harry Boleno, and their English name was Mason. Lizzie Grosvenor is a pretty name, too, for a columbine. Likewise, we add in parenthesis, is Annie Cheshire ; and we much admire, also, Miss Annie Cushnie, both columbines, and her sister Thérèse Cushnie, the latter a famous dancer at Covent Garden, who had " studied hard for two years in Paris, of the best masters ", and was married to Milano, the harlequin and ballet master.

Mlle Henriade must have been another of the French columbines, a dark epical beauty, we would opine, but young and slender, then, in the short skirt " not so ornamented as those of the other Muses ", of a columbine ; and Phoebe Lauri, member of an innumerable stage family, including Charles Lauri, senior and junior, Fanny, Jenny, Edward, Frederic, John, and Septimus. Fanny and Jenny Lauri were both columbines, as well; but for her name only we prefer Phoebe, columbine of the garden and the thatched, tiled dairy. But also there are the sisters Gunnis, both columbines; and we have left till last Mlle Marie Charles, for a particular reason, because she took the part of harlequina, a mime so beautiful in itself, if only as an idea, that even in this spangled company it for a moment takes the breath away. As we conceive of her, there could be two sorts of harlequinas; one with a short skirt or apron worn over her harlequin's fleshings, like the apron of the *vivandière* who, in old prints of the French army, wears nevertheless the uniform of the Lancer, Spahi, Zouave, or whatever regiment she is attached to; or the other sort of harlequina in complete male dress, but perhaps with a bigger ruff or more coquettish hat.

But we continue: grotesques, the Ethair family; Herr Deani, sprite; the Ridgway and Summerell families, sprites; Masters R. and N. Deulin (children of the harlequin); or better still, Signor Plimmerini. These are imps of the pantomime. And who more aptly named than Signor Plimmerini? But, in all this strange company, nothing could be more typical than the Vokes family, dancers of an eccentric genius, with, to all appearance, indiarubber arms and legs. We resume what Blanchard has to say of them. Jessie Vokes was four years old when she first appeared at the Surrey Theatre; Victoria made her début when two years old; Rosina was made use of in long clothes; and as a small child Frederick Vokes was a sprite. They had their own and peculiar, or indeed inimitable style of dancing. As a small boy I myself remember one or more of the Vokes family, but I think a woman only, in the pantomime at Drury Lane, but they must have been dancers of the second or third generation. Jessie Vokes had been taught dancing by the Misses Gunnis,

and by the great clown and dancer, Dicky Flexmore. I have
a distinct recollection of the long, twisting legs, black skin-
tights, and elderly faces of this descendant, or descendants, of so
tremendous a family of ' eccentrics ' and great dancers. Have
we room — or is it too late ? — for Lavater, harlequin ; Stilt,
pantaloon ; and Huline, harlequin ; for we so much admire
their names ?

Here is a last enchantment. In a pantomime taken, most
appropriately, from one of Mme d'Aulnoy's fairy stories, the
part of Apricotina was played by Kate Kelly. She was a well-
known columbine, and it seems probable that she was the great-
niece of Michael Kelly, the Irish singer and musician who in his
Reminiscences has left us the best personal description of Mozart.
This is as it may be, but the name Apricotina reminds us, certainly, of the old Mirabell garden at Salzburg, and we would see
Apricotina in a short yellow skirt, holding a mandoline, and
coming forward to sing — why not ? — in the heavenly ' farewell ' song from Mozart's *Il Seraglio*, music which in miraculous
manner expresses a parting, but not from those one has known
and loved for years, but only, it may be, for a day, for a summer
afternoon in the apricot garden, among the statues and the
fountains — or, even, for but this one evening in the theatre.

Of nearly every columbine, and most of the clowns and
harlequins of the old English pantomime, there is this to be
remembered, that they played dual rôles, in pantomime and ballet.
If they came on at Drury Lane in the Christmas pantomime, or
the Easter spectacle, they were dancers, also, in another season
at the Royal Italian Opera, Covent Garden. Tom Matthews,
Wieland, Dicky Flexmore, as we have seen, were something
more than clowns. They were trained dancers of genius, with
ability either to burlesque or play in straight rôles with the
greatest dancers of the Romantic Ballet. Of the many columbines
of pantomime, it is said so often of one or another that she was

prima ballerina, columbine for one season, and dancing in *Le Diable Boiteux* or *La Fille du Danube* for the next. When we read the typical names — but to dispel monotony we make a selection that we have not had before — pantaloons, Silvester, Tanner, Buckingham ; columbines, Miss Sharpe, Miss Newnham, Annie Collinson ; harlequins, Cormack, Laidlaw, Martin ; clowns, Paulo, or one or other of the great Lupino family ; we know that these dancers and acrobats, interchangeable in their rôles, were all English, or at least, like the Lupinos, had been so long in England that they had become English. It was often the custom, as we have seen, to take Italian names. There were French clowns and columbines. There were, also, Herr Furth, harlequin ;[1] Herr Kohl, pantaloon (the same person, probably, as Herr Cole, pantaloon). Such is the raw material of genius, where the theatre is concerned, and its chances will never be improved by raising the school age until a child cannot live in the theatre until he is sixteen years old or more. The great and immortal Nijinski was born, we believe, to just such a family of dancers and acrobats in a Siberian circus. Their equivalent were the dancers and acrobats among whom we have been moving in the last few pages, persons for the most part closely intermarried, and speaking among themselves, when strangers were about, in *parlare*, that ancient stage slang, now all but forgotten, and made up largely of words of Italian origin, the traditional language of the theatre, but in an Italian as curious but effective as the stage names by which they chose to call themselves.

What shall be the title ? It need not be in English. Shall it be *Arlequin Lingère du Palais* ; *Arlequin Chevalier du Soleil* ; *Arlequin Maître de Musique, ou le Capitaine Scanderbeg* ; or half and half, *La Guingette*, or *Harlequin Turned Tapster* ? Or,

---

[1] " Harlequins were in such request that managers would scour the Continent in search of the finest dancers. Such artists would rank in these days with the finest ballet dancers " (A. E. Wilson, *King Panto*, London, 1934).

in English entirely, though dumb show, *Entertainment between a Harlequin and Two Punches*, or *Italian Night Scene between a Harlequin, a Scaramouche and a Punchinello* ? But there are other glittering titles to choose from : *Harlequin Horace, or the Art of Modern Poetry* ; *Proteus, or Harlequin in China* ; or *Harlequin's Trip to Naples*. We will pause here, again, for there is much to think of. *Harlequin Horace, or the Art of Modern Poetry* could be sensible to so many interpretations. But *Proteus, or Harlequin in China*, is the true and fabulous subject for pantomime, reminding me of what was written by my brother upon Peking, where he says : " I shall, too, continue to call it Peking, and neither Pekin nor the modern Peiping, for it is as Peking that I have always thought of it since I first read its magic name in childhood upon the programme of a pantomime ". In the old pantomimes of *Aladdin* there were nearly always scenes in Peking,[1] and turning to one of the many Aladdins in Blanchard's pages we find old friends : Victoria, Rosina, Jessie, Fred, and Fawdon Vokes ; harlequins, Harvey and Simpson ; pantaloons, Paul Herring and another ; a pair of clowns ; Lizzie Grosvenor and S. Harvey, columbines ; and harlequina, Amy Rosalind. Painted scenes, we imagine, more Tartar than the Tartar City ; red and purple walls, roofs with yellow tiles ; Chinese bridges, junks, and fishing boats. *Harlequin's Trip to Naples* is a project, it may be, still more after our own heart, and one for which we would dearly have loved to give the scenes. Harlequin down on the shore among the *lazzaroni* and the fishing nets, with Vesuvius in the distance and moonlight upon the bay, the line of lights and tinkling guitars. Harlequin at the melon stall, or among the plaster saints. Harlequin among the friars and nuns in a procession, or letting off fireworks. In the puppet theatre among

---

[1] What a spectacle must have been *The Mandarin, or Harlequin in China*, an equestrian spectacle produced at Astley's in 1825 ! This exists as one of West's plays for the juvenile drama. The lines quoted just above are from *Escape with Me!*, by Osbert Sitwell : London, Macmillan and Co., 1939.

the *fantoccini*, or in a huge crowd eating *macaroni*. As *vetturino*, driving a *carricolo* full of fair theatre-ladies round the towns on the slopes of Vesuvius, in and out among the houses and vine-yards, whipping the horses into a gallop. But we have to draw rein ourselves or the pheasant's tail feathers will wilt and fall from the horses' harness, from their manes, and standing erect between their ears.

It may be that the pantomime titles which are more English-sounding are not less poetical. *Harlequin and the Swans*, in which Grimaldi played clown, is a subject beautiful enough in itself if it were not for that episode, of a later date, in which a famous clown, for a wager, embarked on the Thames in a tub drawn by a pair of swans and made his passage from Westminster to London Bridge. *Father Thames and the River Queen* must have been poetry of the same mythology. So, indeed, must have been *The Waterman* and *The Lord Mayor's Fool*, played among the barges of the City Companies, and at swan-upping when the cygnets are caught and branded. The fare is turtle soup, roast beef, and orange jelly with maids-of-honour, and Gog and Magog are the household gods. *Harlequin and Billy Taylor* reads like a pantomime of the village ale-house in some sleepy hamlet under the elms where they still believe in witchcraft, where the old crones wear the steeple hat of Mother Goose and the village boy, cross-gartered, with shorn hair, comes to London to be Prince Charming (but he is all the time Miss Lizzie Gros-venor, or Miss Annie Cushnie !). *Harlequin and the Yellow Dwarf* is not at all difficult to re-create in the imagination ; but *Harlequin and the Queen Bee* could be incomparably more poetical. It could, indeed, draw one aside into another chapter or whole episode. It seems to me (and Leigh Hunt is my authority) that I see harlequin " bridling up like a pigeon ", and " dashing through windows like a swallow ". Honey of Hymettus, and of fuchsia hedges near stone walls, and whitewashed cabins ; honey of the grape vine ; and the orange and the lemon grove ; cactus honey from slopes of the prickly pear ; heather honey and the clown, dressed to match, in ' breeks ' of tartan and a Highlander's red jacket ; honey of the bean field, and beyond, what do we see but harlequin sunning himself in the window of the magpie cottage, close to the climbing honeysuckle ? Honey of the blooming buddleia, which the bees love, before the white lavender comes into flower. Harlequin, with his cocked hat stuffed into his belt, as tall as the Russian sunflower. So many poses or attitudes. But what of his adventures ? The palace of the Queen Bee is like the labyrinth and he is lost among the Death's Head Moths, in one scene, in the maze of yew and privet. Or we find him, at early morning, in the beehive village before columbine has woken in the flowerbed. Or, the next moment, looking over the red wall in his mask, and sliding down the fig tree into the strawberry bed. The transformation scene is the nuptial flight of the bees, and an aerial ballet. And the Queen Bee is the dame of pantomime. Or is she harlequina ?

But for a last title there is *Harlequin and Lord Lovell.* Lovell was, we remark, and is still, a favourite name with Gypsies. We are to imagine harlequin wandering down the rose-hung hedges. This was before the Gypsies had taken to caravans. It was when they lived in tents. Columbine, Fuchsia, Rosina are their daughters, but they can neither write nor spell their names. There are scenes of sorcery and incantation And we are led down an avenue of limes to Lord Lovell's age-old mansion with its mullioned windows. Here we have a play within a play, during the banquet. And music from the minstrels' gallery. For Lord Lovell — none other than Lizzie Grosvenor or Phoebe Lauri — falls in love with Fuchsia, whom harlequin has brought in as a dancer, against his mother's wishes. And love prevails. There is a burlesque marriage, and pantaloon is clergyman. They lead off, for their honeymoon, to the Gypsy tents, where there will be dancing and a harlequinade. And so on. . . .

Why is it such a potent magic ? There must be some reason. I would connect it, for myself, with having been taken to Italy so often as a child. With my first memories of music and entertainment coming from the pierrots' booths upon the Scarborough sands. With having stayed in the old Hotel Brun at Bologna, the town of arcades, when ten years of age, in the next bedroom to the prima donna of the local opera company ; with hearing the snatches of song from next door as she entertained the tenor and other leading members of the company and they rehearsed their songs and talked all day and late into the night, and with having caught sight through the open door on to the passage of the tables and mantelpiece covered with signed photographs of herself and friends in costume. This was Italy. And there was the other Italy of Fra Angelico and Botticelli. But they were, indeed, one and the same Italy — the eternal Italy — until the Fascists threw it down. Now it is gone, probably for ever. It will never be the same. But I am old enough to have remembered it. That is why the mere names of the old harlequins and columbines are so romantic to my ears, even though they were playing in pantomimes that were as English as the pierrots' booths upon the sands.

But word comes that all is ready. We hear the ringing of the entr'acte bell. The scene is built. Already there is the plashing of an oar. It has been but an interlude. But it is now that we are to float with Giulietta past the decaying palaces and on the green lagoon. What we promised is not an entire picture of a dying city but an entertainment among the persons and buildings that are peculiar to our state of mind. Not one city, in detail, but the architectural and musical experience of half a lifetime ; things seen, real or imaginary, on a particular occasion and in company with certain chosen persons.

THE HUNTERS AND THE HUNTED

The theatre is over : the harlequinade is done. The hour is striking. Come down the stair : set foot on to the gangway : step down into the gondola. It is a hot night in August. We are to cross the water for the Fête and Ball of Giulietta in her palace on the Grand Canal.

BOOK 4

FÊTE AND BALL
IN THE HOUSE OF GIULIETTA

FÊTE AND BALL
IN THE HOUSE OF GIULIETTA

(i)

Black-and-White Nun

OF a sudden, it begins to pour with rain.

The palaces over the canal are quite blotted out and hidden in the veil of rain. It rings and jangles like a million coins hurled spinning down upon the waters, and round the gondola. But it is summer rain, and it will stop as suddenly as it began.

For ourselves, it makes a violent change of mood into tense and frightful excitement, mounting and mounting until it is not to be endured. I am ill, now, when I remember the dragging moments. It is the horror and nausea before the Fête and Ball. Hours or months, or they could be years of waiting for the silken, immortal hour. This is what " the princes of the enchanted islands " have broken their bones for, and starved in the gutter. For what ? For the smile of one person out of many hundreds in the audience. We think of them as fabulous and unreal beings, messengers of the spirit, forgetting that they are flesh and bone.

I saw Giulietta this morning, but only for a moment, crossing the hall of the hotel. The time is the present. This happens to everyone. It cannot be the past. It seemed to me that she was enquiring for someone, or had called to fetch her letters. And she got into her motor — I heard the door slam — and drove away. For it is not Venice all the time. It is London or Paris, or anywhere that you choose. It is only Venice at moments, shall we say, at the climaxes of the Fête and Ball ; or as a minute ago, when it came on to pour with rain. It is the tradition, or in the story, that Giulietta entertained her admirers at a Ball in Venice. And so it must be, but we need not be tied down to any time or place.

Of what did the rose and its shadow upon the wall remind me ? Or the voices I heard in my dream, at Hammamet, coming up out of the well ? Or the black-and-white Nuns of the dovecote ? No. No. They are metamorphoses, not of the same, but different persons. Could I send one of the messengers of the spirit, one of " the princes of the enchanted islands ", to touch the rose petals with his wand, it would but make me weep. Neither do I wish for the voice out of the well to come up, embodied. Nor for the ghost of the stepping-stones. Or of the bed of watercress, lying under the white damson bough. For she is still living. The clock points to the eleventh hour. But it is not too late.

But harlequin's silver wand or bat, it seems to me, has changed the Nun of the dovecote and put another in her place. Not the same person, but as it were another Nun of the dovecote, for she has come to live in the same house and resembles her. And this is the mystery. Not a close resemblance, but enough to make the story. Like a sister, or another Nun metamorphosed ; or all things considered, we could say that she has been transformed ; that the wand of harlequin had changed the pumpkin carriage into a crystal coach and that she has driven to the Ball. Better still, that the good fairies were present at her birth, that she was never poor, but in the guise of Giulietta is to entertain her admirers at the Fête and Ball in Venice. The spectacle, therefore, is that of a poor person born to fortune, and not spoiled. Not the same person, for it was another birth, but there are resemblances — and differences — and that makes the mystery.

But I have now to present the world of imagination, in which I live, at its climacteric. That must be done before the fantastic spectacle of the Fête and Ball. All that has preceded has been to that purpose. But there is more besides. A personality, eternal, though only of the moment, has become the excuse or occasion for something that is immortal and can never be repeated. For an entertainment for one summer night only, and never again. But much has come before this. For whom was that palace of the Orient intended in the hunting park? What Sultan, more still, what Sultana was reigning in the Tulip Reign? For what purpose did we wander along the banks of Chrysorrhoas? And why did we describe the castles of *Les Très Riches Heures*? For our own pleasure. For the same reason that we have written of the Humming Birds and the blue-streaked Lories. It is in praise of our god, whoever he may be, but who is in ourselves. Our personal religion or philosophy, and one for which we raise the altar and the statues in our own senses. No other shrine is needed. For he differs from time to time, and except in purpose, he is not the same. But it is the identical god who speaks in the coloured wattles of the Tragopan and in his snow-flecked breast, who is enthroned in glory in the Satyr Tragopan; who calls in the voice of the Turtle Dove and in the eyes of the Peacock's tail; who is no more to be mistaken in music or in a building than in a damask rose or the petal of a lily. Probably there is no further design behind the living architecture of the flowers and birds, no other reason than perfection for its own ends and pleasures. If creed there must be for our religion, let it be this, that it is an end in itself without ulterior purpose.

We promised an entertainment among the persons and buildings that are peculiar to our state of mind, fruits of the architectural and musical experience of half a lifetime. It has been flowering in these pages, but it is not complete. It will end in the Fête and Ball, but we are only in the late morning or afternoon of the day. There are the hours of suspense and agony, and their alleviation. The long middle of the August afternoon, and time to think of what is peculiar and personal in our point of view. We would not tread where other feet have trodden. In so far as it is possible of achievement I would have my world all mine, all mine, and no one else's. What, in our own world, will be happening at this hour? There will be matinées of old musical comedies in the provinces, and it will be near the hour of the interval when teas and ices are passed round. Arcadian afternoons, though jejune, but nearer to the god we worship than in any church or chapel. The god of the silver screen is not ours entirely. He is for others. We respect the old goat of the theatre and the music-hall, who haunts the shadows, to whom were raised the golden proscenium, the gilded balconies and theatre boxes; and who, to our reckoning, guards the convent door.

(ii)

The Sackcloth Capuchins

But these present pages, in which *The Tales of Hoffmann* have been apostrophised from time to time, whence the female characters have drawn their personality and their names as typical figures haunting the imagination of the poet or any artist, and which indicated the place and setting for the Fête and Ball, fixing the occasion, as it were, issuing the invitations to the company and creating, above all, the phantom of Giulietta, are a last opportunity, long denied, to write of a painter who was something of a personal discovery, who will be to some little degree of personal association, and who is not less fantastic in his pictures than the scenes and personages in *The Tales of Hoffmann*. This much we write with assurance, knowing from the title of another of his works how dear to Hoffmann were Callot's etchings; [1] and if Hoffmann loved Callot, how much more would he have appreciated the paintings of Alessandro Magnasco, had he known them.

This, indeed, is an impossibility, for they were not even recognised as the work of a particular painter until recent times. The largest collection, before the recent war, was in the hands of an artist, living in Venice, who had acquired them here and there, thirty and forty years ago, identifying them in his own judgement as works of the same hand, but in entire ignorance of the painter's name. One and all they were by Magnasco, or Lissandrino as was his nickname. But this may not even have been known for certain in Magnasco's lifetime, for his was the brush that painted a large number of the canvases that passed, indiscriminately, as works by Salvator Rosa. He was responsible, therefore, in large part for the legends of the *banditti*. The scenes and the paintings noted by old travellers as being " worthy of the pencil of Salvator ", more often than not were in the mood and inspiration of Magnasco. A Genoese by birth (1667–1749), he worked principally in Milan, with the exception of a few years around 1720 when he lived in Florence under the patronage of Gian Gastone, the last of the Medici Grand Dukes, whose bust at top of the staircase in the Uffizi Gallery was one of the haunting memories of my childhood, standing, as it did, among those of the other members of his family and close to that of Cardinal Leopoldo de' Medici with his wasted features and great Habsburg jaw, a terrifying ghost or apparition of the physical penalties of high descent, but as great a lover of art as his Spanish cousins who formed the great collections in the

---

[1] *Fantasiestücke in Callot's Manier*, 1825.

Prado. Little or nothing, we say in parenthesis, has been written about these busts of the Medici. All we would remark is that a child or innocent coming upon them for the first time, guarding the approach to Botticelli and Filippino Lippi, would form an extraordinary notion of the Medici. Not even the mechanical dolls and automatons of Doctor Coppelius could be more weird and terrifying. Gian Gastone, in comparison with his forebears, was only peculiar and sordid, living the vicious and evil life which is expressed in his fleshy features under the huge curls of his excessive periwig, and Magnasco apart, he does not seem to have been a patron of painting. But the influence of Callot, who worked in Florence, and of his Florentine pupil Stefano della Bella, is evidently in Magnasco's subjects and in his handling. His monkish scenes may be a memory of the great swarms of monks and friars who pullulated in Tuscany during the long reign (1670–1723) of Cosimo III, the father of Gian Gastone. There is less evidence of Roman or Venetian influence upon Magnasco; but Milan had its own masters, now forgotten,[1] while it must be remembered where visual appearances are concerned that Milan remained Spanish, or at any rate under the dominion of Spain, until 1714, when it passed to Austria. Magnasco lived, therefore, under the Spanish effigy until he was nearly fifty years of age, exchanging that for the Austrian Habsburgs who by constant intermarriage were hardly to be known, physically, from the Kings of Spain. A painter, therefore, of the Spanish tendency, passing his life under the far-flung monastic shade of Spain, Spanish, too, in his extremes of poverty and fantasy, but his rapid brush and the *fougue* or speed of his rendering in the fantastic scenes and groups of his creation make of him an illustrator more than a painter, a Callot or a Gustave Doré,

---

[1] Pier Francesco Mazzuchelli, or Morazzone (1571–1626), is the most interesting of these. His painting of *St Francis in Ecstasy*, in the Museo Sforzesco at Milan, a portrait obviously, of some mystic or ecstatic monk of his own time, bears a most striking and extraordinary resemblance to the late D. H. Lawrence.

till we know his huge output and the exceptional feats of which he was capable. There are Magnascos good and bad ; but let us look, first of all, at Magnasco masquerading as Salvator Rosa.

In the dark shadow below a broken arch, of which the core of rubble still stands in place but overgrown with weeds and mosses, a group of ragged soldiers and of Gypsy women or camp followers is carousing. A tattered drum hangs from the broken arch, and from nails in the crumbling wall there hang a breastplate and a bugle. Weapons of different sorts and long-barrelled muskets lean against the wall ; but, also, a string of dead birds is hung up like a gamekeeper's decoy. The scene becomes Italian with the great cracked oil-jar or amphora standing upon a pedestal, with more breastplates hung round it, and in the wild figures of the *banditti*. They are sitting at a trestle table; one of them plays a flute, while his companions are singing, and a woman holds up a naked child. In the distance a pair of figures, witches or *streghe*, show with their white garments out of the shadow. Another painting of the same order is a scene in a cavernous interior, a sort of cellar lit by windows high up in the wall. In the centre, perched on a huge barrel, a magpie is being taught to tell fortunes by a half-naked beggar who is sitting upon the floor. Cages of birds hang upon the wall to remind us of one of the most weird and magical of Cruikshank's etchings for Grimm's *Fairy Tales* ; and a woman in a white dress, but wearing a witch's tall black steeple hat, holds up a naked babe. There are a great number of his bandit pictures, all with the same weapons and breastplates, the same Callot soldiers and witch-like Gypsy women with their children, differently disposed, and assembled in violent contrasts of light and shadow, among ruins or in darkened cellars, to the flickering torchlight or light of a camp fire.

Then there are his monkish scenes, beginning with a series of small canvases ; Capuchin friars, in the brown robes of their order, praying, or in meditation, among wild rocks in a holy cave or *spelunca* somewhere in the waste land or *deserto* of their convent, a series varied in subject and in their attitudes, as in an example in the collection at The Hague, by the monks wearing the white robes of the Camaldolese or another order. This set of paintings culminates in a great meal or *mensa* of the Capuchins in a grotto, an extraordinary and weird scene, with their shaven heads and cowls, their serpentine attitudes, to which the rope belt of the Franciscans or Capuchins gives assistance, and in the odd details of their repast. For contrast, there are his small interiors of convents with nuns at work, plaiting straw, as in one instance.

But the series of small monkish scenes is continued with a painting of a monk being tonsured. His rope belt glides like a snake from his lap on to the ground, he is sitting in a high chair, leaning his weight on one elbow, while he bends his neck down, and there is a curious horror about his shaved head with the ring of hair left round it, about the hand and arm of the monk who clips his neck, and the square vessel for the hair droppings put upon the floor. Yet another of his small paintings shows the friars in chapter, kneeling at foot of the abbot who is sitting in authority in a high chair. They kneel in submission before him, and two of the monks with clasped hands have bowed their heads upon the floor. The scene is of an uncompromising bare-ness, lit only by the feverish light upon their patched garments and bare heads and hands. A crucifix hangs upon the wall, but the spectator has the hidden knowledge that this is a coven of warlocks and that the abbot, of huge stature, is head of the coven.

Or we are shown a library in a monastery, with the members of this curious sect, or sex, turning over the pages of great folios, measuring a globe with compasses in an affected manner, or even prostrating themselves with bowed head and outstretched arms, all under the eyes of the prior who is seated in his high chair or throne, invigilating the coven. Temperamentally quieter and more restrained are the larger convent interiors, where none of the nuns resemble witches, but in a great vaulted chamber with shelves upon the walls and holy texts pasted between the arches, they are employed with spinning-wheel and distaff, or plaiting straw. But the fantasy of Magnasco runs riot in a series of large paintings that must be associated with these monastic and convent scenes and that permit the diabolical or coven element in his imagination to allow itself free rein. That is to say, a first view of any one of these paintings must give the impression that it is a scene of black magic. They are big scenes, crowded with figures ; but the interiors are not those of churches, nor convents, and the population are neither monks nor nuns. They are, in fact, interiors of synagogues ; while the companion pictures, derived certainly from some undiscovered source in a written description or engraving, portray Quaker meetings. Magnasco was a painter who could turn a Baptist immersion into a witches' sabbath, and we could wish for a vast extension of his pictures of Dissenters, and that he could have painted the Mennonite settlements in the early American colonies, the cloister of Ephrata, and such ' peculiar ' sects as the Amish and the Dunkers.

But his monkish subjects are only one half of his creation. This painter, whom we would have chosen to accompany William Beckford on his tour of Alcobaça and Batalha, was also the master of landscape. His numerous Temptations of St Anthony are always landscape paintings, in contradiction to what it might be supposed would be his interpretation of this theme. In one instance it is a scene of fauns and satyrs in a sunlit wood ; only with much searching can the crucifix be found, to prove the subject, a picture with a closed horizon because you cannot look further than the leaves ; but in other examples his blue mountains appear in the distance, recollections, it must be, of the Bergamasque Alps and the hills above Brescia, valleys where the inhabitants of Milan came to spend the summer, and villas where till lately many of Magnasco's paintings were to be found. Others of his landscapes have a mill or old fortress in the centre distance, from the roof of which, in one painting, a net is hung out for catching larks. The country rises in ravines and foothills, like the landscape near the Italian lakes, though never, curiously, is one of the Italian lakes to be seen ; but in the immediate foreground runs a river, and laundry is spread out to dry, an excuse for figures in violent action. For contrast, a more important painting, said to represent the harbour of Genoa, has a mole or quay lined with statues running out into the storm.

But all the painter's genius for the picturesque and the fantastic are to be found in a pair of compositions which have for subject St Anthony of Padua Preaching to the Fishes and Francis of Paola Walking on the Waves. In the first of them, across a stormy gulf full of the crests of waves, a huge tower still surrounded by scaffolding, is building, boats with sails like swallows' wings are scudding in the wind, and standing on a rock in the foreground in the middle of a tree-locked cove or inlet the saint is preaching to the fishes, and not only to the fishes, for every kind of sea bird, and storks and cranes and cormorants, are perched upon rocks or on branches of the over-hanging trees. In the other, across the less stormy, or less choppy waters, there is a high stone pyramid, a town in the far distance, and on the intervening headlands canvas tents or shelters are pitched, of unknown purpose, but which lend shape and significance to the stormy scene. Near to an anchor in the foreground, and close to some kegs and bales and washed-up timbers, the Calabrian saint (founder of the Mendicant Order of Minims) is about to step down into the water and walk upon the waves.

This miracle, could we believe in it (and it inspired Liszt to one of the most romantic of his later piano pieces), proves itself, as we remarked, in the calming and less troubled seas. They form a pair of paintings of a fantastic quality of which no other artist but Magnasco was capable, not great pictures, it may be, but of a surpassing, transcendental strangeness, and so peculiar in manner that they could be mistaken for work by no other hand.

The curious excursions of Magnasco are endless in their variety and scope. In the Poldi-Pezzoli Museum at Milan, hanging near to some splendid portraits by Fra Galgario, there is — or was — the Glorification of San Carlo Borromeo, an architectural scene like a Pannini, but with the characteristic figures of Magnasco. In the same style there are Bacchanales among the ruins ; and for contrast, the little series of episodes from the life of Pulcinella, paintings, if they be by Magnasco, for the attribution is uncertain, done in the local style of Brescia where there was a whole school of painters who devoted themselves to *bambocciate*, dwarfs and hunchbacks, and the masked, white-clad comedy of Pulcinella. There is the Reception in the Garden of a Villa, in the Palazzo Bianco at Genoa, probably one of the last works of the painter, who came back to die at Genoa.[1] The landscapes and hermits of Magnasco are to be seen as nowhere else, upon the staircase of the Benedictine abbey of Seitenstetten, near Linz, in Upper Austria. But there are a pair of little pictures, now separated, that afford us the only view into the painter's life. In one of them an artist, so particularised that there can be little doubt as to his identity, sits before his easel. He wears a curious high cap, a long gown, baggy trousers that suggest the half-Oriental dress of the Genoese sailors, and a pair of entirely Oriental upturned slippers. He has — which

[1] This might be indicated as almost the only one of Magnasco's paintings which is Rococo or eighteenth century in spirit.

was an anomaly in the early eighteenth century — long and furious moustaches, and the impression given is that of an exceedingly tall man, a typical exaggeration, for we know from his contemporary biographer that he was small and wiry. None the less, it must be Magnasco himself, at work in his studio, a high vaulted room of any age, that is the scene, exactly, of his carousals of *banditti*. The breastplates, muskets, all the abracadabra of his brigand or bandit subjects, lie heaped round him upon the floor. In the foreground there is a young girl whom we may identify as the painter's daughter, on whose behalf he returned to Genoa as an old man, and to whom he bequeathed his property in his will. The model from whom he is painting, and of whom we can see his first sketch upon the canvas, is a most extraordinary plumed and tattered vagabond or beggar, whether man or woman it is nearly impossible to say, who has taken up an attitude like that of one of the figures in Callot's *Balli di Sfessania* and is, in fact, a seated beggar in a cloak, but snapping his fingers and thumbs in the movements and gestures of the dance. The other picture represents music, for it would be absurd to call it ' a concert ', in the studio. The same moustached figure, wearing the same Turkish slippers, plays some kind of flute or flageolet. The same young girl, the painter's daughter, joins in the music ; there are other musicians ; the same studio properties, breastplates, muskets, and old pots and pans, litter the floor ; and the studio is the same old vaulted cellar, or one similar, a cavern of gloom as picturesque as any resort of brigands in the Calabrian hills, but one in which it must have been exceedingly difficult to get enough light by which to paint.

Magnasco, according to Lanzi, who knew him personally, was astonishingly quick and impulsive in his handling. It would be quite unnecessary for him to make detailed drawings for his pictures. He took a general subject and improvised in detail ; though we may believe, conversely, that on occasion it would be some little incident, the rope belt of the novice slipping and gliding like a snake in his picture of *The Tonsure*, for an example, that inspired the painting, and that he built up his subject from that one episode. What we have to consider, now, is how lucky he was in his environment. We get little or nothing in his pictures of the fantastic graces of the eighteenth century. Magnasco was not, like Tiepolo or Canaletto, the favourite of rich foreign patrons. Not one of his paintings was ever engraved. He was too poor, too little known, and it is probable too irregular in practice. He painted little or nothing in the way of altar-pieces for churches, and did not work in fresco. The very nature of his monkish pictures made it improbable that his paintings would be found in monasteries and convents. For in their exaggeration and distortion they are near to caricature. The beggar-monks would not appreciate his daemoniac and lurid lights, the emphasis of the painter upon their gesticulations and their bony hands, the moron roundness of their skulls, their paranoiac gestures, and the elongation of their stature. Such a painting as *The Calefactorium* is an assembly, more or less, of demented idiots; it is noisome and pestilential in effect, a scene in the common room, if such existed, of a pauper asylum for religious imbeciles. They are workhouse monks, inmates of some institution, condemned by their own vows to poverty and hunger. Improbable, indeed, that any novice would embrace the faith after a study of these paintings. For they portray a cold and bare existence, the rigours of penance, and abject obedience to superstition. The monks are prisoners of their own faith, of their own will imprisoned and condemned.

In all such paintings it is evident that it is not the religion that interested the artist but its display and opportunity for the wild and picturesque. It was in this respect that we say Magnasco was fortunate in his environment. Lombardy, under Spanish and Austrian rule, was as inexhaustible in subject as we know the old Kingdom of the Two Sicilies to have been. That is to say, it swarmed with monks and nuns. But the artist was not drawn to the richer orders, to the Dominicans or Carthusians in their sumptuous convents lined with marbles. He was the painter, above all, of the Cappuccini, whom we might describe as the beggar or Gypsy monks of the dusty suburbs. They were the mendicant or begging friars and they had monasteries outside every town and nearly every village. As they were mostly poor peasants of no education, and vowed to poverty, these were in effect little more than institutions or workhouses for the vagrant and the old. The inmates did casual labour on the convent property, were sent out to beg in the summer, and returned to the monastery for the winter months. But they were as picturesque to the painter's purposes as any band of tramps or Gypsies. The tradition of Italian architecture left it that there was always something splendid, however tattered and tumble-down, about their background : the high and grandiloquent proportion of wall and doorway, the Mediterranean invention of the pillar and the arch, even though dilapidated and but raised in stucco.

They were the sackcloth friars, the Capuchins, and could have been seen prostrating themselves at a wayside shrine, or as in these paintings, at a crucifix propped up among the rocks. Scenes of apparent improbability, such as the *Monks Picnicking in a Grotto in the Rocks*, he must certainly have witnessed, for these strange beings in their days of plenitude went for ' outings ' and excursions. The writer has himself been present at the opening of a new hotel in a town in Sicily (Acireale) when the monks appeared at the ceremony and ate up all the ices. Some-times, but rarely in these paintings, they are monks of another order, of the Camaldoli, as in one particular painting, where the cenobites in their white robes are digging a grave for one of their number in the convent garden. It is the cloister : skulls and bones of the dead, who are buried without coffins, litter the ground ; but the scene has a beauty of its own by reason of the white robes of the monks, and because the flight of arches that forms the background of the picture conveys the suggestion that, as always with the Camaldoli, the site of the convent has been chosen for its tremendous view.

It is thus at the mother-house of their order in the Apennines, at the original Camaldoli in the Casentino, whence the eyes range down the blue flanks of the mountains to the site of Ravenna and the glittering waters of the Adriatic, and in the other direction in clear weather as far as Pisa and the Tyrrhenian Sea ; or at Camaldoli, above Naples, where " the monastery and church contain nothing worth seeing ", but the view from the terrace carries over the termite city, far below, down to Posilippo where the ashes of Virgil, poet and necromancer, reposed in a grotto under a laurel tree planted by Petrarch overlooking the Partheno-pean city and the Bay, to the site of Baiae hidden under the blue waters, to the isles of Procida and Ischia, to Lake Avernus where Aeneas, in the poem, led by the Sibyl, went down into the infernal regions, and over the fires of the Phlegraean Fields to far Gaeta ; or looking the other way to the open sea, with Capri lying in its bosom, then unwoken from slumber and still pagan in spirit, where the Greek fishergirls went up the steep stone steps with their creels upon their heads through the vines and lemon terraces to Anacapri, where we might hear the ghost of a taran-tella in the shade of an olive tree where the shepherd is piping to his goats, and then to the smoking crater of Vesuvius, to Sorrento of the guitar and tambourine, to Torre Annunziata and Torre del Greco whence sail the coral fishers, to the ilexes of Portici, and the phantom, flat-roofed houses, white as Pulcinella, along the vine-clad plain. At some such monastery of the Camaldoli, where, hot and tired after the climb, you may ask for wine of the white-robed hermits or for milk at the near-by cabin door, before looking at the view, we would find a refectory or chapter house hung with paintings by Magnasco. But we should look in vain. The taste of the cenobites is for Carlo Dolci and his school. It is of that they dreamed, whether at Camaldoli, among the chestnut woods of La Verna, or amid the fragrant boughs of Vallombrosa. It is but our own imagination that would credit the ascetics, here or in any other place, with the desire to have their eccentricities and the wild beauty of their setting perpetuated by this master of the monkish picturesque. He had to work for himself alone. This great Genoese, or we had better call him Lombard, follower of Callot was constrained to follow his own tastes and inclinations, and those must have led him to anything but riches. It seems probable that he seldom, if ever, worked to commission but merely sold from time to time what paintings he had ready in his studio. From the nature of his subjects there can be little likelihood that any patron would choose and order a painting from Magnasco ; a tonsuring, a scene of monks doing penance, or the *calefactorium* or *scaldatoio*. It must have been left to the painter, and the patron had to take what had not been sold, or was on hand.

His works bear the character of inspired and furious im- provisations. Of most of them he must have lost sight the moment they were painted. In common with his contemporary composers, who saw little, if any, of their music printed in their lifetimes, Magnasco can never have seen an exhibition of his own paintings. There were but the contents of his studio which were continually changing. Nor, like other painters, had he the opportunity to gaze long upon his pictures enshrined for ever above an altar. In consequence, they show progression by instinct rather than by reflection. They were produced hap- hazard, not according to a fixed plan. Were it not known that such is not the case, and that Magnasco lived for nearly the whole of his working life in Milan, we might be led to conjecture from the nature of his subjects that he lived the life of a vagabond painter and moved from place to place. The same, or recognisable, scenes occur so seldom in his pictures, except for the vaulted room or cellar which his imagination has transformed from his studio into a bandits' den. Neither is any particular monastery to be identified. It has never sufficient of architectural feature to connect it with any other scene. It is just a convent of poor Capuchins. What appealed to Magnasco was the monks, and not the monastery. And even the monks themselves are anonymous. No one of them is ever to be known again. It is like arriving in a strange world of Chinamen who are not to be told each from each ; and before we have time to know them we have moved on to another. This is especially the case in such scenes as his interiors of convent libraries, where the effect is entirely that of a world apart, with strange inhabitants. They are externalised ; rendered by someone who is outside them, as it might be a painter working upon scenes in a lamasery in Tibet.

In his rôle of spectator, these are not the paintings of a fellow worshipper or Christian. But neither are they deliberately satirical in intention. Their purpose really is something akin to the *terribilità* of certain of the later Italians, a state of mind like the furious realism of a Caravaggio, a division or mood of what are rightly termed the ' mannerists '. But with Magnasco the key or explanation is in the picturesque. It is that, and only that, which is the secret. What interested him was the *pittoresca*, subjects that from their strangeness lent themselves to painting. A Romantic painter, therefore, and one of the early manifestations of the Romantic movement. But there are no traces in his pictures of any literary inspiration. What, if any, were the poems that inspired him, for the poets, certainly, would have been in trouble with the Inquisition ? But it is not that he hated or despised the monks. There is nothing in his paintings of the hatred of the political cartoonists. His are never the fat monks of Rowlandson or Gillray. Not an overfed or jovial friar is to be found anywhere in his pictures. They are all gaunt and emaciated, the victims not the rebels of their system.

The romantic spell which had been cast by Callot over the Gypsies and vagabonds, more still, for it was his particular discovery, over the actors of the Italian *Commedia dell' Arte*, has been extended by Magnasco into the enclosed world of the monks, but it is still governed by Callot's principles that it must be poor and tattered. He lets it be understood that it is a world in ruins. We get the same sense of ruin in Magnasco as from the actual ruins of Pannini ; and indeed, one half of Pannini, and that the least known, consists in his paintings of the architecture of his own day enlivened with figures of ladies and gentlemen in contemporary fashion, with gilded carriages, prelates and cardinals, and " lackeys in their harlequin liveries ". But in Magnasco's pictures there is never a new building. All is old and poverty-stricken, though grand in proportion. It is the Spanish decline interpreted ; the ruin resulting from exhaustion and from the discovery of the New World. In Magnasco is to be found, for the first time, the play of hermits, bandits, monks, and vagabonds, in the wreckage of a yet recent world. Not a single building in the background of any of his pictures could be ascribed to a date more than a hundred years before the painter's birth. His bandits are gathered together in ' blitzed ' buildings unrepaired after the Spanish wars. The ruins are because there has not been enough money to restore or mend. They are victims of an economic crisis, and one prolonged indefinitely for the reason that it could neither be cured nor understood.

What a glorious spectacle, though, must have been the Italian Renaissance in decline ! More than anywhere else in Venice ; but even in Milan the Spaniards succeeding to the Sforzas encouraged the decay with all the indolence of Spain.

In 1590 the city contained a quarter of a million inhabitants, and a hundred years later in Magnasco's lifetime was composed principally of monks and beggars playing the part of 'unemployed' in our industrial age. We may wish in vain that the painter had set forth upon his travels. But, perforce, he had to be content with what lay near to hand, in the towns of the Lombard plain, or among the hills of Brescia and Bergamo. Probably he did not travel because he had no need to. His scenes derived, at little or no encouragement, from his imagination, a reflection which brings us back into our own threadbare world and to the new devastation, to the litter of broken machinery, to families living among ruins, to the migrant hordes of the homeless and dispossessed, and to these coming winters which will be more raw and terrifying than any since the Thirty Years' War. Now, even now, while the trials of the ogres are in progress, in this year when the gas chambers were choked with dead and the furnaces of the crematorium only failed for want of fuel.

No wonder, then, that our tastes are drawn, one moment, to the Dutch masters of still life, to de Hooghe and Metsu, to those quiet interiors where nothing moves and everything is embalmed in light; and in another mood to Hieronymus Bosch, Goya, Magnasco, Cruikshank, to the masters of terror, great or little, and can bear nothing in between the two extremes of delight and pain. We would know more of painters such as the 'ecstatic' Morazzone, but in the same breath are delighted that none but a few have heard of him and that his pictures are unknown. It is a pleasure to hear of a piece of early music unpublished, or an old house that has not been photographed. In certain circumstances we could prefer to write a book that would not be printed. It is a preference that things should be held in private, not in public ownership; that all secrets should not be known and publicised; and we look back with envy upon such a state of ignorance as reigned in Toledo after the Great War, in 1919, when you could go round the smaller churches and there was no guide-book to tell you what paintings by El Greco you might find. It was in this manner that I saw the glorious Assumption of the Virgin in San Vicente ; the Baptism of Christ in San Juan Bautista, below the town ; a picture of St Martin on a white horse dividing his raiment with the beggar ; and a little picture of the Infant Christ walking with the giant St John Baptist, Toledo upon its hill in the background ; four pictures more exceedingly curious in every respect than any written description could have led one to believe, more curious, also, now and always, than any modern paintings seen a few days before in Paris, for the first time abroad after long war-imprisonment in England, then as now. After El Greco, a long way after him, Magnasco, but this, too, was a delight in things forgotten or unknown.

(iii)

Daughters and Sons of Albion

But the women are lingering before their mirrors. We must go.

It is London after all, for I hear the old woman with the hurdy-gurdy. It is not so long since. But time passes quickly, and she must be dead. Yet her tunes come into my mind. I hear the ' drone and tinkle ' of the hurdy-gurdy, and I cannot move or speak. It makes my hair stand on end and I feel it in the pores of my skin.

For it is like coming back, at dead of night, to an empty house and looking up at the windows ; or worse still, the house is not empty but lived in by others. It is so fearful, so appalling, to know suddenly that one is young no more. Why should the hurdy-gurdy play such a trick upon me ? What are the words of *Der Doppelgänger* : " Why, why does it mock the torments I endured there all those years ago ? " For I knew it would be London. I said so in the beginning. But it matters less when men grow older. Their nature is that of plants or trees that do not flower. Therefore, the ghost or wraith of myself, physically, has no fears for me.

Oh ! but twenty years have lasted no longer than that simple tune. It is that which is the agony, and how little and how much has altered. It is only human beings that have changed. This must be more terrible for one who has been told, and who knows, that he can never have had the high spirits of the young. Those others are consoled more easily. But it is awful to be walking with open eyes, and ears that remember an old and trivial tune of no meaning, none at all, but that recalls the very light and air of being young. Of no message, in itself, but only from association so that I would even be ashamed to write down its name. I remember, of course, other tunes of the same time, and this was certainly no new tune then. It must have been composed soon after I was born, so that, however meaningless, it must have, and not only to myself, something of eternal or universal meaning.

How curious to hear it again, to have it turning, turning in one's mind like some kind of reproach or taunt ! None the less, it will not go. It comes back again and again. It is irrelevant, and only a coincidence, or it is trying to convey to me some hidden meaning which I would sooner not know. But, of course, I understand it all the time. What it means is only too plain to me. It would have it that I should have lived my life another way. The bait or taunt works, too, that in any case life could have been different, but it is now too late. And it is so near, still. It is in one's ears and before one's eyes, but gone, all gone.

It may be that one is more susceptible, at certain moments,

to this music. What does it say? That we must part. Ah! humble, dear being, who played not long ago while I was young myself, and whom I might have passed, not knowing, in the bluebell wood across the colliery line. Or in another season, blackberrying. Since then, for a long time sheltered and now, when the leaf is turning, going out into the world of discontent to live on the hill, above the church and the same bluebell woods, now but the husks of themselves. But which will be magically beautiful again, for a few days or a week or more, long before the pale barley ripens, pale as the hair of the little girl whom we saw coming down by the gasworks, past the Domesday mill, into the haunted shadows. The bluebell woods are a childhood perpetually renewed, by that the more poignant. Then that tune was in the air, or another like it. Ah! I have lived before upon the groundsel paths, among the slag heaps; but now, no longer. I must forswear my youth. This is all that is left of it: the shadow of a person, and an old, old tune. Who could doubt that such things are sent to make us feel unhappy? We need only to think of the questions asked of any mirror. Of how pathetic are the few personal possessions. " That table or chair I bought myself. It belongs to me. I shall take it with me when I go." Going whither? To the paper husks of the bluebells that shake and rattle in the wind. To flowering ghosts, dandelion clocks, pink willowherb; later, to where the blackberries have withered on the briar. Dear, humble being, wandering with your thoughts with pale skin and accent. Must we, then, part, when so many doors are opening, when in our world of imagination it is too late to turn back, and the years of living are more than half done.

The doors are opening but the rooms are empty, or so it seems to me. For, spiritually, the forced sale has taken place. The removal van stands at the door. It takes so little to be happy. But this one does not realise when one is young. Or not with a temperament like mine. Now, all I would wish, in this winter of the spirit, is to fall asleep and wake up in a luxury of light and warmth ; not to have every morsel of coal dragged unwillingly from the bowels of the coal mine ; not to have all food weighed and balanced up in calories, with so many million deaths anticipated, calmly, from cold and starvation ; but to pass on to the light and warmth of life ; even to walk in the fish market, where the god of the statue holds a net and trident and we behold the riches of one world in the spoils or loot of another ; to forget or have in my shadow the crying wraith ; to hear no more of tears and weeping, for I cannot bear it and will go down with it into the cold. Now, at this moment, among the thatched cottages gone out to tell the tale of sorrow, and will creep back under the old stone wall, as night is falling, looking like a pale wan ghost, and take no food, accept no comfort.

As I write, the winter owl is hooting ; the grass is numb and cold. No. The light and warmth must come from within now, more than ever before. The fire cannot kindle of itself. The lamps must be relit again. There are but few who have saved their matches. And they are poets, painters, writers, not men of science. Those are mending the fuse, but all we get are lightning flashes, and in the glare we see our own white faces. When it is repaired there will be no mechanism to turn it off. A blinding light, all night long, outside your window, noises in the pipes, and motor engines starting up : mechanical clocks that tick once, loudly, every minute, or the shaman-drum of the refrigerator. It is not warmth or light, or peace or life. It is a mocking and a counterfeit. The sown grass is growing on the roof garden above the model flats, each with bathroom and kitchenette, grass of the common burial ground, no more nor less ; there is constant hot and cold water, an insolent porter, and the elevator groans all day and night. Or you may have a country cottage, with rockery, five minutes' walk from the suburban station. The same persons in the same compartment, every morning and every evening, till :

> Home is the sailor, home from sea,
> And the hunter home from the hill.

Listen ! Listen ! It is as we promised. The old hurdy-gurdy or *orgue de Barbarie* grinds out a pastoral tune : " When the court, soon after the Restoration, visited Tunbridge Wells, there was no town, but within a mile of the spring, rustic cottages, somewhat cleaner and neater than the ordinary cottages of that time, were scattered over the heath. Some of the cabins were movable, and were carried on sledges from one part of the common to another. To these huts men of fashion, wearied with the din and smoke of London, sometimes came in the summer to breathe fresh air and to catch a glimpse of rural life. During the season a kind of fair was daily held near the fountain. The wives and daughters of the Kentish farmers came from the neighbouring villages with cream, cherries, wheatears, and quails. To chaffer with them, to flirt with them, to praise their straw hats and tight heels, was a refreshing pastime to voluptuaries sick of the airs of actresses and maids of honour." It is Lord Macaulay in his *History of England* (i. 346). But his testimony is proved in the person of the Frenchman de Grammont, from the reign of Charles II. The account of the one, indeed, is based obviously upon that of the other. Here, then, is de Grammont : " Tonbridge is at the same distance from London as Fontainebleau from Paris. All that are handsomest and best of both sexes meet at the waters during the season. The company, there, though always numerous, is always select. As those who seek to amuse themselves always outnumber those who come for their health, a sense of joy and pleasure pervades everything. Constraint is banished, a friendship is established on first acquaintance, and the life which one leads there is delightful. For lodgings one has clean, comfortable cottages, standing detached, and scattered at half a mile from the waters. The morning meeting place is at the point where the fountains are. It is a wide avenue of tufted trees, under which those who take the waters walk up and down. On one side of this avenue is a line of shops, filled with all kinds of trinkets, lace, stockings, and gloves, in which there are lotteries as at a fair. On the other side of the avenue is the market, and as every one goes to choose and bargain for his own provisions, nothing is set out which is unpleasant to look upon. Pretty, fresh-coloured village girls, dressed in clean linen, little straw hats and natty little shoes, sell the game, vegetables, flowers, and fruit. It only rests with oneself to live as well as one likes. There are tables for high play, and a facility for love affairs. As evening closes in, every one leaves his own little palace to meet at the bowling green. There, if you like, you may dance in the open air, on a turf as soft and compact as the most beautiful carpets in the world."

Look deeper ! These are the idyllic or ' Keatsian ' scenes of Samuel Palmer. The capital of his pastoral kingdom was Shoreham, near Sevenoaks, where he spent four or five years under the influence of William Blake, immediately before, and for some time after, the death of his master. Here, we are told, he drew and painted continually, read poetry, and went for long moonlight walks in the country round. As we have seen, he is not the only witness. But from this stage Arcadia, for their accounts read like a pretty scene in a musical comedy, the painter has withdrawn into the haunted solitude of Blake's cottage, where the farmer's daughter, neat-waisted, tight-heeled, and in her little round straw hat, finds no entry. Neither bowls of cream, nor baskets of cherries, nor the tender wheatear,[1] tied in pairs, come to the door. Or, if they do, they are brought by visionary persons in another garb.

[1] *Saxicola Oenanthe*, the English ortolan, used to be snared in great numbers in Kent and Sussex, but is nearly extinct.

The Daughters of Albion, barefoot, bareheaded, in long fluttering gowns, dance on the hillside. They are the sacred milkmaids, virgins, or not, of the sheepfold; the population of the woodcuts made by Blake for Thornton's *Virgil*, first inhabitants of a primitive new world. The creations of an old man, a prophet, or an 'Ancient', spectral emanations of 'The House of the Interpreter' in Fountain Court. Yet it is another generation who haunted the mind of the younger painter. The landscape is not so primitive and bare. This is not the country of the Weald or Downs, where the only features are a stone circle or a grove of trees. To Blake, who had never been to Greece or Italy, that was the ancient world. But, also, Blake's theory of antiquity came from the Bible. He belonged to an older generation than that of Palmer. None the less, these paintings and drawings are a development of his genius that Blake himself was too old and big to undertake, and that was only possible to a young man who, after it, would take another direction, or do nothing more. None the less, they spring as directly as by word of mouth from William Blake. Whether Samuel Palmer read the poetry of Keats we do not know. It is more than probable, considering the circle of his friends, and were this proved, by that addition of imagery and feeling it would explain the transcendental poetry of his drawings and rare paintings.

His pears and apples are in exaggerated blossom, during the few days while the red shows in the white. No other hand, indeed, has ever painted such pear or apple trees in blossom. They are like the disintegration of a bright cloud with its locks or particles held in suspense, before precipitation. They gem the boughs. It is the living tree, leafless, but struck into flower. But the cumulus forms of his fruit trees are in near relation to the passing clouds, entities that are magnificent in their short hour, but at the mercy of the winds. Perhaps he only painted them in their season, for a spring or two, and then the mood had gone. But there is evidence that his rhapsodical or ecstatic visions were built up from close and careful study. His preliminary drawings are most accurate and painstaking.

During his period of inspiration the immediate neighbour-hood of Shoreham became transformed or transcendentalised. It would be invidious, then as now, to search that country within the radius of a walking distance, and seek to identify his subjects. For they are the fusion of real and unreal. Their components have no more factual truth than the contrasts or comparisons that are assembled in the making of a poetical image. The clue to their formation lies, probably, in his long moonlight walks. Those were the touchstone, or transforming agent, and gave him his poetical or distorting lens. He was, further, in an intoxication from reading poetry. That his trance or possession lasted for as long as four or five years is a matter of surprise. Nevertheless, this is the period of time, more or less, during which Millais was inhabited by his youthful genius ; while minor Pre-Raphaelites, among them John Brett, painter of *The Vale of Aosta* and *The Stone-Breaker*, were inspired for about as long by the Pre-Raphaelite ideals before they turned ordinary and proceeded upon their normal courses. The apprenticeship may be easier, though, when the doctrine is the mere rendering of detail, for that makes its own measurements or demands on time. It cannot accomplish itself in less than the year or two that it takes to write a book or paint a picture, and once repeated, the span of a few years is quickly done, and the inspiration goes, never, in most cases, to return again. Samuel Palmer was in compact with his inspiring genius, and this is typical, for some time after Blake had died. The nature of their relationship is exactly that of the artist who needs peace and quiet in order to snatch at his recollections of some personal but fading vision, in this instance, the giant character of

Blake, who cannot have been less wonderful and portentous, in his own way, than his contemporary Beethoven. We may even wonder if Blake was not more inspiring in his personality than in his works. His drawings and engravings may be but the poor reflection of what he seemed to be. To his little group of admirers he was the one 'Ancient' in the modern world. He was the only living person with visionary authority, not that they believed, literally, in his visions, but he must have seemed to them to be the only spiritual genius in a material world.

While the trance or focus was before his eyes Samuel Palmer could continue with his pastoral and moonlight paintings. A gloss or parallel to the truth of appearances, for a private selection or anthology of the finer passages from Kilvert's *Diary* taken, chiefly, from the years he lived at Clyro, and consisting of this mid-Victorian curate's descriptions of thunderstorms and starry nights, of haywains heavy laden coming slowly down the country lanes, would make the test or give the titles, even, for Palmer's rural idylls. For Palmer, curiously, but not for Blake's other disciple, Edward Calvert, whose pastorals are more Virgilian, less poetical it may be, but more full of emblems.

With Calvert, the beehives are set up in order in the orchard, the wattle fences are like mushroom rings upon the hills ; and in *The Chamber Idyll*, the most beautiful of his few woodcuts, the Daughter of Albion and her pastoral lover take their moonlit pleasure in a cabin formed of the trunks of trees stripped of their bark, locking into each other at the corners with nicest precision, and with the over-arching part of the roof only ornamented with such plain sculpture as the woodman's axe can execute. Again, the same maiden with her long gown billowing in the wind crosses a wooden footbridge into a flowering mead or eyot ; and were we to wait till the moon shows over the hill, we would see the outline of the shepherd's crook coming down among the millstones, and the tall shapes of other maidens descending the hillside in the evening towards the cyder feast.

If we would look round us for such magical blossoming, for such transcendental moonlights and harvestings, it is to discover that they depend upon a mood, or are only to be found in the company of a particular person. It may happen, once only, for a few days in a lifetime. And never again. A summer ravishment like that of eating under the strawberry net. In Blake, as in Palmer or Calvert, there is a Druidical simplicity in pastoral forms. Bucolics of thatched roof and leaded casement, of wooden trenchers, honeycomb, and stoneground loaf. Of the oaten moonlight and the hunter Orion walking on the hill.

(iv)

Fête and Ball in the House of Giulietta

The red apple tree has been left standing on the plot of grass before the door and in that early September morning looking out of window while it was still misty, they could have been red oranges except for the way they hung down from the leaves. The house is walled with red tiles in the local manner and roofed with slabs of stone. Black-and-white Nuns from the dovecote clapped their wings, the apple tree broke into blossom in its season, and young persons came in laughing from their ride over the common. For mile after mile one could walk in the moonlight and only meet motor after motor along the country lanes.

By day, what lovely gardens ! Tall hollyhocks and lime-washed orchards, the laburnum and the beehives in a row. No " fisherwomen in high white caps like towers and huge glittering golden earrings lining the railing of the pier ", for that is the first sight of abroad. No blue mountains or swift rivers. No laundry spread out to dry upon the river bank. No oleander flowering. No peasants lumbering down the hills with loads of charcoal. But the magnet draws the needle, the moth flies to the candle flame. " The long ranges of columned palaces . . . the mighty cornices . . . the marble by the boat's side . . ." We are upon our way. To that land " as rich in works of arts as Italy or Spain, or it is, in fact, Italy but everything is different and more beautiful than the reality, an Italy which never existed, or is not to be found, at least, among the creations of her own masters ".

This house of the dovecote and apple tree, in my life of the imagination, has been the place of metamorphosis for not one, but two persons, and that is why I have mentioned it from time to time in these pages. It must be accepted that many of the persons who play a large part in our shadow world, that is to say, as motives or forces for our inspiration, are not necessarily and always the persons whom we have known best in life. This may have particular application to poets, more than to other artists, and many historical examples go to prove it. But, in fact, nearly all artists are inspired outside their lives, that is to say, by persons or circumstances unknown to them through actual contact. It is, even, the most ordinary and comprehensible form of inspiration ; while, to a particular type of mind, such persons unknown, or little known and not enough, tend to become as important and eternal in our shadow world as those things or persons of the past with whom, from constant association, we feel we have passed our lives. They may produce a sharper and more finished image than some that are of daily contact. At least, they are no less real than any journey into history, that is to say, into the entire past until such time as we ourselves remember it. To this extent is every imagination, every shadow world, a mixture of real and unreal.

There is the obvious, and what is not obvious at all, but

concealed and hidden. A place or a person, seen only once, and that for no more than a few moments, may affect our whole lives and be the constant subject for our thoughts. The extent to which this is true in poetry and in music can never be determined, but it must be very great. We would prefer to think of it, in symbol, as the black and white halves of the mask, both entirely different ; and yet both the same. One, or both persons, from the house of the dovecote and apple tree ; or even the mistaking of the red apples for red-gold oranges in the misty morning. The three loves of our Prologue, according to this rule, may be their separate selves, or one and the same person. Or there is the probability that their total adds up into a fourth embodiment, " whom we have but mentioned, and who may be another person altogether, or all three loves in one ". We would mention, once again, that our goddess for the Fête and Ball is Thalia, the Muse of Comedy, whom we meet, now, hurrying from her dressing-room, at a corner of the painted ante-room, in a hat like a little straw boat or basket heaped with cherries, wearing her dress " that is shorter and not so ornamented as those of the other Muses ", holding her mask in her right hand, and in her other hand her shepherd's crook. But her staff is a glass wand, of the same crystal as the coach of Cinderella.

There is a kind of wreathéd music playing from a hidden orchestra, which in meaning and intention is like the strophe or simple measure sung by the *contadini* and the peasantesses, one of the most magical of Mozart's inventions, during the wedding scene in *The Marriage of Figaro* and coming immediately after the mounting, sparkling march, made out of nothing, but as brilliant of opportunity as a new pack of cards. To this music of the wreathéd simile we have come up the staircase, or along the corridor, and in an immortal moment that, like the old tune of the hurdy-gurdy makes our hair stand on end, makes us unable to move or speak, and makes us thrill or tingle in all the pores of our skin as though in the presence of the goddess herself, and of the inspiration of all poetry and music, we behold the beautiful Giulietta, who is tall and dark, with her black hair, that is intensely raven-black, but, curiously, with a few white hairs in it, dressed or arranged like a stiff black casque behind her head, like a black headdress, almost; a pale, broad forehead, huge black eyes of an unimaginable depth and blackness, filling, most of the time, the entire eye-surface, but with very white eyeballs; a lovely regular nose; full and beautifully cut red lips; and a face, in spite of its lovely modelling, remarkably round and moonlike, looking in the lowered lights, if there is ever excuse for that to happen, round and simple like a pierrot's face and, like that, full of all moonlight poetry, till the lights go up again. In her hand she holds a cigarette. She is smoking, mostly; but, if not, holding a silver cigarette case in her red-nailed fingers. Her dress, for in this moment we see her standing up as though to receive her friends and admirers, is half white, half red, that is to say, one half of her dress, mask-like, is pure white, and with classical lines of great simplicity of cut and drapery, and the other a bright red, but of the same lights and depths as the pure white, and matching with it, the red and white, again, being of the same note or tone as her black hair and her tawny or fading-magnolia-petal skin. The dress has long tight sleeves, and those, and the straight folds of the dress, following the lines of her figure, make her, perhaps, taller than is the truth. It is to be noticed that the curious and mask-like emptiness and alternation of the red and white gives us her, one moment, as a tall woman with black hair and eyes wearing a milk-white, curd-white robe, of entire simplicity, like white doe-skin, like the white chamois belly, a fuller whiteness, that is, than the white of linen, and that this brings out the rounded modelling of her features, like the face of a pierrot in white porcelain, with the lights of china on it; and again, when the red of her dress is turned towards us, which is as though we looked at the other cheek of the mask, in profile, then we behold this same beautiful Giulietta in a metaphor, as it were, not of the moonbeams and the pierrot in her appearance, for the red holds the light, does not absorb it like the white, but we are left to imagine her in that moment, not standing in the ballroom, but riding, swimming, moving in the sunlight, and this brings the appropriate red and white to her face. This beautiful figurante says a few words to everyone, and we pass on. For a moment, the brighter colours of the Caribbean are in our eyes and ears. Flowering trees ; the blue jacaranda, the golden sugar cane, the haunting rhythms of the habanera. But it is only while crossing the floor away from her, and for a step or two. And then it links again with the wreathéd music of our entrance, that is to say, of the staircase and corridor.

Someone, who might be Queen Henrietta-Maria in her portrait by Van Dyck, appears standing by her horse's head under a painted archway. She wears a hunting dress, and the plumed hat of a Cavalier. At her side, in the picture, stands the court dwarf, Sir Jeffery Hudson. It is among the most poetical and aristocratic of portraits ever painted. A string of huge pearls, straight from the seas of Ormuz and the Indian ocean, is looped round the crown of her plumed hat. It is so long since I have seen the painting that I have little memory of the colour of her hunting habit, but in shape it was a ghostly anticipation of the next century. A skirt that in queenly fashion touched upon the ground ; an Amazon bodice ; riding boots of soft leather there must have been, but they were concealed ; and she had exquisite long sleeves and gloves. I describe this portrait because it is one of those things I mentioned that, once seen, haunt the mind and are at the back of its imagery, and because this Queen or Amazon setting forth for the chase is so much the antithesis of Thalia and the Muses of our time. Granddaughter-

in-law of Mary Queen of Scots ; and herself the great-grandmother of the Young Chevalier ; the daughter of Henri
Quatre, who hunted in the forest of Fontainebleau, to whom the
phantom dark huntsman appeared, and who danced the farandole
under the old oak trees of Béarn with the pretty peasant girls.
She has not the dusky shade in her of Jeanne Duval, diluted
through who knows how many generations, and more probably
come to that other by mere chance resemblance, and casting her,
in any event, for the fabulous beauty of her rôle. This portrait
of a French Queen of England by Van Dyck we have to regard
as a phantom of high breeding, near, so very near to the golden
age, for she was alive in the time of Shakespeare, and to whom,
instinctively, we bow our heads on approaching, and while
speaking. I remember her whenever I see a bush of white
lavender, which she is said to have introduced from Orleans.
She is supposed, too, to have loved pinks and carnations, which
reminds me of the rouge on her white cheeks in her portrait by
Van Dyck that hangs in my home, and is on the wall in the room
below me as I write this.

The friends and admirers of Giulietta whom she is entertaining
at the Fête and Ball there is no need to describe, for upon this
imaginary occasion which resembles nothing else in the world
except the Seville or Venice of Count Almaviva, they are friends
and admirers, one and all, not rivals. To those who love such
things, the music and the intrigues of *The Marriage of Figaro*,
always ending happily without hurt feelings, are playing continually. It is their immortality ; and to lesser degree, the same
night, and every night, the beautiful Giulietta is entertaining her
friends and admirers in Venice. It is for this reason, to get the
reality or continuity, that I have written at intervals in these pages
" It is raining ", or " It pours with rain ". For we all know
the sound of summer rain during a party, and how that brings
with it a sudden chilling of the temperature, and an intimation

PETER SCHLEMIHL SELLS HIS SHADOW
Etching by George Cruikshank, 1822

that the day or evening is both mortal and immortal like our own affections, which we know are impermanent, but like to think will last as this living moment when it came on to rain. Or we may, even, not be emotionally interested, but mere spectators, members of the audience, as it were, during a performance of the music.

Many persons, therefore, dead and living, are present at the Fête and Ball. But we are dumb witnesses, and do not have to speak, any more than if we were sitting in the stalls. And it is, indeed, at moments like a performance in a theatre, for the scene changes ; or it is as though we moved from room to room. The page of Cleopatra steps ashore from the golden barge carrying the crown of Egypt on a cushion ; we are seeing the page-girl in the fresco[1] who played, or her prototype, a part in our lives during the years of the old woman with the hurdy-gurdy. An exquisite easel-painting of her, head and shoulders only, is in the Scuola dei Carmini. I was haunted with visions of her " Climbing like Cupid down the slanted air ", and the metamorphoses of her physical appearance which obsessed me particularly on summer afternoons while sailing a boat in a high wind upon a lake at home in Derbyshire made me think that this " minion was Charon's daughter ", and indeed of her original, the painter's model, the father according to tradition was a gondolier, and in the transmutation of my thoughts and images of her I was led to imagine how :

> In the orange wood she tried her armour,
> And this page of Venus in that mimic barrack
> Made from the battlements with beacons hung
> Shone in bright mail that was a traitor to her breasts,
> For it hid the white doves that ever move with Venus ;

and then again after the dying of this ghost, when her shade

[1] *The Banquet of Antony and Cleopatra*, by G. B. Tiepolo, at the Palazzo Labia, in Venice.

or substitute was transformed, wondrously, into another person, the new image became metamorphosed for *The Battles of the Centaurs*, and took the form of Hippodamia, " In beauty as the Argolide, the golden land ", and I wrote of " Her smoky fairness and her fair gold fronds " in one of the pair of poems that I intended to be in the style of the Florentine cassone panels that were painted by Piero de Cosimo and other masters with subjects such as these. The subject of the poem was *The Battle of the Centaurs and Lapithae*, and the occasion for the battle, according to Dr. Lemprière, in language that it is irresistible to quote, was a quarrel at the marriage of Hippodamia with Pirithous, where the Centaurs, " intoxicated with wine, behaved with rudeness and even offered violence to some of the women that were present. The Centaurs had been invited to partake the common festivity, and the amusements would have been harmless and innocent, had not one of their number attempted violence to Hippodamia. The Lapithae resented the injury, and the Centaurs supported their companion, upon which the engagement became general. Many of the Centaurs were slain ", till at last, in words become over-familiar from the reading of war communiqués, " they were obliged to retire " into Arcadia, leaving :

> . . . Hippodamia on the hoof-marked moss
> Ringed with that crescent moon a hundred times,
> In faunal emblem,

till in course of time, by easy metamorphosis, Hippodamia becomes Olympia ; Olympia, " in whose silence lies her provocation ", and " who is of the sort that will burn our youth through in suspense and agony ". But many, if not the majority, of the guests at the Fête and Ball, are ideas, not persons. And not ideas only, but sensations, as of fruit gathering, ever among the most lovely sensations of the living, as upon an only imaginary occasion which from its imagery has become part of permanent experience, when :

PETER SCHLEMIHL'S SECOND ENCOUNTER
WITH THE MAN IN GREY
Etching by George Cruikshank, 1822

. . . Midas, the miser, took me back with him
And we lived, in an instant, where that noon was left
Gilding the ladder foot at each gold tree,
Where he spared no wealth of his
And the climbers, like Hylas and like Ganymede,
Seemed stolen into heaven . . .
And they threw the sprigs of flame to us and climbed
    yet further,
Fighting at the cherry heart,

till :

Midas, the miser and the spendthrift, wept,
His men, on their ladders, let the cherries fall
And dropped from the heavens where they worked and sang
To weep with Midas.

To this extent must all poems be capable of interpretation by their creators, and I would infer from this that the Fête and Ball, being no actual occasion, has not to be bounded by what is probable, but is to be regarded as a poem, a piece of music, or a painted fresco.

But, at this moment, we are in an endless, boundless plain that exhausts itself in the distance, and runs on, and we are waiting in a peculiar apprehension as though about to behold something most curious, which is either a symbol in itself or the key to what will happen in the future. It is announced by the shrieking and screaming of the population, and by the barking and howling of dogs. "Come at once," a voice says, "that you may lose nothing, for the very moment of beginning is as curious as anything else of this strange affair." We are prepared in an instant, ready to see and hear all that is to take place. Groups of women and children are already gathered on the roofs of the buildings, and all are screaming, and dogs are howling, and all eyes directed to the prairies in the West, where we behold at a mile distant a solitary individual descending a prairie bluff and making his way in a direct line towards us. Everyone joins in the general expression of great alarm, as if they are in danger of instant destruction, but the figure discovered on the prairie continues to approach with a dignified step and in a right line towards us. All eyes are upon him, and he at length makes his appearance coming up the staircase and into the middle of the ballroom floor. All the friends and admirers of Giulietta stand ready to receive him, which they do in a cordial manner by shaking hands with him, and recognising him as an old acquaintance. He comes up, grasps my hand, kneels down behind me, and, with wonderful dexterity, I see him loosening my shadow from the ground from head to foot ; he lifts it up, he rolls it together, and at last puts it into his pocket. He then stands erect, bows to me, and returns back to the rose grove, at which moment I think I hear him laughing softly to himself. But he comes back again, takes my shadow out of his pocket, and with a dextrous fling it is unrolled and spread out on the ballroom floor, in the full glare of all the lights, so that he stands between two attendant shadows, mine and his — and walks away. It is Schlemihl, the favourite among her admirers, the man without a shadow, a figure contingent to the story, but of no other importance to ourselves who are but spectators.

There are arrivals, too, by water.

But it is the turn of the hired dancers, and of a young girl, more particularly, whom we saw arriving as though being smuggled in, for she was muffled up in a long coat and had some sort of handkerchief or bandana upon her hair. But the music begins, and we recognise her as she appears in the door of a house upon the stage. For her it must be, and yet she is transformed. They are dancers of the music hall. She sings a line or two in a cracked, but not unpleasant voice, for it has a little animal warmth and pathos, amounting even, if one shuts one's eyes, to a personal fascination. And, a moment later, she has begun to dance. A figure of extreme lightness, for she seems to leap into the air, be held there, and descend slowly. Again and

LADY IN RIDING HABIT
by Gavarni: " La Mode ", 1830

again, held up at arm's length by her pair of partners, and no sooner foot to ground than leaping up again, but always slowly and as though blown from each to each, wearing a dress that in its simplicity is an exaggeration of a walking dress, to music that, in its popular idiom, is of pleading tone as though trying to get her real partner, with whom she has not danced yet, to come home. And in a moment, he has left the two young girls with whom he was dancing, the music alters, quickens, and they dance together, the pleading tones of the first part being changed, subtly, but noisily, as though with the honks of motor horns, ghostly synonyms for noise and traffic, till the last bars leave them leaping, one behind the other, into the wings.

They come back, once more, to take the applause and there is then the spectacle of the dancers walking off on their bird feet, for their tread is different from that of other human beings. It has been so for thousands of years till they have become a caste, a race apart, to be known in the street, at the station, on the platform of the Underground, by the little leather case they carry with their dancing shoes, so much so, that every time we see them it is like coming across the Gypsy tents or caravans, or something as strange, if we prefer it, as the coloured tipis of the Blackfoot Indians, tents of deerskin, painted in bright colours, with a broad band at the base painted with the planets, and above, some totem peculiar to the person, a bear, a river, a red mountain, revealed to the painters of these signs under the influence of a drug, and only worked by them in that condition, the whole encampment of tents with the painted tipis in the middle being struck and moved in a few moments, to spring up again like a ring of mushrooms in the huge green plain.[1] We conceive of

[1] Walter McClintock in *The Old North Trail* (Macmillan and Co., London, 1910) describes the ' White City ' of the Blackfoot Indians during their annual Festival of the Sun. The designs for their painted tents were always secured through dreams, after long fasting, and became the exclusive property of their owners. At the bottom, there is an

the dancers, then, as being, in the Gypsy phrase, 'born in the tents', by which they mean of true blood, not half-breeds, and this would apply, more particularly, to 'troopers' or vaudeville dancers such as those whom we have just seen, who are really and truly of a race apart, and even bound by contract not to marry for so many years, according to their terms of partnership.

There are two worlds, and the shadow is falling out of one of them ; while the other world is but a shadow or pretence and its real life goes on behind it. . This is the contrast, and we are to suppose that it was, at one time, the substance of the one and the impermanence of the other that lent beauty to the latter, in the eyes, at any rate, of painters who by the risks of their profession lived in between, belonging neither to the one world nor the other. But now the two worlds are trembling on the scales, and we may be approaching a time, typical of revolution, when the only life of pleasure is that played upon the stage, when actors and dancers draw large salaries and the other world is ruined. Then what has fled will not be pitied.

So the shadow is falling out of one world. Already, " with wonderful dexterity " it is being loosened or unshackled from where it is chained to our feet, from where it runs along the grass, or across the ballroom floor, if, that is, one or more of the lights is lowered, which is the moment when we behold that moonlit pierrot face, spiritual sister to *Le Grand Gilles* of Watteau,

encircling band of dark colour representing the earth. Within this band is a row of disks, called ' dusty stars '. The Indians have given the name ' dusty stars ' to the puff-balls which grow in circular clusters upon the prairies, because they are supposed to be meteors, fallen from the night sky, and sprung up in a single night. They call them ' dusty stars ' because they emit a puff of dust when pressed. Above is a row of rounded or pointed projections representing mountains. Higher up is the design of animal, bird, sacred rock, thunder-trail, or other emblem. Surmounting all, an encircling band of black represents the night sky, on which are portrayed the sun and crescent moon, the constellations of the Seven Brothers and Lost Children (The Bear and Pleiades), and a Maltese cross, the emblem of the Morning Star, also representing the Butterfly or Sleep Bringer, which brings dreams to the owner. These painted tipis and their symbolic decorations are now, unfortunately, a thing of the past, and their circular encampment is no longer to be seen in the endless plain, below the snow-capped Rocky Mountains.

imbued with the same poetry, and with that same rounded modelling of the face-bones. Soon the shadow will be lifted up, it will be rolled together and folded, and put into a pocket. But, a moment later, one or more of the guests, as we have seen, is given back his shadow. It is unrolled and spread out at his feet upon the ballroom floor, seeming to give him his passport or permit into that alternate world of pretence or shadow in which, as we have said, the real life is concealed or hidden, which can mean nothing more or less than that his instructions are that he must live apart and as an artist.

There is a minor immortality, which is not of the world, and that may be a matter only of coincidence, in the sense that understanding or sympathy are born again. The one ghost transmutes into another. It is as though the breath, dying at the lips, is breathed in again by someone else, and never lost. The shades of persons are immortal to this degree. The drama is eternal, and that is its hope, for there is no other accommodation, and no certainty of a world to come. None need despair, for it is an affair of numbers. Nevertheless, we hear tears and weeping. I have been too near, in life, to the long wall that goes up the hill, past the cemetery, and down at the other side into the smoky town. In itself like some kind of ghostly metamorphosis, for it is incessantly the Northern speech, it is that which so affects me, so that, to my imagination, that is the language of sorrows and disappointment, and of the world of shadows worn thin. I see the house of the minister, with the clipped laurels, and passing I see and hear him while he mows the lawn. There is a bay tree in a sheltered corner, and the hated Michaelmas daisies are in flower.

The burden of this, at least, is to lift up the mask and look beneath it, to live between the spectacle of the two worlds, and enjoy them both. But a pleasure in work, only, for the drama is more sad than gay ; or so we may think, being caught in the trough between two wars, and in the ensuing tidal wave. Where are the sounds of laughter that were promised in the first page, in our Prologue ? Instead, so near the end, there is the noise of tears and weeping. But music is playing. Music of the time and moment, banal and meaningless, as befits a present time which has no meaning, and is still prostrate and exhausted. But, by its very emptiness, it takes on our own feelings and emotions, and becomes transformed or transcendentalised until it is no longer the simple tune from which it started. Perhaps the same process has overtaken persons, and has transformed the Fête and Ball. Looking at that round and moonlit face, am I imagining, one moment, that I see it sheathed in the turban of an Antillaise ? An eared or horned turban, a folded handkerchief or bandana ? But of the race of comedians to which it belongs, by descent from Watteau and from the phantom which beset or haunted the life and mind of Baudelaire, and ruined him, this is the Eared Pheasant or Crossoptilon, the " Mephisto of the breed ". The twisted ears or ends of the handkerchief lend this appearance to that moonlike face. All the rest is imagination. For *Le Grand Gilles* is not only and entirely a statement of fact. There is more besides. It is a painting by Watteau and, probably, his masterpiece. By the same token, the phantom of Giulietta is a haunting on the part of the talent or spirit that is in her beholder.

But we would lose, or cast off, the last links with the actual, for it is not our purpose to examine and report on things with the eye of the photographer. These are scenes that could not be photographed, for they are too subtle for the camera. The phantom of Giulietta fades as we look at her, or rather, springs into another appearance altogether, in the full glare of all the ballroom lights. Yet ghosts, we remark, are more convincing that are seen in daylight, or among a crowd of persons. The phantom, nevertheless, is in the eye of the beholder. To

GENTLEMAN IN HUNTING COAT
by Gavarni: "La Mode", 1830

persons of our particular temperament it is as though we were born and predestined to such visions or exaggerations that, in their extreme instances, may amount to something much less than the truth. Of such, we could say that it is only by their own shortcomings that they will not fulfil themselves as works of art. For their only purpose is that they should be judged as that. In any other light they can but fade and fail, just as much as their creator can imagine for himself no other career but that of writer. But of works that find their own shape and, as in this example, are a transmuting or translation of a common theme. Seen in this context, the whole occasion of the Fête and Ball has one depth or aspect in which it consists of nothing but the agonies and doubts of waiting. It could become a hallucination of long corridors and ante-rooms. Until we have taken that vow to remain, for ourselves, outside its complications, to be spectator, not participant, at that moment, shall we say, in which our shadow was given back to us by the spirit or person who had bargained for it. This was equivalent to the issuing of an order that, spiritually, we should be exempted from its troubles. A kind or degree of consecration, telling us that the spectacle of the two worlds was to be our subject, the world of substance and the world of shadow, or if we prefer it, the parable of the hunters and the hunted.

The scene burns up, immediately, as though with the increase or addition of every light that can be turned on. The music marches to a climax. But it is not military. Dandini, the baron of pantomime, in a suit of pale pea-green walks, like the master of ceremonies, at the head of the procession.[1] But he pauses, even so, to tap with his fingers and take a pinch of snuff. After making a turn of the ballroom, we see him leading by the hand Olympia, who is an automaton no longer. The shadow of a mandoline and its ribbons upon part of the white wall reminds

[1] " Jellicoe in pale pea-green " occurs in a poem by William Blake.

us of Antonia. It is in sign that she is but a shadow now, or has gone to another continent. But the phantom of Giulietta is still entertaining her friends and admirers.

We hear the neighing of a horse, a noise which will throw the inhabitants of the water-city into consternation, for a horse has never been seen here before except the bronze horses of St Mark's. In a sort of vision we behold Giulietta standing on the steps of a country house and by a painted railing. She is dressed in her hunting habit; a top-hat with a veil tied round it in the fashion of 1830; and the habit itself is of dark-blue cloth with full sleeves and sloping shoulders; a black cravat, like a man's, knotted into an elaborate but loose bow; the bodice is thin and pointed at the waist, the skirt long and full and to the ground; and the train lifted up and carried over her right arm between the wrist and elbow. In her other gloved hand she holds a riding switch. Her companion is described in the fashion plate as wearing a coat of red casimir, and white buckskin breeches; and we could add that the leather of his riding boots is most soft and elegant, that his coat is pinched in at the waist with tails cut almost as wide as the skirts of a dress, that this is accentuated because his right hand is thrust into his pocket, that he wears a black hunting cap, has whiskers and hair combed out above his ears, and that the collar of his red coat is cut extremely high as a backing for the most fanciful of cravats, consisting of a winged collar of linen, of which we can see the corner against his cheek, a loose stock wrapped round that, and below it, both super-fluous and necessary, like the auxiliary engine on a sailing yacht, a little tight and compact bow tie. Even the art of knotting and tying such cravats is lost, no more to be recaptured than the ghosts of Byron or d'Orsay, a fabulous elegance, therefore, and the same which we impute to Giulietta about to set off hunting.

A farewell only in symbol, for we are not to see her climb

into the saddle. There are to be no more Amazons in top-hats and veils. It is another splendour come down to the circus ring. But a vision that is not incongruous because here, or in another room, there are white cloud horses in fresco upon the ceiling. The scene could be the Palazzo Rezzonico, upon the Grand Canal, in Venice. This is one of the palaces built by Longhena, the architect of the Salute, in the white Istrian ; it has a Renaissance façade chequered with time so that there is dark shadow, and snow as of Poseidon's hair and beard, upon mask and pilaster and rustication, and where the weeded foundation comes up like a wharf out of the slimy tide, close to the mooring posts ; it has a splendid stair, a ballroom, and a saloon with the white horses of Tiepolo upon the painted ceiling. But at the same time the scene more nearly resembles the ' set ' in which Giulietta entertains her friends and admirers in the opera. Old scenery, borrowed, as it were, from Covent Garden, or another old opera house, and it matters not at all how badly it is painted. The setting may be a Louis XV saloon, but as imagined by an Italian scene painter of 1860 ; or more likely, a drawing-room in Venetian Gothic because of the implications in the name of Giulietta. A saloon, probably in ivory and gold, with excessive frames and mirrors ; or a room with pointed windows and a balcony, with walls of crimson brocade and sham Titian portraits. It is better so. For we would not have it that there is anything personal. It is a hired room in a palace or, if we like, the whole floor of the *piano nobile*, which means the great staircase and the set of rooms leading into one another upon the first floor. Of which we see room after room in perspective ; or it may be, the characters coming in up the wide and shallow flights of steps, and from the landing.

The beauty of such a dilapidated, tawdry scene is that we are left to fill in its details to our taste. Or it may mean that our time has lost the power to create its own settings. It can but copy, or go rigid. The long autumn shedding of the leaves is not for us, just as surely as we are removed an aeon from the " green livery of May ". The scene painter's Rococo, or his setting for the barcarolle in a palace upon the Grand Canal, we have to choose between these, but either is right and proper, and the rest is nothing but imagination.

Are we to describe the sudden thunderstorm within the ballroom ? The loud knocking, downstairs, upon the door, which resembles that moment when Count Lindoro, in the guise of a drunken dragoon, breaks into the house of Dr. Bartolo ? In the next act he will secure admission again disguised as a teacher of music, but his interview with Rosina will be interrupted by Don Basilio. This, and no more, is the thunder, which has not the boom and rattle of artillery. Nor, yet, the thud and crunch of falling buildings. Instead, it is but pleasantly sinister for a few moments, and it cools the air. Mere stage thunder ; or our own directions that " It is raining " or that " It pours with rain ".

The curtain is lowered, and the interlude portrays a storm of rain and thunder, no different from the rain and thunder upon the night of our Prologue. In the light, therefore, of this drama, while there is darkness upon the stage, we come forward for our farewell. For this is a kind of writing that we shall not attempt again. We behold the characters for the last time as they come forward to take their bows, before they disperse and return to ordinary. But the programme directs that the play will end with a bravura and finale of light and graceful melody. So, when the lights go up again, it is full daylight, and the fantastic edifice of the Fête and Ball has been dissipated in a breath.

EPILOGUE

THE shadows attenuate and grow taller. We are to visit a pastoral scene so extraordinary and improbable that it is difficult to believe it true. The Daughters of Albion are to darken and come smooth and tawny. It is another continent and a scene so old that it is to-day but could be ten thousand years ago. Before the Pharaohs and in the age of giants. But their fierceness and great strength have been exaggerated in the legends. These giants are tall and gentle. We hear the lowing of herds. They are the shepherd kings. More curious still, the giants have enslaved the Pygmies.

A land of milk and honey lies open into the mountains, a pastoral land of lakes and extinct volcanoes. Its human dwellings are villages of beehive huts, hamlets not so far apart that the shepherds cannot walk with their slow tread from each to each, and come from many directions to the pale meadow or pasture lying in the middle, for it has gone ashen from the hot sun even at this high altitude. They start on their journey before dawn, and it is at this hour coming out of the shadows that we see the first of the shepherd kings advancing towards us, a figure so incredible and cast in so strange a canon of proportion that it is like the dream, come true, of a sixteenth-century ' mannerist ' or of one of the heresiarchs of painting. But he comes nearer, and we see that he is dressed in a long robe reaching to the ground, and that in his hand he holds a long pastoral staff or wand. In his long gown he is a giant of the fairground walking upon stilts. But men on stilts have a peculiar way of walking. If you look closely you can see them lift their stilts. The most skilful of them could not tread like this shepherd king out of the shadows.

But he is followed immediately by two more giants, and we hear him laughing and talking to them over his shoulder. The tropical dawn, too, is as dramatic as a sudden lighting of the circus tent. We are so close to the Equator that it springs into full radiance in a moment, and by its sudden impact we see the patterns of their robes. The leading giant is in a white gown with great wide-spaced rings or black moons upon it. His companions are wearing robes of brick red, and black, but the pattern in both instances is of widening circles or parhelions, like mock suns, spaced with magical instinct to the huge stature of their wearers. And now from all the gallery forests the shepherd kings are appearing, singly, and in twos and threes, each with his tall staff or wand of kingship in his hand, while the serfs drive in the cattle, hurrying and running in contradiction to their sandalled masters.

The herds are lowing, and to this extent it is like a cattle market in any other land, though no one would foresee this pastoral civilisation, these knights or nobles of the shepherd's crook and this aristocracy of stature and slow movement in the flowerless fields. We cannot dismiss it from our imagination that they are in some shadowy way related to the Pharaohs, but before the fixing and hardening of the Pharaonic forms into an unchanging architecture and to statues and emblems that never altered down the ages. To ante-dynastic Egypt, therefore, and to the early kings before the thirty dynasties began to reign, and before the invention of the hieroglyphs that chained them for thirty centuries or three thousand years.

Their gigantic stature imparts to them a sacerdotal air, but not so much as though they are the priests of religion, but rather that they are the gods themselves, for our instinct tells us that their minds are not capable of theological invention. They are gentle pastoral gods or shepherd kings from so profound an antiquity that they belong to another creation of human beings and must be considered, individually, as gods or kings. It may be no more than the results of a milk diet which turn them, not into gigantic warriors but giant shepherds. They seem to be conditioned by lands of milk and honey and to require cattle, in order to remain fixed in their physical peculiarities. When this can happen, and for this reason, their aspect suggests an antiquity much greater than the actual truth. They become immensely tall and supine, or at any rate not warlike, and their attitudes of dignity make them into shepherd kings.

Whatever the reason, there could be no other pastoral scene in which the ordinary canons of stature and proportion are so severely broken. Many of the shepherd kings are seven feet six inches high, and even taller in appearance because of their thin, straight figures and long robes. Their plumed diadems make them more enormous still, and the patterns of their robes are as though calculated to draw further attention to their height. So, also, is their habit of walking with long staffs or wands. But the humped cattle are wealth and pride of the shepherd kings, great beasts of dun or fawn, or with coats like lions, and wide branching horns. The giant shepherds, who are incurious about the past and know nothing of their own history, can trace back their cattle for many generations and have a multitude of words to describe the different dapplings and markings of their herds. Almost the majority of words is devoted to this purpose in their laconic language, and something, it may be, of this invention and ordering has gone into the bold patterns of their gowns. It is a Druidical simplicity, but omenless and without ulterior meaning. They have no priests or magicians, being, in our eyes and to our interpretation, so many potential, but ineffectual gods or kings. Not for a moment are they to be regarded as peasants. They are landowners and aristocrats. Here, in their own pasture lands, the patterns of their dresses are suns or moons or Saturn's rings, circles like silver necklaces, or shapes that could represent the planets but, as we have said, of no prophecy or import.

It can only be that the workings of their instinct are towards a big and primitive simplicity, disdaining the trivial. No one, so far as we know, has yet made a study of their textiles. We are ignorant, therefore, of the technique of their manufacture. Yet these robes of giants are marvellously adapted to the great height of their wearers. They are of another style from the stuffs of Nigeria or the French Sudan, negro Emirates that in our world dying of civilisation are among the only living traditions of textile design. But neither are they related to the pagan stuffs of tree bark manufactured by the Congo tribes, materials reaching back, in origins, to the negro kingdoms of Dahomey and Benin. Two Belgian Catholic missionaries have been working for over thirty years on the customs and folklore of the Ruanda-Urundi, but their findings have not yet been published. It would be interesting to know their legends, and whether there is any memory of a golden age, of the reign of magic, and a time when the gods lived as kings upon the earth, for that would be sure indication of some surviving echo of the Pharaohs. More probably there is nothing, and the haunting of these sable ghosts has no explanation. They have but sprung up again in a propitious soil.

The shepherd kings dwell deep in the interior of Africa, so remote that no one knew of them till 1906, or proved the legend of a race of giants. In the Belgian Congo, in a great tongue of land a hundred miles long and as many broad, between Lake Tanganyika, Lake Edward, and Lake Victoria.[1] The Pygmies are their serfs and till the soil for them, and there is a half-caste race that comes between. But few, then, of the pure-blooded dwarfs and not more than a dwindling twenty thousand of the giants. They are of the same race as the Nilotes and akin to the

[1] Ruanda-Urundi was included in the former German East Africa until 1919.

giant, but not so gigantic Dinka and Shilluk, whose country is the White Nile five hundred to a thousand miles above Khartum, of the same stock, probably, as the Zulu, lion-crowned Masai, and Matabele. But the Nile banks have wrought a difference in the Shilluk and Dinka, and made them herdsmen, too. The Dinka go naked and pass long hours gazing out over their herds and standing on one leg. The Shilluk, who are often as tall as seven feet and slender in proportion, wear cloaks of vermilion reaching to their hips. These they let fall readily, and stand leaning on their long spears, their faces rubbed with ashes and their hair dyed red with clay, looking like spectral, moonlit giants out of another world. Both tribes have beautiful wide horned cattle with fawn or grey skins, but they are naked savages too low in the human scale to hold our minds for long.

Seeing them, our first thought must be to wish that there were a race with a higher civilisation, but cast in the same attenuated canon of proportion. With their great height and slender build they are the aristocrats of the negro world and serve to remind us of how many negro types there are besides the black slave of the plantation and the Moor Othello. Only Shakespeare, who imagined his Moor to be a full-blooded negro, allowed him the instincts of a ruler and a great man in his own land and made him other than a slave or blackamoor. This was his instinct, for he cannot have had experience of any but the first African to come to hand.

The more interesting negro races remained hidden until recent times, the first to emerge only a hundred years ago being the Zulu impis or regiments of King Tchaka. Here, at last, after millenniums of slavery, was the negro warrior, but reduced now, in our day, to be bedecked with plumes and draw a rickshaw in the streets of Durban. The Zulus are negroes with the stature and physique of warriors, but the Nilotes or negro shepherds emerged much later from the living past. Neither are they typically the negro but may have some strain of the Ethiopian in them, which means that for all their darkness of skin they have straight features and are chocolate or copper coloured, not the hue of basalt or ebony, with enormous lips and rolling eyes.

Anyone seeing the Dinka or Shilluk must have the impression that those tribes have lived in the Sudan from before the Pharaohs, but even in the absence of all history or traditions of their own, it would appear that they have been here no longer than since the fourteenth or fifteenth century of our era. It was at that time, and coming from one general stock, perhaps towards Abyssinia, that they spread forth into other parts and developed their peculiar characteristics. The Nilotes are nearly related, too, to the Herreros, a tribe living near the Atlantic coast in former German South-West Africa, and who were cruelly reduced by the German colonists in two long wars. They, also, are of the type of shepherd kings, being tall, slender, and aristocratic in appearance, but among the Herreros the women are more interesting than the men, for they are characterised by all travellers as the most lovely of all coloured races. Like shepherd queens in their turbans and red gowns, or priestesses of Venus Callipyge, the especial goddess of the Africans, they are dedicated to the old rites and, childless and barren, may have disappeared in another generation that has never heard of them and has no paintings, good or bad, of the beautiful Herrero women.

Time among the Ruanda-Urundi is of no consequence. They are as careless of it as of the past. Their day is not divided into hours. The whole day is given up to talking and wandering slowly, staff in hand. It is with them as with the sacred bulls and cows. They live out their lives and have no more conjecture than the animals. They are no more conscious than the trees or birds of their descent from ancient times. It places them on both a higher and a lower plane than other human beings. It is by the questioning of such supine confidence that we are drawn to believe in anthropomorphism and could credit a crocodile, a goat, a peacock, with a soul, more still, with human knowledge, as though the animals have had existence, at some time, as human beings and have risen or fallen from their former state. Such is an explanation of the half-human, half-animal idols of pagan religions. It is one of the earliest fantasies of human beings when they look round and wonder who they are. But it is also scarcely credible that the Pygmies and giants should be found living so near together and in the legendary or fabulous circumstances that imagination would create for them, as slaves and masters. In near proximity, too, to the gorillas and giant pachyderms, to the elephant and rhinoceros that are sole survivors from the age of monsters.

But the shadows lengthen. From an alteration as simple as a change of diet the stature of the shepherds may diminish in another few generations and there will be no more left of them than the giant skeletons found in the Grottes des Rochers-Rouges at Mentone, troglodytes who lived ten, or twenty, or fifty thousand years ago, and who from their numbers seem to have been no more than a family of giant fishermen who came down from their caves to collect shellfish and look for what they could find in the rock pools. Giants of the kitchen midden, but it is to be presumed that they were not alone. There must have been other giants along the seashore. These could not have been the only individuals. There must have been a scattered tribe. Then, as now, we could have seen their long shadows lengthen in the evening.[1]

But this is not the shadow of a naked man at the foot of the red rocks, or coming in out of the sea. What we behold is the decline or darkening of the golden age of flocks and herds. This is the cattle kingdom ; the landscape of the megalith but without

[1] Cf. *Les Grottes de Grimaldi*, by chanoine de Villeneuve, Imprimerie de Monaco, 1906.

the rude stone monuments, for these giants do not concern themselves with problems of time or calculations of the stars. In mind they are no more conscious than the giant hollyhock which comes up in the garden, sown from seed, has its time of glory, and then withers with its spire of crowns. It goes back to the soil, unless forgotten in some corner we see its spike or rattle which is as dead as the old bones in the cave. But these giants, if ever found, will be in proximity to skulls and horns of cattle. This race of giants has horned cattle in proportion to them. And no other possessions but a few pots. No crowns or diadems, no idols, and few weapons. They leave the world, like the animals, with little or nothing more than what they brought with them, except a bowl to feed from, and a long staff or wand. So many cattle kings, reigning at once, need no memorial. For the dynasty is the whole race, and every individual. But to make the mystery insoluble to future ages the giants should be buried, on occasion, with the skull or thigh bone of a Pygmy.

It darkens. The lowing of the herds comes from a distance. They are returning to their villages. The wide horned cattle are driven into the enclosure and the living fence or palisade is lifted and put back in place. It must be a youthful world still, where there are lions to prey upon the herds. Youthful, yet very old. So old that it is before kings and queens had even a heap of stones to mark where they were buried. This has been a vision of the golden age. Where every shepherd is a king and all men are giants, in the land of milk and honey, in long gowns, with the wand or sceptre in their ebon hands.

THE END